PRACTICAL ANIMAL ECOLOGY

PRACTICAL
ANIMAL ECOLOGY

W. H. DOWDESWELL
Winchester College

METHUEN AND CO LTD
36 ESSEX STREET · STRAND · LONDON

Preface

The six years which have elapsed since the publication of my previous book, *Animal Ecology*, have been a period of great advance in the teaching of elementary ecology. The encouragement given by some universities has been most heartening, and many excellent courses are now provided by the Field Studies Council and Local Education Authorities, which are of particular value to schools situated in urban surroundings. Moreover, where circumstances have allowed, it is clear that many schools have been experimenting with courses of their own, making use of such natural facilities as they may have at their disposal. The beneficial results are reflected in a number of ways, not least in examination papers.

This is, perhaps, an appropriate moment to take stock of our advances from the practical standpoint. During the last few years, progress has been made in many aspects of ecology, such as the biology of soil and the structure of small communities of animals and plants separated from one another by minor ecological barriers. This has necessitated fresh modes of thought and the evolution of new methods, many of which can be mastered with profit by the elementary student. The present book can therefore be regarded as a much expanded version of the last chapter of my previous one and is concerned largely with practical techniques and their application in the study of ecology. The two works are complementary, the former providing a theoretical background for the latter.

In conformity with present trends in field-work, I have included two chapters on the ecology of soil, a subject which is admirably suited to study at school. A further two chapters have been devoted to quantitative aspects and the use of statistics which, I hope, may prove useful both to schools and in university courses. Throughout the book emphasis has been placed on the inter-relationship of animals and plants, but space does not permit of a detailed treatment of plants by themselves. Several excellent works on plant ecology already exist and references to these are given in the Bibliography. This aims to cover a wide field, particularly the means of animal identification.

As before, I have assumed an elementary knowledge of comparative anatomy and physiology such as is usually acquired during the first and second years of school sixth form work. It may be objected that some of the topics discussed are outside the scope of ordinary classwork. These have been included, nonetheless, with the object of helping students who may be working on individual projects of their own. Once a basic knowledge of the subject has been acquired, this is undoubtedly the way to derive the maximum benefit from ecology at school.

I would like to take this opportunity of thanking particularly Dr E. B. Ford, F.R.S., for his invaluable help and encouragement, and for reading the whole of the typescript. He has also kindly allowed me to reproduce part of a paper of his on the mathematics of the capture-recapture method of estimating numbers, as Appendix B. My thanks are also due to Mr W. B. Yapp for permitting me to summarize his account of the line transect method of counting animals, as Appendix A. Most of the apparatus I have described was constructed by Mr A. J. Lewington and Mr A. S. Mitchener in the school workshop. It is no exaggeration to say that, had it not been for their technical skill and imagination, much of this book could never have been written.

The following have kindly provided me with photographs and diagrams; it is a pleasure to acknowledge their valuable help: Mr W. M. M. Baron (Plate 4), Mr S. Beaufoy (Plate 10), Mr J. Clegg (Plates 8 and 9), Dr H. B. D. Kettlewell (Plate 6), and Dr D. P. Wilson (Plates 11b, 14, 15 and 16). Mr R. Ward drew all the pictures of apparatus (except where otherwise stated) and Mr W. M. M. Baron kindly contributed Figs. 47, 54 and 55. Mr A. S. Mitchener prepared most of the figures in Chapters VII–IX, other than those of apparatus. I am also indebted to various authors and publishers who have allowed me to reproduce figures and drawings: the source of each is acknowledged in the text. Dr F. B. Hora first drew my attention to the phenosafranine method of oxygen determination (Chapter II) and my thanks are due to him for much kindly advice.

It is also a pleasure to acknowledge my most grateful thanks to Mrs J. H. Preston for her infinite patience in preparing the typescript and for valuable help with the Bibliography, and Index.

Winchester
  October, 1958

The need for a reprinting has enabled me to make certain corrections and adjustments in the text, also to rewrite the Bibliography bringing it up to date.

Winchester
  August, 1963

Contents

Plates

Figures

CHAPTER I

Introduction

Animal Communities

One of the fascinations of ecology as a subject both to study and to teach is its diversity. The various types of habitat occupied by animals and plants are innumerable; so too, are the modes of life of the organisms themselves. Animals, for instance, can be classified broadly into terrestrial and aquatic forms. Yet many species such as woodlice, are so poorly adapted to life on land that they can only forsake the humid conditions in which they live for short periods at a time. Others, again, although truly terrestrial as adults, possess an aquatic larval stage and have to return to the water to breed. This is true of most amphibians and many insects such as the mosquito.

But in spite of their complexity, it is nonetheless true to say that all animal communities have certain fundamental features in common. In the first place, they are all ultimately dependent upon plants since these are the only organisms capable of autotrophic nutrition. Examination of any animal community will reveal a complex set of food relationships (*food chains*) existing between the different species. Large carnivores prey upon smaller carnivores and if we pursue the food sequence we soon reach the herbivore stage. Most herbivorous animals feed, at least partly, on green plant material. But this is not always so. In regions where light cannot penetrate, such as in caves or on the ocean bed, herbivores have to subsist entirely on organic debris (detritus). This is derived from the dead remains of other animals and plants reduced to a suitable state of decomposition by the action of bacteria.

Again, all animal communities are subject to changes in their physical environment (*climatic factors*) such as temperature, light and humidity. Most free-living species possess a fair degree of adaptability and are able to withstand variations such as the extremes of temperature existing between summer and winter without difficulty (*eurythermous*). On the other hand, conditions in some habitats tend to remain remarkably uniform. Thus the beds of the great oceans and the sources of mountain streams, by virtue of their almost constant temperature, tend to promote colonization by a group of organisms (*stenotherms*) which are incapable of existing anywhere else. Typical among these is the small freshwater turbellarian *Planaria alpina* which is generally regarded as a relict species from the Pleistocene ice ages and is confined to areas of cold water arising from natural springs. Many internal parasites and symbionts have carried their habitat preferences to extremes. Tapeworms (Cestoda) are notorious in this respect, the majority inhabiting the small intestine of vertebrates, most of them warm-blooded. Some of these parasites have acquired a remarkable degree of specificity, being confined to hosts belonging to particular genera or even to single species. For instance, the African ostriches and South American rheas both harbour a species of tapeworm (genus *Houttynia*) which occurs in no other birds. The Australian cassowaries and emus on the other hand, are parasitized by the genus *Railietina*. Thus, comparative parasitology can sometimes provide valuable evidence, not only of the peculiar preferences of the parasites themselves but also of the evolutionary affinities of their hosts.

Study of the requirements of tapeworms has shown that a relatively constant physical environment is by no means their only necessity for a successful existence. Certain other factors are also of importance, in particular their diet which consists of carbohydrates obtained from the host's food and certain specific nitrogenous compounds derived from the intestinal wall. The availability of these substances determines the number of parasites that can live in a single host.

Ecological factors such as food, living space and density are termed *biotic* and operate in all animal populations irrespective of whether they are parasitic or free-living. Most animals can tolerate a fairly wide variation of diet and should one constituent become scarce they can readily turn to another. In any habitat the balance between carnivores, herbivores and scavengers or detritus feeders is therefore exceedingly complex and often varies at different times of the year with the availability of particular foods. Some species, however, rely entirely on a single diet and their survival is, at times, apt to be somewhat precarious. Thus the small moth *Tortrix viridana* feeds exclusively on oak leaves and, in years of abundance, may defoliate large areas of woodland. If, as occasionally happens, the supply of leaves is exhausted before the insect has completed its larval cycle, the caterpillars die of starvation. Similarly, among carnivores, many of the ladybird beetles prey entirely upon aphids whose abundance is thus closely related to that of their predators.

Under natural conditions all wild animal populations spend a large proportion of their time feeding or avoiding being eaten. In so doing, each species comes to occupy a distinct position (*ecological niche*) in its own biotic environment denoting its relationship to other members of the community, particularly in terms of its feeding habits. Neal has used the following classification of niches in woodland:

VEGETARIANS

(1) LEAF, BUD AND SHOOT FEEDERS
    (a) *Defoliators*   e.g. caterpillars
                                  snails and slugs
                                  rabbits, mice, voles, deer
    (b) *Miners*   e.g. caterpillars

(2) SUCKERS OF PLANT JUICES
    (a) *Sap feeders*   e.g. aphids, bugs, frog-hoppers
    (b) *Nectar feeders*   e.g. butterflies, moths, bees, flies

(3) FRUIT AND SEED FEEDERS e.g. weevils, caterpillars
                                    wood-mouse, vole, badger
                                  nuthatch, chaffinch, thrush

(4) GALL FORMERS   e.g. gall wasps, gall midges
(5) BARK FEEDERS   e.g. bark beetles
                                  wood lice
                                  millipedes
                                  grey squirrel, rabbits

(6) WOOD BORERS — e.g. wood wasp, moth larvae, beetle larvae

(7) ROOT FEEDERS — e.g. moth larvae, beetle larvae

(8) FUNGUS FEEDERS — e.g. beetles, fly larvae, spring-tails

CARNIVORES

(1) PREDATORS — e.g. ladybirds, lacewing larvae syrphid larvae, beetles
centipedes
insect-eating, mollusc and worm-eating, large carnivores
fox, badger, stoat, hedgehog

(2) BLOOD SUCKERS — e.g. mosquitoes, flies
spiders

(3) PARASITES — e.g. fleas, ticks, ichneumons, chalcid wasps, tachinid flies

SCAVENGERS

(1) OMNIVORES — e.g. badger

(2) FEEDERS ON SUBSTANCES OF VEGETABLE ORIGIN
e.g. spring-tails
earthworms
mites

(3) FEEDERS ON SUBSTANCES OF ANIMAL ORIGIN
(a) *Dung feeders* — e.g. flies and their larvae, beetles
(b) *Carrion feeders* — e.g. fly larvae, beetles

The degree of competition for particular niches is determined to a large extent by the size of the animals concerned, the nature of their feeding methods and the extent to which they themselves constitute the food of neighbouring species. The greater the number and variety of niches in a particular locality, the more numerous and diverse will the animal population become.

But the balance between an animal community and its environment is never static for long. Climatic and biotic factors are in a constant state of flux, particularly when influenced by human interference, and this is reflected to varying extents in the behaviour of the populations concerned. Favourable conditions with a suitable climate, an abundance of food, and a relative lack of predators and parasites, may bring about an enormous increase in the numbers of a species. Such outbursts are well known in the common white butterflies *Pieris brassicae* and *P. rapae*, and the depredations of their larvae may cause great losses to market gardeners. On the other hand, adverse circumstances such as disease may reduce the density of a usually common species to an abnormally low level, such as has happened in the rabbit population of parts of Britain as a result of myxomatosis. Recent evidence suggests that the density of wild animal populations is to some extent self-regulating and that when numbers become excessive the inevitable effects of food shortage and disease are supplemented by those of 'biological stress'. This is no doubt due to a complex and highly variable set of factors, as yet largely undetermined. Among higher vertebrates the psychological aspect may be of importance as in the establishment of territories by birds during the nesting season. On the other hand, the characteristic 'crash' in numbers which invariably follows plagues of the voles *Microtus arvalis* and *M. agrestis* seems to be due to a form of physiological exhaustion (shock-disease) resulting from the increased competition for limited food and living-space. In lower forms, too, physiological factors must frequently play a part in density-regulation, as in the swarming behaviour of locusts.

Some animal populations, such as the mammals of North America, fluctuate in numbers with remarkable regularity. In Britain the Short-Tailed Vole exhibits a four-yearly cycle, while partridge populations appear to fluctuate with a periodicity of between nine and ten years. In spite of intensive study, we are still far from understanding fully the reasons underlying these cyclical changes.

Practical study of ecology

Of the various aspects of biology, ecology is one that demands an essentially practical approach. For there is only one place in which to study the relationship between animals and plants and their environment – in the natural setting where they live. In the following chapters I have attempted to suggest various ways in which such studies can be carried out.

From this brief introduction it will be seen that ecological studies at any level must invariably include some or all of the following aspects:

(i) *The identification of the animals and plants.* This is an essential preliminary in all biological work and, fortunately, is a much simpler matter than it used to be. Plants, in particular, are now well documented and the numerous good 'floras' (*see* Bibliography) make identification down to species a comparatively easy matter. The identification of animals is less simple, but the publication by the Systematics Association of a bibliography of key books for the identification of the British fauna and flora[1] has greatly simplified the task of finding appropriate works covering the taxonomy of particular groups. An argument sometimes advanced against the introduction of ecology into the biology course at schools is that the essential preliminaries consume such an inordinate amount of time. This is hardly a valid argument, for in elementary studies involving communities of animals, a reasonable compromise is to identify the majority as far as their genera, and a few of the easier groups, for which simple keys are available (e.g. freshwater planarians and leeches) down to species. Such a procedure is perfectly justified provided a clear distinction is made between organisms occupying different ecological niches.

(ii) *The study of life cycles and behaviour.* A feature of all animal communities is the great diversity of habits among the various species. If we are to gain a true idea of the relationships of the different forms it is essential to discover something of their life cycles and the phases of behaviour through which they pass at

[1] Smart and Taylor (1953). *Bibliography of Key Works for the Identification of the British Fauna and Flora.* (London: The Systematics Association, c/o British Museum.)

different times of the year. The natural history of many British species is now adequately described in the text-books but information gained in this way can never supplant that derived from actual observation in the field. Furthermore, it will soon be apparent, even at an elementary level, that large gaps in our knowledge of the commoner animals still remain to be filled. One of the fascinations of ecology as a subject is that no two habitats are exactly alike and the habits of the various colonists often vary appreciably from place to place. In a sense, therefore, the study of any community is an original contribution to knowledge. Here is an almost unlimited field for the enthusiastic naturalist who is prepared to devote the time and patience necessary for accurate observation and recording.

(iii) *The influence of ecological factors.* We have seen how such factors can be subdivided for convenience into two kinds – climatic and biotic. Variations in the composition of soil (*see* Chapters VI and VII) may also play an important part in determining the kinds of animal and plant communities that can exist in a particular place. Factors of this kind are known as *edaphic.* Their interaction is often highly complex and many of them still remain unidentified.

But despite the limitations in our knowledge of ecological factors in general and the relative crudity of our methods for studying them, we now know enough to enable us to apply specific techniques to particular types of problem. Many of these can provide reliable information with a minimum outlay in time and apparatus. As such, they can usefully be employed in elementary studies of animal ecology and a selection of them will be described in the following chapters.

(iv) *Numerical aspects.* The density of a population is the outcome of competition between animals of the same and different species and provides a measure of the biological success achieved in a particular locality. This is an aspect of ecology which is often overlooked at an elementary stage, possibly on account of the supposed difficulty in making reliable estimates of numbers in a reasonable time. In certain circumstances, using appropriate sampling methods, it is quite easy to obtain results of sufficient accuracy for comparisons to be made between the conditions in one locality and another. Such studies (described in Chapters III–V) are well worth while, for they enable observations which may previously have been purely subjective to assume a more precise and objective form.

CHAPTER II

Measurement of Climatic Factors in Air and Water

In this chapter simple methods will be described for measuring some of the more important climatic factors that influence the lives of animals. The various procedures considered have been used extensively in the field and found to give reliable results. Most of the apparatus can be constructed quite easily in a laboratory or workshop, and the various components needed are relatively inexpensive. The application of these methods to specific problems in ecology is considered in Chapters VII–X.

TEMPERATURE

The ordinary mercury or alcohol thermometer, although an accurate instrument, has distinct limitations when used in biological field-work. It is easily broken and, moreover, it must be withdrawn and examined each time a temperature is taken. For measurements of the temperature gradient (thermocline) in localities such as ponds, the latter difficulty can be overcome to some extent by the use of a maximum and minimum thermometer. This involves taking a series of separate readings at successive depths – a laborious procedure, which has the added disadvantage that continued raising and lowering of the thermometer may cause a mixing of the water in the different temperature zones.

Such problems are overcome by the use of an 'electrical thermometer' which gives continuous readings as the temperature changes. These instruments are of two kinds:

    (a) those which measure variations in the current generated by a thermocouple[1]

[1] If two wires of different metals are joined end-to-end and their extremities subjected to different temperatures, an electric current will pass between them. A thermocouple consists of a number of such wires connected together in order to increase the output obtained.

(b) those which measure variations in the resistance of a substance subjected to changing temperature (thermistor).

Thermocouples have certain inherent disadvantages in that they are difficult to construct and cumbersome to use for measuring the small temperature changes likely to be encountered in biological work. They have now been largely superseded by the much simpler and more robust thermistor.[1] This consists of a capsule of a complex metal oxide whose resistance decreases rapidly with increasing temperature.

When used as a resistance on one side of a simple Wheatstone

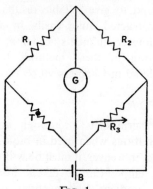

FIG. 1
Circuit of Wheatstone
Bridge

Dowdeswell: *Animal Ecology*
(Methuen)

Bridge circuit and balanced by a suitable variable resistance on the other (Fig. 1), the changes in the thermistor (determined on some empirical scale) can be plotted against actual temperatures (obtained from a waterbath using a sensitive mercury thermometer) and a convenient conversion graph thus obtained. The Wheatstone Bridge can be mounted in a small box (Plate 1a) and is quite cheaply and easily made. The galvanometer must be a moving-coil instrument (an ex-government milliameter, costing about a pound, can be adapted for this purpose) and the power supply can be provided from a single torch cell. The resistance thermometer will be found to be very sensitive, settling down at a new temperature in a few seconds and giving readings to an accuracy of $0.1°$C. or better. Using a null-galvanometer sufficiently robust for work in a small boat, a sensitivity of $0.02°$C. has been attained.

Many kinds of thermistor are now available with a wide range of sizes, mountings and temperature characteristics. Most of them

[1] Obtainable from Standard Telephones and Cables Ltd; price about fifteen shillings.

are extremely durable and can withstand rough treatment such as being buried in the soil or inserted in the bark of trees, for considerable periods. It is sometimes said that the characteristics of certain types of thermistor tend to change with increasing age, but experience over the last five years does not suggest that such alterations are of frequent occurrence. Nonetheless, it is

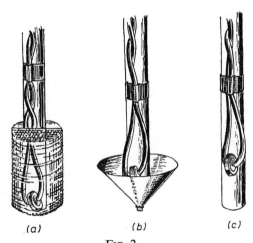

(a)   (b)   (c)

FIG. 2

Mounting a thermistor (a) in perforated zinc cage (b) protected by metal ferrule (c) on pole, unprotected

undoubtedly a wise precaution to recalibrate a resistance thermometer from time to time.

An important point to remember when using thermistors in water is that their leads must be well insulated. Friction with stones and vegetation quickly destroys insulation, so when mounting a thermistor (for instance on the end of a wooden rod as in Fig. 2c) it is desirable to enclose it in some kind of protective housing. For temperature measurements in open water a small perforated zinc 'cage' can be easily made (Fig. 2a). In sand or mud, a conical metal ferrule (Fig. 2b) will be found to give good protection. For studies in deeper water (generally from a boat) the thermistor must be attached to a line with markers on it at

31

appropriate intervals to indicate the depth. This should be made of nylon (or some other plastic) which does not shrink when wet. The type of housing will depend on the depth and nature of the bottom but it must be sufficiently heavy to sink easily.[1]

LIGHT

For approximate comparisons of illumination and turbidity in shallow water, a white metal disc about 8 inches in diameter can be attached at right angles to the end of a rod calibrated in feet. Measurements are made by noting the depth at which the disc is just invisible. This rather crude apparatus (generally known as Secchi's disc) has the advantage of being cheap and easy to construct. However, it has obvious limitations and cannot be used as a means of obtaining absolute measurements of light intensity.

By far the most convenient and accurate method of measuring illumination is by means of a photo-voltaic light-meter. A photographic exposure meter can be adapted for this purpose but it has the double disadvantage of expense and of needing recalibration if actual measurements of light are to be made. Furthermore, such instruments are not waterproofed and can only be used in the dry.

Photo-voltaic cells cost only a few shillings and a good light-meter can easily be constructed in the laboratory. The best type of cell to use is one which has been specially treated to withstand exposure to daylight. Although slightly less sensitive than most, it has the advantage that its rate of deterioration is much slower.[2] It can be conveniently housed in a Perspex container about $3 \times 2.5 \times 0.1$ inches, the various sections being sealed together with chloroform. The metal contacts are of phosphor-bronze sheeting,

[1] For a detailed account of the use of thermistors for measuring temperature in deep water see:

Mortimer, C. H. (1953). 'A Review of Temperature Measurement in Limnology.'

Mortimer, C. H., and Moore, W. H. 'The Use of Thermistors for the Measurement of Temperature in Lakes.'

International Association of Theoretical and Applied Limnology, Communications Nos. 1 and 2.

[2] Manufactured by Megatron Ltd, 115a Fonthill Road, London, N.14.; cost about six shillings.

corrugated to ensure a springy mounting with good electrical connections. The method of assembly is shown in Fig. 3. When completed, all joints and apertures in the apparatus (particularly those through which the leads pass) are sealed with Chatterton's compound or any other waterproof adhesive. Finally, the whole

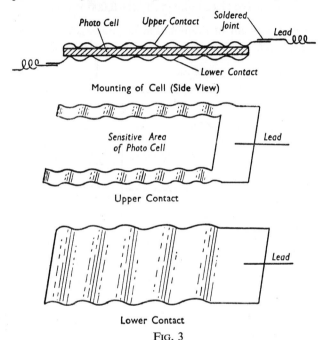

Mounting of Cell (Side View)

Upper Contact

Lower Contact

FIG. 3
Method of mounting a photo-voltaic cell
Dowdeswell and Humby: *School Science Review*, No. 125, Nov. 1953

surface is painted with dull black paint except that immediately above the sensitive part of the cell. It is important to remember that the leads from the cell must be well insulated throughout their lengths, particularly if they are likely to come into contact with water. The assembly can be conveniently mounted on a calibrated stick (*see* Plate 1b) or in any other way desired.

The meter (a 0–0·5 ex-government milliameter is suitable) is mounted in a separate box and provided with two shunts in order to increase the range or readings (*see* Fig. 4). Using the resistances shown in Fig. 4 the approximate range of the instrument is as follows:

Open circuit . . . .   0–300 ft-candles
Shunt No. 2 (90 ohms) . 250–2,000 ft-candles
Shunt No. 1 (20 ohms) . 1,000–8,000 ft-candles.

The normal gradient of illumination in ponds is covered by the open-circuit scale, while the maximum light intensity on land

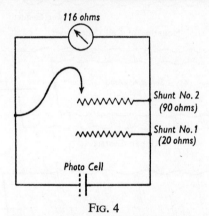

FIG. 4
Circuit of photo-voltaic light meter
Dowdeswell and Humby: *School Science Review*, No. 125, Nov. 1953

(direct sunlight) is about 4,500 ft-candles and well within the range provided by Shunt No. 1.

The simplest method of calibration is by comparison with a commercial light-meter such as that used by the British Electricity Board. Alternatively, standardized electric lamps can be used operating under carefully controlled conditions.[1]

HUMIDITY

Various sorts of hygrometer are now made. One type depends on the change in length of a paper strip or hair according to the

[1] For details of this method of calibration see Dowdeswell, W. H., and Humby, S. R. (1953). *School Science Review*, **125**, 64.

amount of moisture in the atmosphere. Such instruments, although convenient to use, suffer from the disadvantages of being easily damaged if carried about and of requiring constant checking if accurate measurements are required. They are not, therefore, of much use in the field.

Dry-bulb temperature	Wet-bulb depression										
	0·5°C	1·0°	1·5°	2·0°	2·5°	3·0°	3·5°	4·0°	5·0°	6·0°	7·0°
0°C	91	82	73	65	56	48	39	31%			
2	92	84	76	68	60	52	45	37	22%		
4	92	85	78	70	63	56	49	42	29		
6	93	86	79	73	66	60	53	47	35	23%	
8	94	87	81	75	69	63	57	51	40	29	18%
10	94	88	82	76	71	65	60	54	44	34	24
	1°	2°	3°	4°	5°	6°	8°	10°	12°	14°	
15	90	80	71	61	52	44	27	12			
20	91	83	74	66	59	51	37	24	12		
25	92	84	77	70	63	57	44	33	22	12	
	2°	4°	6°	8°	10°	12°	14°	16°	18°	20°	25°
30	86	73	61	50	39	30	21	13	5		
35	87	75	64	53	44	35	27	20	13	7	
40	87	76	66	56	47	39	32	26	20	14	1

TABLE 1. Wet- and dry-bulb humidity values. (*From Kaye and Laby.*)

If a series of measurements is required in a particular locality, the most suitable kind of hygrometer is of the wet- and dry-bulb type. This consists of two thermometers mounted side by side, the bulb of one being covered by absorbent material dipping into a small water reservoir. Latent heat of evaporation will result in the wet bulb being at a slightly lower temperature than the dry and the difference between them can be used to determine the relative humidity of the atmosphere.[1] This is obtained by reference to the simple conversion table above (Table 1). The only precaution

[1] This is defined as the ratio of the mass of water vapour per unit volume of air to that of a similar volume of saturated air at the same temperature. It is usually expressed as a percentage.

necessary when using a hygrometer is to ensure that it is in a shady place and not exposed to direct sunlight. In its usual form, the instrument takes some time to settle down to new conditions. However, equilibrium can be rapidly attained by attaching a strong piece of string to the top of the mounting and swinging the instrument round for a short time. This is a hazardous procedure and may well result in a high mortality of thermometers! A far better device is the whirling hygrometer (Fig. 5) which gives quick and accurate readings, and has been specially designed to

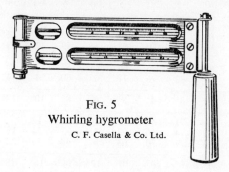

FIG. 5
Whirling hygrometer
C. F. Casella & Co. Ltd.

withstand rough treatment.[1] Estimates of relative humidity are made in the same way as with an ordinary wet- and dry-bulb instrument.

Measurements of humidity in microhabitats such as bushes or tufts of grass present obvious problems. One way of overcoming them is to use the resistance thermometer (p. 30) with two thermistors – one wet and one dry. Estimates of relative humidity can then be made as with a wet- and dry-bulb hygrometer. By adjusting the length of the leads from the thermistors, readings can be taken at any convenient distance from the habitat itself.

Another method which is suitable for microhabitats involves the use of paper impregnated with cobalt salts.[2] Cobalt chloride paper is prepared by dipping filter paper in a 25 per cent aqueous

[1] Manufactured by C. F. Casella & Co. Ltd, Regent House, Fitzroy Square, London, W.1.; cost about three pounds.

[2] For full details of preparation and procedure see Solomon, M. E. (1945). 'The Use of Cobalt Salts as Indicators of Humidity and Moisture', *Annals of Biology*, **32**, 75–85.

solution of $CoCl_2$. $6H_2O$ and allowing it to dry. There is a close relationship between the colour and the atmospheric moisture, the paper being blue at low and pale red at high humidities, with a series of lilac colours in between. The length of exposure required varies with the amount of moisture and the temperature, but about 2 hours is normally sufficient. Standards for comparison are best prepared by exposing pieces of cobalt chloride paper to air of different relative humidities, determined by one of the methods already described. The coloured papers are then sealed in liquid paraffin between two pieces of glass. Relative humidities ranging from 40 to 70 per cent can be measured by this means to an accuracy of about 2 per cent. Beyond this range the error increases to approximately 5 per cent. For higher humidities, cobalt thiocyanate is preferable to cobalt chloride, and it has the added advantage that equilibrium is normally reached in about half an hour. The methods of preparation and standardization differ somewhat from those of cobalt chloride paper and certain corrections are necessary to allow for changes in temperature. Detailed consideration is outside the scope of this book but full particulars are available elsewhere (Solomon (1945) – *see* footnote p. 36).

In certain types of ecological study we frequently require information, not so much on relative humidity as on the *evaporating power* of the air. Thus, while the humidity may remain constant, the higher the temperature the more rapid will be the water loss from a damp surface. The potentiality for evaporation is measured as the *saturation deficit* – the amount by which the partial pressure of water vapour in the air falls short of the partial pressure at saturation point irrespective of temperature. This can be determined from readings on a wet- and dry-bulb hygrometer.

Estimates of relative humidity and saturation deficit have one important limitation, namely, that they only provide information about conditions at a particular moment. Wind is obviously a vital factor influencing the rate of evaporation, since the humid atmosphere surrounding moist surfaces is constantly being replaced by drier air, except on comparatively rare occasions when the air itself is saturated. Wind-speed varies from one minute to the next, hence it may be important to introduce the time factor into a study of humidity.[1]

A useful instrument for measuring the total evaporating power of the air in a particular locality over a given period of time is the *atmometer*. Many forms of this instrument are now available; one

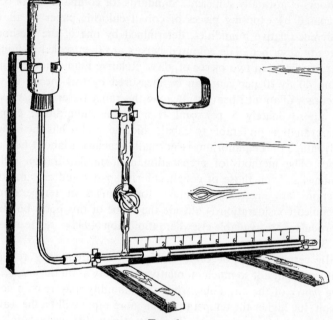

FIG. 6

Portable atmometer for short-term measurements of evaporation

which has been found convenient and reliable for field use is shown in Fig. 6. This consists of a porous tube made of unglazed earthenware which is attached to a capillary tube and reservoir. A second capillary tube fitted with a suitable scale is joined to the base of the reservoir. The whole apparatus is filled with *distilled* water.

[1] Wind-speed can conveniently be measured in the field by using a thermistor in conjunction with a portable Wheatstone Bridge of the type already described (p. 30). For full details of construction and use of the apparatus *see* Penman, H. L. (1949). 'A Portable Thermistor Bridge for Micro-meteorology among Growing Crops', *Journal of Scientific Instruments*, **26**, 77–80.

Evaporation from the surface of the porous tube results in replacement of water from below and hence in the movement of the column in the right-hand capillary tube. This is timed over a given distance and a number of readings taken in order to obtain a mean. The resulting figure will be proportional to the rate of water-loss. After each measurement the moving column is refilled by turning the tap of the reservoir.

Values obtained in this way are purely empirical but they provide a useful means of comparing the evaporating power of the air in different places over short periods. Sometimes it may be necessary to determine the average rate of evaporation in a particular habitat over several hours. Such measurements demand a rather different type of atmometer such as that designed by James (Fig. 7). It works on the same principle as the instrument already described but the reservoir is much larger (250 c.c. flask) and the porous tube is connected to it by ordinary glass tubing, sealed at the end, but with a small hole made in the side about an inch from the top. This is covered by a short sleeve of tightly fitting rubber tubing which acts as a valve allowing water to pass from the reservoir into the porous 'candle' but not in the reverse direction. Comparisons are made by weighing the whole apparatus and determining the loss in weight over a given period.

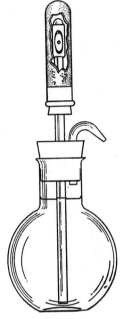

Fig. 7

Atmometer for long-term measurements of evaporation

Tansley: *Intro. to Plant Ecology* (George Allen & Unwin Ltd.)

The successful use of all types of atmometer depends on the effectiveness of the porous surface. Tap water should never be used in the apparatus as minerals, particularly calcium compounds, soon block the pores. A weak solution of mercuric chloride will keep the 'candle' free of algal growth and its surface should be scrubbed occasionally with a stiff brush and distilled water. In order to prevent evaporation when the apparatus is not in use, the porous tube should be covered with a plastic bag which will tie at the neck (obtainable from most biological dealers). This will obviate the need for continual refilling.

CURRENT

A rough estimate of the rate of flow of a stream or river can be obtained by floating a light object such as a table tennis ball and timing its passage over a known distance. This method has obvious limitations – it only records the speed of the surface water and the measurements represent an average of the conditions over the stretch in question.

The simplest type of current meter consists of a single Pitot tube – an L-shaped piece of glass tubing, the vertical length being about 2 feet and the horizontal limb about 4 inches. When immersed in a current with the horizontal limb pointing upstream, the height of the column in the vertical limb can be determined by means of a graduated scale. The faster the current, the greater the pressure it will exert at the mouth of the tube and hence the higher the column will rise. The velocity of the current at a particular depth can then be calculated from the formula

$$v = \sqrt{2hg},$$

where v=the speed of the current,

g=the acceleration due to gravity (32 ft/sec^2 or 981 cm./ sec^2),

h=the height of the column.

In practice, this simple apparatus gives no more than the most approximate estimates of current-speed. The chief limiting factors in its use are:

(a) the height of the column is never more than a few inches above the level of the water. Hence, considerable errors may arise due to parallax;

(b) nearly all flowing waters are subject to some degree of turbulence. This causes oscillation of the water column and makes it difficult to obtain an accurate average reading.

40

A more reliable instrument based on the same principle is shown in Fig. 8. This consists of two Pitot tubes joined together at one end by a central U-tube and with right-angled pieces of copper tubing attached to each of the lower ends pointing in opposite directions. The U-tube is half filled with a fluid which is easily visible against a white background, such as aqueous borax carmine or orange G. The whole apparatus is assembled on a board provided with a scale to indicate the depths of the copper tubes below the surface of the water. When the meter is immersed in flowing water with one tube pointing upstream and the other down (*see* Plate 2), the resulting difference in air pressure on the two sides will cause a displacement of the liquid in the U-tube. The *difference in height* of the two columns is measured against a piece of graph paper mounted behind the tube and this figure will be proportional to the speed of the current at that particular depth.

Calibration can be carried out with sufficient accuracy for all ordinary purposes by selecting suitable stretches of a stream or river where the current is uniform (as judged by the floating object method) and taking a series of readings at the surface. Differences in height of the liquid columns may then be converted into feet per second by a simple graph which can be conveniently mounted on the back of the board near the top and waxed in order to make it waterproof. The apparatus is inevitably somewhat cumbersome to carry

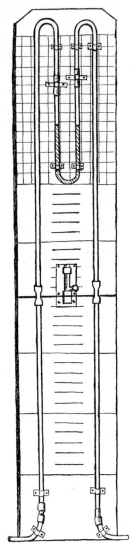

FIG. 8
Current meter
(*see also* Plate 2)

about, for if parallax errors in reading the height of the liquid columns are to be avoided, the board must generally be at least a yard long. This difficulty can be partially overcome by using two boards of equal length hinged in the middle and providing detachable rubber junctions for the tubes on each side so that the meter can be folded up. It is advisable to fit screw clips at either end of the U-tube to stop the liquid flowing out when the meter is placed on its side for transport. When the apparatus is removed from the water it will usually be found that the liquid columns remain at different heights indicating unequal pressure in the two side tubes. This is due to air locks caused by pockets of water becoming trapped in the right-angled tubes at the bottom. They can usually be removed by tapping the board on each side or inserting a pipe cleaner or grass stem. It is important that this procedure should be carried out before each reading is taken if consistent results are to be obtained.

More accurate measurements can be made with electrical devices such as the Ekman current meter which is used extensively in oceanography. But they are not easily home-made and are rather expensive to buy.

GASES DISSOLVED IN WATER

(i) Sampling methods

A preliminary necessity for the analysis of dissolved gases is a means of obtaining samples from particular depths and keeping them out of contact with the air. The sampling of surface water generally presents little difficulty. All that is required is a bottle with a tightly fitting stopper. This is removed under water and the bottle is allowed to fill on its own. Care must be taken when replacing the stopper to ensure that no air bubbles are trapped inside.

Sampling below the surface necessitates the use of a container which can be opened when the appropriate depth has been reached. The apparatus shown in Fig. 9 is simple and works well. It consists essentially of a long glass tube joined to a narrow board calibrated in feet. One end of the tube is attached to a mouthpiece and the other fits on to a container with a volume of about 100 c.c. This is a piece of wide glass tubing with a cork at each end into which is inserted a small glass tube fitted with a short piece of rubber tubing and a clip. It is important that the two glass tubes should end flush with each cork otherwise air bubbles will be trapped inside the container. To take a sample the apparatus is lowered to the required depth with the clip at the mouthpiece closed. When this is opened the container fills and water which has been in contact with air is drawn off into the tube above. Sucking is only necessary at shallow depths (about 2 feet or less) when there is a possibility that some water contaminated by contact with air may still remain in the container.

Once the sample has been obtained the clip at the mouthpiece is replaced and the apparatus withdrawn from the water. Clips are placed at both ends of the container which is then removed. Any water remaining in the long glass tube is now released and a fresh container fitted on. As a check on the accuracy of sampling, it is advisable to take at least two separate samples at each depth. Containers are easily made and it is normally desirable to have about six available at once.

There is an obvious limitation to this simple device, namely, that it becomes exceedingly cumbersome if required for use at depths of more than about 5 feet. For deeper waters it is necessary to have a weighted apparatus which can be let down on a line or wire fitted with markers to indicate the depth.

Fig. 9
Sampler for use in shallow water

The method described by McLean and Cook[1] (Fig. 10) is reliable and works well. It consists of a bottle (about 250 c.c.) fitted with a rubber stopper and weighted by a piece of thin lead piping wound round the bottom. The double right-angled glass tube on the left is the water inlet and passes through the cork to the bottom of the container. The tube on the right fits flush with the cork in order to avoid trapping air bubbles, and passes into a second, smaller bottle (c). This serves as an overflow for the water from the larger container which has been in contact with air when the container was empty. The whole assembly is enclosed in a light wooden frame and slung from a central metal ring (d). The outgoing tube (b) is supplied with a short length of rubber tubing closed by a piece of solid glass rod. As long as this remains in place, no water can enter the apparatus but the tube and bung can easily be removed at the appropriate moment by pulling the thin string (a). Water then rushes in and fills both bottles.

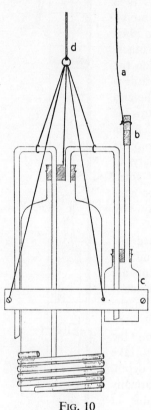

FIG. 10
Sampler for use in deep water

After sampling, the apparatus is raised to the surface; the rubber cork in the larger container is carefully removed and replaced by a glass stopper. The water in the small bottle which has been in contact with air is rejected.

[1] McLean, R. C., and Cook, W. R. I. (1946). *Practical Field Ecology*, George Allen & Unwin.

44

(ii) *Estimation of oxygen*

(a) *Phenosafranine method.* When dissolved in an alkaline solution, oxygen will readily oxidize ferrous iron to the ferric state. The reaction can conveniently be represented as,

$$2\ FeO + O \rightarrow Fe_2O_3.$$

In a titration, the end-point can be determined by adding a small quantity of a dye such as the red phenosafranine which is *reduced* to a colourless compound by the first drop of excess ferrous salt. The alkaline medium is provided by Fehling's solution B (prepared by dissolving 173 gm. sodium potassium tartrate and 120 gm. sodium hydroxide in 1 litre of distilled water). This serves to prevent the precipitation of iron hydroxide, also the hydroxides of calcium and magnesium, when hard water is being tested.

From this equation we see that 11·2 litres oxygen are equivalent to 2×56 gm. ferrous iron. Hence 1 c.c. oxygen is equivalent to $\dfrac{2 \times 56}{11 \cdot 2} = 10$ mg. ferrous iron.

It thus follows that

10 mg. ferrous iron is equivalent to $\dfrac{1 \times 1000}{50}$ c.c. O_2 per

litre of water $= 20$ c.c. O_2 per litre.

∴ 1 c.c. O_2 per litre (using a 50 c.c. sample) $\equiv \dfrac{10}{20}$

$= 0 \cdot 5$ mg. ferrous iron.

If we prepare a standard solution of a ferrous salt (ferrous sulphate) such that 1 c.c. contains 0·5 mg. ferrous iron, then 1 c.c. of it will represent 1 c.c. of dissolved oxygen per litre *provided we take a 50 c.c. sample.*

The amount of $FeSO_4 . 7\ H_2O$ (Analar purity) required for a solution containing 0·5 mg. ferrous iron per c.c. (equivalent to 0·5 gm. per litre) can be calculated as follows. The molecular weight is 278.

Hence, 56 gm. iron are in 278 gm. ferrous sulphate.

45

$$\therefore 0.5 \text{ gm. iron is in } \frac{278 \times 0.5}{56} = 2.48 \text{ gm. ferrous sulphate.}$$

A solution of 2·48 gm. per litre is approximately 0·25 per cent.

Experience shows that standard ferrous sulphate at this concentration gives results which are consistently too low. Evidently, the reaction between dissolved oxygen and ferrous iron is not strictly stoichometric. A slightly lower concentration must therefore be found by trial and error, and a figure of 0·22 per cent generally proves to be satisfactory. In order to avoid any possibility of premature oxidation, the ferrous sulphate should be dissolved in 1 per cent sulphuric acid. Standardization can easily be carried out using air-saturated distilled water prepared by bubbling with an aquarium diffuser or simply by pouring water from one container into another for about ten minutes. A table of oxygen saturation in water at different temperatures is shown on p. 49 (Table 2).

With a little practice, the following technique will be found easy to follow and to give reliable results. Standard ferrous sulphate solution is contained in a burette which should be fitted with an extended jet. Pipette 50 c.c. of air-equilibrated water into a boiling-tube. Add approximately 5 c.c. Fehling's solution B and *2 drops* of 1 per cent aqueous phenosafranine solution. 1 per cent methylene blue is a suitable alternative indicator but the end-point is a little less precise. Titrate this mixture against standard ferrous sulphate stirring carefully all the time with a glass mixing rod. Note the reading when the colour disappears. Repeat the operation running in the ferrous sulphate quickly until near the end-point. The standard solution is such that 1 c.c.=*1 c.c. dissolved oxygen per litre.* Compare the result obtained with the table of figures for saturation (Table 2, p. 49) and calculate any correction factor necessary. If this is outside the range of 0·9 to 1·1, it probably indicates a faulty technique. Estimates of dissolved oxygen in unknown water samples can now be made in the same way.

Once this simple procedure has been mastered the method will be found to give consistent results which are quite accurate enough for most purposes.

(b) *Winkler method.* The Winkler technique of oxygen determination, although giving greater accuracy than the phenosafranine method described above, is more laborious to carry out and less suitable for class work. If manganous hydroxide is added to a known volume of water containing dissolved oxygen, a proportion will be converted into manganic hydroxide. This is dissolved in a non-oxidising acid such as concentrated hydrochloric (free from chlorine) or, better, ortho-phosphoric and made to react with potassium iodide. An equivalent quantity of iodine is then liberated and this is titrated against a standard solution of sodium thiosulphate with starch solution as indicator. The reactions can be represented as follows:

$$2Mn(OH)_2 + O + H_2O \rightarrow 2Mn(OH)_3,$$
$$2Mn(OH)_3 + 6HCl \rightarrow 2MnCl_3 + 6H_2O,$$
$$2MnCl_3 + 2KI \rightarrow 2MnCl_2 + 2KCl + I_2,$$
$$2Na_2S_2O_3 + I_2 \rightarrow Na_2S_4O_6 + 2NaI.$$

The following reagents are required:

A. 40 per cent manganous chloride solution.

B. 33 gm. sodium hydroxide and 10 gm. potassium iodide dissolved in 100 c.c. distilled water.

C. N/80 sodium thiosulphate solution. This must be standardized in the usual way against standard potassium dichromate or potassium permanganate. The solution does not keep well and the appearance of a precipitate is a sure sign that it is no longer fit for use. Deterioration can be delayed to some extent by the addition of 5 c.c. chloroform or 3 gm. borax per litre but, even so, a routine check should be carried out every few weeks.

D. Concentrated hydrochloric or ortho-phosphoric acid.

E. Starch solution, prepared by boiling some starch with distilled water in a boiling-tube and pouring a little of the product into boiling water in a beaker. The solution must be cooled before use because the blue substance formed with iodine is destroyed by heat.

Procedure

Carefully remove the stopper of the container and, for a 70 c.c. sample, add 0·5 c.c. of solution A and 0·1 c.c. of B. For larger volumes proportionately more of the two solutions should be used. Replace the stopper making sure that no air bubbles are included. Shake well and leave to stand for five minutes. A brown precipitate of manganic hydroxide appears and the oxygen in solution is now 'fixed'. This procedure can easily be carried out in the field but the final stages are best completed in the laboratory.

About 2 c.c. concentrated hydrochloric or ortho-phosphoric acid are now added, the stopper being carefully replaced once more. On shaking, the precipitate disappears, the liquid becoming a clear golden brown colour on account of the iodine which has been liberated. Extract 25 c.c. in a pipette and titrate against N/80 sodium thiosulphate using starch solution as indicator. This must be freshly prepared and should not be added until the yellow of the iodine has nearly disappeared. The procedure should be repeated at least twice for each sample.

The calculation is then as follows:

1 c.c. N/80 sodium thiosulphate is equivalent to 0·1 mg. oxygen. Let V be the volume of thiosulphate used, and v the volume of the sample.

Then $$\frac{V \times 0·1 \times 1000}{v} = \text{mg. oxygen per litre.}$$

Now   1 c.c. N/80 thiosulphate $\equiv$ 0·0001 gm. oxygen,

$\therefore$ 1 c.c. N/80 thiosulphate $\equiv \dfrac{0·0001 \times 22{,}400}{32}$ c.c. oxygen.

Hence $\dfrac{V \times 0·0001 \times 22{,}400 \times 1000}{32 \times v} = \dfrac{V \times 70}{v}$

$= $ c.c. oxygen per litre at N.T.P.

It will often be convenient to express the oxygen concentration of a water sample as a percentage of saturation for a particular temperature. This can easily be done by reference to Table 2 (p. 49).

Winkler's method has been found to work well in practice and, apart from the accidental inclusion of air bubbles in the

PLATE 1

(*a*) Portable Wheatstone Bridge and mounted thermistor (see also Figs. 1 and 2)

(*b*) Light-meter and mounted photo-voltaic cell (see also Figs. 3 and 4)

PLATE 2

Current meter in use (see also Fig. 8)

samples, the errors involved are small. The potassium iodide in solution B oxidises slowly on keeping and the appearance of the yellow colour of free iodine is a sign that a fresh solution is needed. The thiosulphate deteriorates quickly and must be renewed after a few weeks. The only other significant source of error is the presence of nitrite – a rare occurrence in natural water. (For detection and estimation *see* p. 147.) When present in a sample it must first be oxidised to nitrate with potassium permanganate the excess permanganate being neutralized with potassium oxalate solution.

Temp. (°C.)	*mg. Oxygen per litre water*	*cc. Oxygen per litre at N.T.P.*
5	12·3	8·68
6	12·05	8·49
7	11·80	8·31
8	11·55	8·13
9	11·29	7·95
10	11·03	7·77
11	10·79	7·60
12	10·56	7·44
13	10·34	7·28
14	10·11	7·12
15	9·88	6·96
16	9·68	6·82
17	9·48	6·68
18	9·28	6·54
19	9·08	6·40
20	8·92	6·28

TABLE 2. Oxygen dissolved by distilled water when saturated with air at different temperatures.
(*After Roscoe and Lunt.*)

Certain types of static water such as stagnant ponds, frequently contain appreciable quantities of organic matter in suspension or solution. This must be removed if an accurate oxygen estimate by the Winkler method is to be obtained. A simple procedure is to oxidize the organic substances with bromine and to remove the excess by addition of sodium salicylate. The following additional reagents are therefore required:

A. 3 gm. potassium bromate, 20 gm. sodium bromide and 25 c.c. concentrated hydrochloric acid made up to 100 c.c. with distilled water.

B. 10 gm. salicylic acid and 20 c.c. of 15 per cent caustic soda made up to 100 c.c. with distilled water.

Procedure

To the sample of water add 0·5 c.c. of solution A per 100 c.c. Restopper and immerse the container in water in the dark for 24 hours. Now add 0·5 c.c. of solution B, shake well and allow to stand for 15 minutes. Subsequent procedure is as for a normal Winkler test.

(iii) *Estimation of carbon dioxide*

The amount of carbon dioxide in natural waters will generally vary inversely with the dissolved oxygen when living plants and animals are present. Before attempting an estimation it is important to determine the pH (*see* p. 52) of the sample in question.

(a) *Acid waters – dissolved free carbon dioxide*

Free carbon dioxide will only occur in acid waters. If a solution of sodium carbonate is added to the sample, the CO_2 will form bicarbonate according to the equation:

$$Na_2CO_3 + CO_2 + H_2O \rightarrow 2NaHCO_3.$$

Phenolphthalein is a suitable indicator for this reaction since it is colourless in the presence of bicarbonate but turns pink when free carbonate appears.

The following reagents are required for the test:

A. N/100 sodium carbonate solution. This can be conveniently prepared by dissolving 0·53 gm. of pure anhydrous Na_2CO_3 – dried in an oven at 103°C. for an hour – in 1 litre of distilled water. The solution does not keep well and it should be standardized each time before use against N/100 HCl.

B. One per cent phenolphthalein solution in 50 per cent alcohol, neutralized with dilute sodium hydroxide.

To 100 c.c. water sample add 10 drops of phenolphthalein solution. Run sodium carbonate solution from a burette until a pink colour is produced which does not disappear within

5 minutes. The chief difficulty with this titration is to avoid the formation of bicarbonate by contact with the air. Error on this account can be reduced to a minimum:

(i) by *gentle* stirring during titration
(ii) by the use of a container such as a measuring cylinder which presents the minimum surface of the water sample to the air.

If x=the number of c.c. of N/100 sodium carbonate required by 100 c.c. sample of water, then the normality of $CO_2 = \dfrac{x}{10,000}$.

A normal solution of CO_2 contains 22 gm. per litre.

∴ the sample contains $2 \cdot 2x$ mg. per litre, i.e. $2 \cdot 2x$ parts per million.

Alternatively, the result can be expressed as c.c. per litre at N.T.P. by multiplying the above figure by $0 \cdot 509$.

(b) *Neutral and alkaline waters – combined carbon dioxide*

In neutral or alkaline waters, any carbon dioxide present will be in the form of bicarbonate – mainly that of calcium and magnesium. This can be conveniently determined by titration with a dilute acid using a suitable indicator.

The following reagents are required:

A. N/100 hydrochloric acid. This can be easily standardized against *freshly prepared* sodium carbonate solution (*see* previous test). The acid can be stored for a long time without any change of normality provided it is kept in a clean, well-stoppered bottle.

B. B.D.H. '4·5' Indicator,[1] or alternatively, a mixture of 0·02 per cent methyl red and 0·1 per cent bromo-cresol green in 95 per cent alcohol. In each the colour change is from blue through grey to a pale greyish-pink. The end-point (=pH 4·5) is taken as the first appearance of a pink tint.

To 100 c.c. of water sample add a few drops of indicator and titrate against N/100 HCl, shaking well. A pilot sample should first be titrated in order to obtain a standard colour for the end-point.

[1] Obtainable from the British Drug Houses Ltd, Poole, Dorset.

51

The amount of combined carbon dioxide is generally expressed as the equivalent quantity of calcium carbonate per litre. Let $x=$ the number of c.c. of N/100 HCl needed for 100 c.c. water sample. The equivalent weight of $CaCO_3$ is 50. Hence the amount of CO_2 expressed as $CaCO_3$ will be $5x$ mg. per litre (or $5x$ parts per million).

HYDROGEN-ION CONCENTRATION (pH)

The accurate estimation of hydrogen-ion concentration necessitates the use of electrical apparatus. This is cumbersome, expensive and not easy to use in the field. Fortunately, the range of pH likely to be encountered in ecology is a relatively small one extending from about 4 on the acid side to 8·5 on the alkaline. Moreover, most plants and animals are able to tolerate quite large variations in the pH of their surroundings. Hence, more approximate methods of measurement can be used by biologists in the field than would be tolerated by chemists in the laboratory.

The colorimetric method is by far the most convenient for making quick determinations of pH. If the variations to be measured are likely to extend over only a narrow range, individual indicators may be used which change colour at known pH values, e.g. bromo-cresol purple which changes from yellow to violet between pH 5·2 and 6·8. However, it is generally more convenient initially to use a multiple indicator such as the B.D.H. Soil Indicator with a pH range of 4 to 8, the colour changes corresponding to steps of 0·5 pH. Special test tubes are available with two graduations, the lower indicating the amount of liquid to be tested and the upper the volume of indicator to be added. The two are shaken together and the resulting colour is matched against those on a standard chart of pH values.

Having obtained an approximate estimate in this way, a more accurate determination can be made by using a capillator with single indicators such as bromo-cresol purple, already mentioned. The method consists essentially in mixing a small amount of water (or soil) with indicator, and transferring it to a capillary tube for matching against a carefully prepared standard. Accurate readings to the nearest 0·2 pH are obtainable by this means. British Drug Houses Ltd. produce a number of different capillator outfits[1] several of which are transportable and ideal for use in the field. A wide range of indicator papers is also sold by dealers; alternatively they can be prepared in the laboratory by dipping filter paper in the required indicator solution. An appropriate series of colour charts is available for matching. This means of pH determination combines the advantages of simplicity and ease of transport but is less accurate than the capillator method.

The accuracy of standard indicator colours can easily be checked with liquids of known pH. Manufacturing chemists such as the British Drug Houses Ltd. produce a series of buffer solutions[2] differing from one another by 0·2 pH and extending over a wide range of acidity and alkalinity.

DISSOLVED MINERALS

(a) Estimation of chlorides

The sea water around our coasts varies little in composition and can be regarded, for all practical purposes, as containing 3·1 per cent chlorides of sodium and magnesium. In estuaries, however, the fluctuations in salinity may be considerable as the state of the tide changes. Such variations often exert a profound effect on the animal and plant colonists of the estuarine zone.

The density of the sea is a function of its temperature and salinity. Hence, a quick estimate of the total chlorides in a sample can be made with a thermometer and sensitive hydrometer, using the conversion graph (Fig. 11). This simple method may well be precise enough for many kinds of ecological study.

If greater accuracy is needed, the chloride can be estimated chemically by titration with silver nitrate using potassium chromate as indicator. To a 100 c.c. water sample add a few drops of potassium chromate solution. Titrate against N/100 silver

[1] These range in price between one and four pounds.
[2] A buffer solution is one whose pH is practically unchanged by dilution and remains constant on addition of acid or alkali.

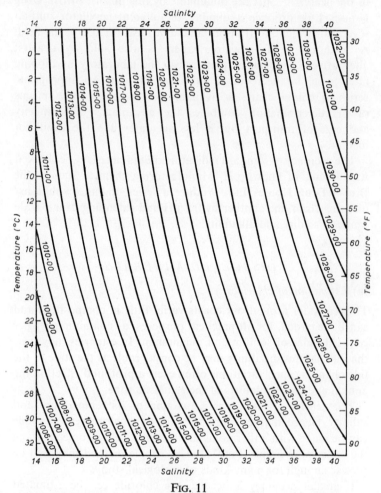

FIG. 11

Graphs showing the relationship between temperature, density and salinity of sea water

Based on Admiralty Chart No. C.6104 with the permission of the Controller of H.M. Stationery Office and of the Hydrographer of the Navy

nitrate stirring constantly. The end-point is reached when a permanent faint red colour of silver chromate appears.

1 c.c. of N/100 silver nitrate $\equiv$ 0·000355 gm. chloride.

(b) *Determination of hardness*

The hardness of water is generally due to the presence of the salts of calcium or magnesium or both. These often play an important part in determining the distribution of animals. Not only are they essential constituents of the outer covering of many arthropods and molluscs, but they are also intimately concerned in controlling the permeability of living tissues to water and solutes.

(i) *Temporary hardness.* This is due to the bicarbonates of calcium and magnesium and can be estimated in the same way as combined carbon dioxide in neutral and alkaline waters (p. 51).

(ii) *Permanent hardness.* This is mainly caused by the chlorides and sulphates of calcium and magnesium. The method of estimation described by Knowles and Watkin is easy to carry out and works well in practice. If a known volume of standardized sodium carbonate solution is added to a water sample, the soluble chlorides and sulphates present will be precipitated as insoluble carbonate. The residual sodium carbonate can then be determined by titration with sulphuric acid and hence the amount used in precipitation can be found.

To a 250 c.c. sample of water add 50 c.c. N/10 sodium carbonate solution. Boil for at least half an hour in order to convert any bicarbonate present (as temporary hardness) into insoluble carbonate. Filter into a 250 c.c. volumetric flask, washing the precipitated matter well with hot distilled water. Allow the filtrate to cool and make it up to the required volume with distilled water, shaking well. Titrate 50 c.c. of filtrate against N/10 sulphuric acid using methyl orange as indicator.

1 c.c. N/10 sodium carbonate $\equiv$ 0·005 gm. calcium carbonate.[1]

[1] The hardness of water (both temporary and permanent) is generally expressed as equivalent parts of calcium carbonate per 100,000.

Thus,

50 c.c. filtrate required v c.c. N/10 sulphuric acid.

∴ 250 c.c. filtrate would require $5 \times v$ c.c. N/10 sulphuric acid.

But 50 c.c. N/10 sodium carbonate were originally added.

∴ $50 - 5v$ c.c. sodium carbonate were used.

∴ hardness $= \dfrac{(50 - 5v) \times 0.005 \times 100,000}{250}$ parts of calcium carbonate per 100,000.

An alternative means of determining the total hardness of water now widely favoured, makes use of a colorimetric procedure. Once the various stock solutions have been prepared, this method is much quicker than that already described and gives results of equal or greater accuracy. It depends on the ability of disodium ethylene diamine tetra-acetate (sodium versenate) to form stable un-ionised complexes with Ca^{++} and Mg^{++}. Similar complexes are also formed with a number of other ions such as Cu^{++} but these are normally present in natural waters in such relatively small amounts that they make no appreciable difference to the final result.

When the dark blue dye eriochrome black T is added to solutions containing calcium and magnesium ions, a complex is formed which is pink in colour. This can be changed back to blue again by the addition of sodium versenate solution which removes the Ca^{++} and Mg^{++} from the dye complex to form the corresponding versenate complex once more. The change in colour of the dye thus provides a convenient and precise end-point.

Another common dyestuff, ammonium purpurate, reacts in a similar way to eriochrome black T but forms a pink complex *only* with Ca^{++} (not with Mg^{++}). This is changed to the normal purple colour of the dye by the addition of sodium versenate. Thus, eriochrome black T can be used as a convenient indicator for the estimation of calcium and magnesium together (total hardness) while the ammonium purpurate reaction enables the calcium alone to be titrated without interference from magnesium (which can be derived from the difference between the two estimations).

The following reagents are required:

A. *Standard sodium versenate solution*

Dissolve 2·5 gm. sodium versenate in 2 litres of distilled water. Add 13·5 c.c. N NaOH (solution E) and make up to 2,500 c.c. Adjust this solution against standard calcium chloride (solution D) so that 1 c.c. is equivalent to 0·1 mg. of Ca^{++}, using eriochrome black T as indicator.

B. *Indicator for total hardness titration*

Add 1 gm. eriochrome black T and 1 c.c. N Na_2CO_3 to 30 c.c. distilled water. Mix well and make up to 100 c.c. with isopropyl alcohol.

C. *Buffer solution*

(Required for total hardness titration only.)

   (i) Dissolve 40 gm. borax in 800 c.c. distilled water

   (ii) Dissolve 10 gm. caustic soda and 5 gm. sodium sulphide ($Na_2S.9H_2O$) in 100 c.c. distilled water.

Mix these two solutions and dilute to 1 litre. This buffer solution serves both to control pH at the appropriate level (pH 8–10) and also to eliminate the effects of the ions of copper, iron and manganese where these are present simultaneously.

D. *Standard calcium chloride* (stock solution)

Add 0·125 gm. calcium carbonate to 100 c.c. distilled water and 25 c.c. N/10 HCl. Make up to 1 litre. This solution is equivalent to 50 mg. per litre of Ca^{++}, i.e. 50 parts per million.

E. *Caustic soda solution*

N NaOH, i.e. containing 40 gm. per litre.

F. *Indicator for calcium only*

Grind together in a mortar 0·20 gm. ammonium purpurate and 100 gm. NaCl. Keep dry in a well-stoppered bottle as the aqueous solution is unstable.

Procedure – Calcium only

A colour standard must first be prepared for matching that of the unknown. 10 c.c. of standard calcium chloride solution (D) are diluted to 100 c.c. with distilled water (equivalent to 5 p.p.m. of Ca^{++}). 2 c.c. N NaOH are added together with approximately 0·2 gm. of calcium indicator (F). 5 c.c. of standard versenate solution (A) are now run in so that the indicator assumes the purple end-point colour. This is unstable and unfortunately fades in a few hours. The difficulty can easily be overcome and, incidently, the need for preparing subsequent standards avoided, by preparing a dilute solution in isopropyl alcohol of the dye dahlia violet. The two coloured liquids should be poured into Nessler tubes standing on a white background and a match obtained by looking *down* on to the columns from above. It will be found that the addition of a trace of methyl red is necessary in order to obtain a perfect resemblance to the colour of the ammonium purpurate end-point. The resulting dye solution is quite stable and will keep indefinitely.

Having obtained a standard, 100 c.c. of the unknown sample are treated in the same way, versenate solution being added until the colour exactly matches that of the standard. Each c.c. of standard versenate required to titrate 100 c.c. sample $\equiv 0·1$ mg. Ca^{++} in 100 c.c., i.e. 1 part per million.

Total hardness

100 c.c. sample of water is slightly acidified by adding N/10 HCl and then boiled for a few minutes. 0·5 c.c. buffer solution (C) is now added and about 5 drops of eriochrome black T indicator (B). The sample is now titrated with standard sodium versenate, the end-point being reached when the blue colour appears. The temperature of the sample has little effect on the accuracy of the test with fairly hard water, but in soft waters titration at approximately 70°C. is found to sharpen the end-point considerably.

The volume of versenate used per 100 c.c. sample in the first titration (Ca^{++} only) is now subtracted from the amount used in the second ($Ca^{++} + Mg^{++}$).

$$1 \text{ c.c. difference} \equiv 0·061 \text{ mg. } Mg^{++} \text{ per 100 c.c.,}$$

i.e. 0·61 part per million.

The old method of determining the total hardness of water by shaking known volumes with standardized soap solution is a rather tedious procedure. The results obtainable are never as accurate as those derived from the methods already described.

The estimation of other dissolved minerals such as the compounds of nitrogen and phosphorus, can be carried out by methods similar to those used in soil analysis. Some of the standard techniques are described in Chapter VI.

CHAPTER III

Collecting and Marking Methods

The ecological study of any community inevitably involves, sooner or later, the collection of specimens of the various animal species. These will exhibit a great diversity of behaviour and modes of life so that a variety of different collecting methods will have to be adopted. On some occasions it will only be necessary to obtain a few individuals for identification. On others, collection may be quantitative with the object of obtaining a random sample of the population as a means of estimating its density.[1]

A knowledge of animal density is of value, not only as a quantitative guide to distribution, but also because it is frequently possible to relate variations in numbers to the influence of certain predominant climatic factors. Moreover, it is well known that rapid fluctuations in density provide the most potent means available for bringing about evolutionary adjustment in wild populations. With a few exceptions, notably some of the larger birds and mammals, it is hardly ever possible to count a whole animal community. Hence, a system of random sampling must be devised; the more representative the samples, the better will they reflect the conditions in the populations from which they were withdrawn.

COLLECTING METHODS

(1) *Flying insects*

For catching day-flying species a suitable net is required with a short stick 2–3 feet long. This is best obtained from a dealer. Entomological nets are more or less of a standard pattern with a jointed frame to permit folding and a diameter of about 18 inches. The net bag is made of leno and this should be black (not green or white, as often sold) so that the insects inside can be seen more

[1] This is most usefully expressed as the economic density – the number of individuals per unit of *inhabited* area.

easily. When collecting larger species such as butterflies, the so-called Kite net will be found the most convenient shape and size (Fig. 12). The cost is about thirty shillings but the expense is well worth while.

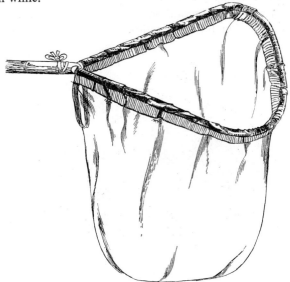

FIG. 12
Kite net

In ecological studies it is frequently necessary to kill the insects for ease of transport and subsequent study in the laboratory. The most satisfactory killing bottle is one containing about a half-inch layer of a mixture of potassium cyanide and plaster of Paris. It should have a wide neck; a 1 lb. jam jar with a well-fitting cork will be found ideal for most purposes. Many corks are far from gas-tight and, if used as they are, the killing bottle will deteriorate rapidly. This difficulty can be easily overcome by dipping the cork in molten paraffin wax in order to block up the pores. The cyanide bottle has the advantage over other kinds of being easy to prepare, lasting well, and being harmless to most insect pigments. Remember that the gas is *poisonous* and must not be inhaled. Delicate insects such as butterflies are liable to be damaged by rubbing

61

against the rough surface at the bottom of the jar. This can be avoided by inserting a thin layer of cotton wool kept in position by a little paste or glue.

Before attempting to collect a sample of insects in a particular locality it is a wise precaution to study the behaviour of the animals first. Careful observation will sometimes reveal the

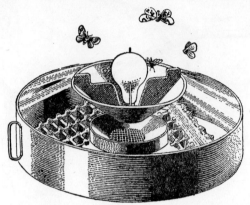

FIG. 13
Mercury vapour light trap (commercial pattern)
Watkins & Doncaster

presence of ecological barriers such as areas of vegetation or patches of light or shade. Moreover, it must be borne in mind that the behaviour of the two sexes is often different; while one may be an active flier, the other may prefer to remain close to the food plant. Such a consideration is obviously important if a truly random sample of the population is to be obtained. A little time spent in preliminary studies of this kind may well save an unnecessary expenditure of labour later on.

The methods of collecting night-flying species have recently undergone a revolution with the discovery that the eyes of many insects (particularly moths) are extremely sensitive to ultra-violet light. Various forms of trap containing mercury vapour lamps are now in use, a typical commercial example being shown in Fig. 13.[1]

[1] This is the kind supplied by Messrs Watkins & Doncaster, 110 Park View Road, Welling, Kent.

The total cost is about sixteen pounds; this includes a choke (about five pounds) which is essential, as the lamp cannot be connected direct to the mains. An efficient home-made version is illustrated in Fig. 14. This utilizes the same M.V. lamp and choke as its commercial counterpart, but consists of a wooden box two foot square and about nine inches deep. The bottom is fitted with

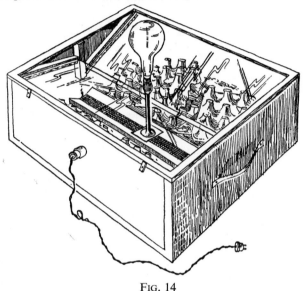

FIG. 14
Home-made type of mercury vapour light trap

an opening covered by perforated zinc to let out rain water. The top is almost closed by two overlapping pieces of glass with a vertical gap of about an inch between them. The metal stem carrying the M.V. lamp projects upwards above the glass. Once attracted into the trap the moths tend to settle down among the egg cartons placed inside. They can be examined by drawing out the glass which is fixed in grooves so that it may slide outwards. The wire leading from the lamp is attached to the choke which, in turn, is connected to the mains. Apart from the lamp and choke, the cost of the parts is small; it should be possible to construct the complete apparatus for about eight pounds.

(2) *Small animals in vegetation and on trees*

Small species, e.g. certain beetles, spiders and larvae of many insects tend to remain among the vegetation within a few inches of the ground, and search for these may have to be made by hand. On occasions, e.g. during warm weather when the animals are active, a 'sweep-net' will often be found helpful in

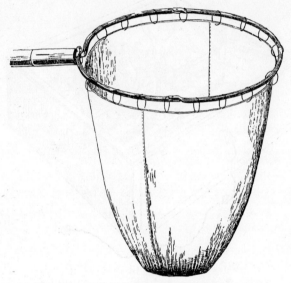

Fig. 15
Sweep-net for use in low growing vegetation

sampling such communities. Its construction is similar to an ordinary entomological net except that the stick is generally longer (about 4 feet) and the frame is made of metal with a stout bag of linen or thin canvas (Fig. 15). Another useful method of collecting spiders and small insects is to sink jam jars in the ground flush with the surface, into which the animals will fall. The mouth of the jar should be covered over lightly with leaves or similar vegetation to keep out the rain.

Where the ground is reasonably flat as in fields and open down-

PLATE 3

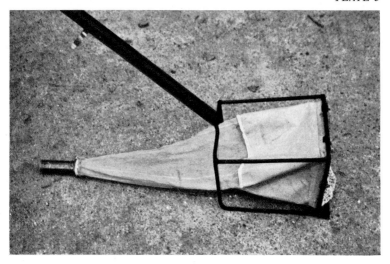

(*a*)

(*b*)

Net for quantitative collecting in water. (*a*) Ready for use. (*b*) Secured
for transport

PLATE 4

(a) Holding a young blackbird for ringing

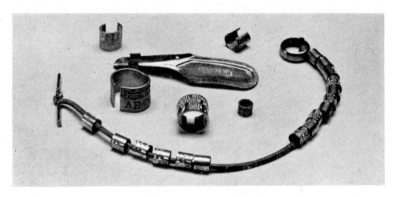

(b) Various types of B.T.O. rings and a celluloid coloured ring (*front right*); tool for opening a coloured ring (*middle*); convenient method of carrying rings in the field (*front*)

land, a type of drag net can be used such as that shown in Fig. 16. This consists of a light tubular metal frame to which is attached a canvas bag. The kind of tubing used to house electric light wires (conduit tubing) is ideal for this purpose and welding can be carried out easily by any blacksmith. On stony surfaces it is advisable to cover the leading edge of the frame with a slit piece of rubber hose pipe bound with wire in order to avoid excessive wear. Although originally designed for collecting lepidopterous

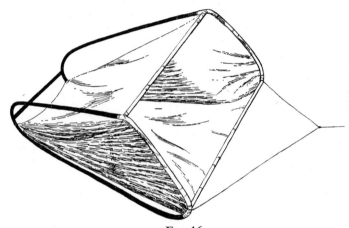

FIG. 16
Drag net for use among low growing vegetation on land

larvae off grass stems at night, the net will be found useful for all the small arthropods and molluscs which abound in low growing herbage.

The inhabitants of taller vegetation such as bushes and small trees, can frequently be dislodged by beating with a stick and collected in a 'tray' underneath. This should be made of a piece of strong fabric about 1 yard square kept taut by a collapsible wooden frame. The standard pattern Bignell beating tray (Fig. 17) can be purchased, but a suitable substitute can easily be made in a laboratory or workshop. An inverted umbrella will be found quite satisfactory for most purposes.

The sampling of colonies of small insects inhabiting rather

inaccessible places such as the rough bark of trees presents a particular problem for it is often difficult to prise them out with a knife without damaging them. An empty wash-bottle with a nozzle of suitable size will be found helpful. The insects can generally be sucked into the flask without difficulty but it is

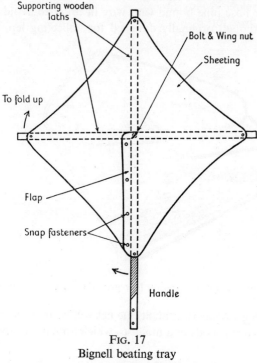

FIG. 17
Bignell beating tray
Neal: *Woodland Ecology* (Heinemann)

important to remember that the inner end of the exit tube must be covered over with a piece of muslin of gauze.

(3) *Larger land animals (birds and mammals)*

The trapping of birds is now widely practised as part of the national ringing scheme organized by the British Trust for Ornithology. Many methods are in current use and an admirable summary of the best of them has now been published as a small pamphlet.[1] Bird traps, in general, are of two kinds.

(a) *Man-operated.* These are efficient but have the disadvantage that they require constant watching and therefore involve a great wastage of time.

(b) *Automatic.* Many designs are available and these are undoubtedly best for all ordinary purposes. When using a trap of

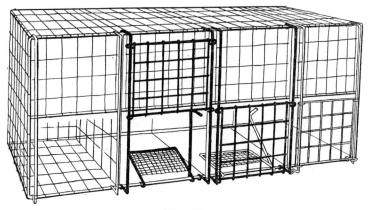

FIG. 18
Potter trap for birds

this kind it is important to make sure that it is visited and emptied at regular intervals (not longer than one hour) otherwise the birds inside are liable to be damaged by battering themselves against the sides. Two other important points should also be borne in mind:

(i) Traps should never be sited in places frequented by cats
(ii) They must never be left 'set' when not in use.

Among the smaller traps, one of the most satisfactory is the Potter trap (Fig. 18). This consists of several compartments each provided with a vertically sliding door. When the trap is set each door is held open by means of a wire support attached to a small

[1] Hollom, P. A. D., and Brownlow, H. G. *Trapping Methods for Bird Ringers* (Field Guide No. 1), 1955, published by the British Trust for Ornithology, 2 King Edward Street, Oxford.

platform below. A bird entering a compartment is bound to alight on the platform and its weight is sufficient to release the door above. The pattern normally used is made of stout wire and is best obtained from a dealer.[1]

Another satisfactory model which can easily be constructed is

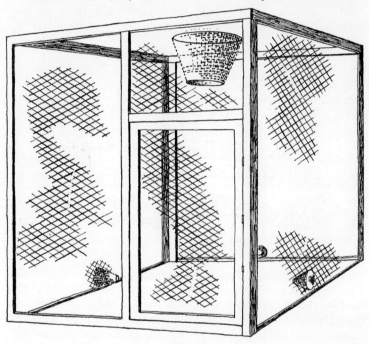

FIG. 19
House trap for birds

the House trap. This is simply a large wooden cage (of approximate dimensions, $6 \times 4 \times 4$ ft) covered with fine mesh wire netting (Fig. 19). It is provided with a door at one side and one or more narrow entrances. These can either take the form of small 'funnels' of wire netting around the bottom of the trap or a single large funnel at the top. The diameter of these entrances must obviously depend on the size of the birds to be caught but, in

[1] Manufactured by The Greenrigg Works, Woodford Green, Essex.

general, the smaller they are the better. Once inside the trap very few birds manage to find their way out again. The difficulty inevitably arises of securing the birds once they are inside the cage. This can be overcome effectively by providing a small wooden extension on one side at a convenient height from the ground (dimensions approximately $3 \times 2 \times 2$ ft). The end of this is closed by a piece of glass which must face towards the maximum amount of light (i.e. South). The birds will tend to fly down the extension towards the light at the end and can then be collected without difficulty.

A variety of baits can be used depending on the natural preferences of the birds to be caught. Bread and corn are both satisfactory, and a special 'bird cake' is obtainable from dealers which is particularly attractive to insectivorous species. It is advisable to scatter bait around the outside of a trap as well as inside it when it is first set up. Bird trapping should be discontinued during the breeding season, i.e. from about mid-March to September.

Although it is easy to trap individual birds, it is extremely difficult (if not impossible) to obtain a random sample of a population by this means. The establishment of one or more traps in an area inevitably upsets the natural distribution of birds and a rapid movement takes place towards the new source of food. The use of numerous trap sites also baited localities without traps will overcome this difficulty to some extent. However, there is a deeper problem associated with the psychology of the birds themselves. Records invariably show that while some individuals evidently regard a trap as a good source of food and are prepared to be caught several times a day, others, once captured, become trap-shy and never appear again. The number of recoveries thus tends to bear little relation to the size of the population as a whole. This is an important point to bear in mind when considering the applicability of the capture-recapture method (*see* Chapter IV, p. 94) to the study of bird communities.

The systematic trapping of mammals presents far greater problems than that of birds. In this country it has so far been confined largely to field mice and voles. The simplest type of home-made trap is that originally developed at the Zoological Museum, Tring (often referred to as the 'Tring' trap). It consists of a wooden box (Fig. 20) of approximate dimensions 6×3×3 inches. One end is closed by a piece of perforated zinc which slides into two slots at the sides. The other is fitted with a thin metal

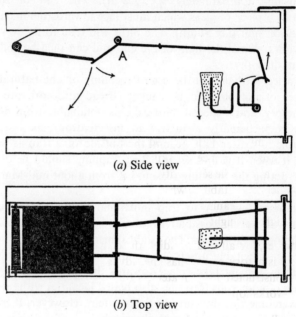

(a) Side view

(b) Top view

FIG. 20
'Tring' mammal trap
Chitty: *Journal of Animal Ecology* (C.U.P.)

door attached to a spring. The mechanism for setting the trap is shown in Fig. 20a. When the trigger A is released the door shuts, clearing the floor so as not to damage the animal's tail. The mouse is easily removed by withdrawing the perforated zinc and covering the exit with a small bag. Blowing through the other end of the trap will often help to induce the mouse to run into the bag. The trap sites can be conveniently marked by sticks conspicuously coloured or fitted with small white flags. Most small mammals are nocturnal so that a night's capture can be removed the following morning. However, some species such as bank voles are active by day and night and, on occasions, a stay in the trap for 24 hours may be unavoidable. In such circumstances a high rate of mortality may occur during cold weather. This can be overcome to a considerable extent by removing the perforated zinc at the end of the trap and replacing it with a small metal box containing bedding materials (dry hay or bracken) and a supply of mixed grain. Various baits have been used but coconut has been found most satisfactory. It should be renewed at frequent intervals.

More recently an improved type of trap has been designed by Chitty and Kempson, made of sheet aluminium alloy.[1] Its advantages are:

(i) A semi-automatic method of setting which is not influenced by individual differences in skill

(ii) An adjustable sensitivity to weights ranging from 1·5 to 8 gm.

(iii) Increased stability when set

(iv) Ease of cleaning

(v) Lighter weight.

However, for all small studies, the original model will be found quite satisfactory and it has the advantage of being cheap and easily constructed from materials that are likely to be available in any workshop.

(4) *Small animals in mud*

Mud is never an easy medium to sample as its consistency and depth vary so greatly. An approximate idea of the animal colonists in the upper layers can be obtained by using a drag net (Fig. 21). This consists of a strong metal framework to which is attached a heavy net bag about 18 inches deep, weighted at the back. The net is pulled along by a cord attached as shown in the diagram. Various sizes of net can be obtained (or made) for use in different circumstances and the depth of mud sampled can be increased to

[1] For full details see Chitty, D., and Kempson, D. A. (1949). 'Prebaiting Small Mammals and a New Design of Live Trap', *Ecology*, **30**, 536–42. The trap is now manufactured at a cost of about fifteen shillings by The Longworth Scientific Instrument Co. Ltd, Thames Street, Abingdon, Berks.

FIG. 21
Drag net for use in water

FIG. 22

Sampling
device for use
in liquid mud

some extent by weighting the metal frame in front so that it sinks more readily. The obvious objections to this method are that collecting is only possible in the top few inches and that representative samples are difficult to obtain from small areas.

Mud-dwelling animals frequently exhibit a marked vertical zonation, thus necessitating a sampling device capable of operating at particular depths. The apparatus shown in Fig. 22 works well in the sort of conditions existing on the bottom of ponds and slowly flowing streams where the mud is soft and fluid. It consists of a metal container (e.g. a cocoa tin) to which is soldered a conical ferrule in order to aid penetration into the mud with the minimum of disturbance. The tin can be closed by a swivelling metal lid operated by a stout wire from the end of the pole to which the assembly is attached. The pole itself is calibrated at six-inch intervals in order to facilitate sampling at particular depths. The apparatus is lowered into the mud with the lid closed and is opened when at the required depth. The lid is then closed again before the sample is brought to the surface.

72

The equipment is simple to make and easy to use, but its limitations are that it can only function in soft mud and at shallow depths (not more than about 6 feet).

A convenient means of sampling in firmer mud is shown in Fig. 23. This consists of two lengths of galvanized iron gutter piping about 3 feet long, hinged together down one side so that they can be closed to form a tube with a locking-device made of a piece of heavy steel wire running through metal 'eyes'. A wooden handle is fitted at one end attached to one half of the tube only, the other half being left free to open and close. At the other end is a 'flap valve' consisting of two semicircular sheets of metal hinged together in the middle and fitting tightly against the sides of the tube when closed. When the apparatus is pushed into the mud the valves open and the tube fills. When it is withdrawn the valves close leaving a core of mud inside the cylinder. This is easily removed when the lock is undone. The advantages of this apparatus are that samples can be taken within a small area and at specific depths. Moreover, the core of mud obtained preserves to a considerable extent the original zonation of layers and the animals contained in them. Obviously this method could not be used at depths of more than about 4 feet.

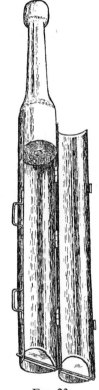

FIG. 23
Sampler for use in semi-solid mud

Sampling at greater depths demands a heavier and more complex type of equipment. An excellent design of 'grab' has been described by Allan but the constructional details are outside the scope of this book. These can easily be obtained by reference to the original account.[1]

[1] Allan, I. R. H. (1952). 'A Hand-Operated Quantitative Grab for Sampling River Beds', *Journal of Ecology*, **21**, 159–60.

(5) *Aquatic species*

Generally speaking, the collection of the various species occupying aquatic habitats presents little difficulty. Molluscs, for instance, are relatively immobile and many of them tend to cling to the surface of stones and vegetation. They can often be collected by hand with the aid of a penknife or section lifter. Capture of the more active species requires some kind of net and a great variety

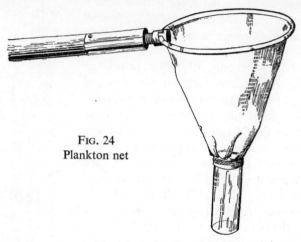

FIG. 24
Plankton net

of types is now available. The smaller of these are operated by hand; the larger ones can be towed behind a boat. Some typical examples are shown in Figs. 24–25. In elementary fieldwork the demand is nearly always for the type of net suitable for collecting in ponds, streams and rock pools. Its diameter should be about 9 inches and the length of the pole about 5 feet. An essential feature is that it must be able to withstand hard use without bending or breaking; this is where the commercial products often fail. By far the best pattern available at present is that designed at the Windermere laboratory of the Freshwater Biological Association.[1] The frame is made of $\frac{3}{8}$-inch gauge duralumin tubing which is brazed into a solid dural block with a hole down

[1] Obtainable complete from the laboratory; The Ferry House, Far Sawrey, Ambleside, Westmorland.

the centre through which a spigot attached to the end of the pole can pass. This is secured by a wing-nut on the inside. The net bag is attached to a length of thick copper wire and fits inside the main frame, the ends of the wire passing into two holes, one on each side of the dural block. It is held firmly in position by bindings of copper wire. The shape of the frame is either of the conventional circular kind or that shown in Fig. 25. The latter is infinitely

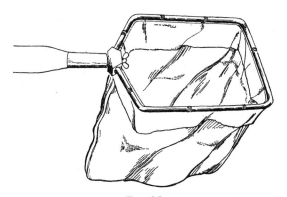

FIG. 25
Net for general collecting in water

preferable for most purposes and enables the net to be laid flat on its side if required.

The size of the animals retained in a net is, of course, determined by its mesh. Three grades are normally used for ecological work:

No. 1, 20 meshes per inch. For larger animals;
No. 2, 60 meshes per inch. For zooplankton;
No. 3, 180 meshes per inch. For phytoplankton.

The nets are made of bolting-silk which is rather expensive but they have a long life if treated carefully and dried well after use. No. 1 nets are plain bags; numbers 2 and 3 are conical and open at the apex so that a suitable container for the plankton can be attached. This usually takes the form of a glass tube but the small rubber funnel now used at Windermere is preferable as this avoids

75

the danger of chafing the silk when the net is packed and is much easier to empty.

As is well known, most plankton is sensitive to changes in light intensity. For this reason, plankton nets should always be *black*, as a white net acts as a reflector causing the animals to swim away from it. This can easily be demonstrated in an aquarium with small crustaceans such as *Daphnia*.

The quantitative sampling of aquatic animals presents considerable problems. On the rare occasions when a species is wholly confined to the surface of stones or mud it may be possible to use the botanical method and throw down a quadrat[1] in a number of different places selected at random (*see also* Chapter IV, p. 91), the animals found within it being counted and collected. The size of the quadrat used will obviously depend on several factors such as the nature of the habitat and the density of the population.[2] For instance, the slowly flowing stretches of the River Itchen are densely colonized by the small snail *Hydrobia jenkinsi*, which is confined almost exclusively to the surface of the mud on which it feeds. A quadrat of 6-inch side has proved quite large enough to obtain adequate samples of the population. For less dense communities a larger size may well be needed. In muddy areas it is advisable to paint the quadrat a bright colour in order to identify it easily.

Few aquatic habitats are, however, as uniform and easy to sample as that just described. More often the sampling of even a few square feet demands the use of a number of different collecting methods. This may not be too difficult in static water, particularly if some kind of 'grab' (*see* p. 73) can be constructed. But in flowing water, the situation is complicated by the fact that the removal of stones and vegetation for examination inevitably causes many of the organisms clinging to them, or sheltering underneath, to let go and be washed away. It is here that the 'square' type of collecting net (Fig. 25) is such an advantage compared with more conventional forms. When lying on its side it can

[1] A sampling square of known area.

[2] For ease and accuracy of counting, it is advisable to divide a quadrat by cross wires into a number of smaller areas. Thus, a six-inch quadrat can conveniently be divided into nine two-inch squares.

easily be propped up by a piece of stick or small metal spigot constructed for the purpose. If placed downstream of the area to be sampled it will catch all those animals which would otherwise have been lost in the current.

Undoubtedly, the ideal procedure is to obtain a complete representative sample in a single operation. This can be achieved in shallow pools, streams and rivers by using the kind of net shown in Plate 3; a modification of the type designed by T. T. Macan. It consists of a stout box-like metal frame of dimensions $8 \times 11 \times 12$ inches attached to a stout wooden handle. Electric light conduit tubing, similar to that used for the land drag net (p. 65), is a good material and can be easily welded. The lower leading edge of the frame is fitted with a metal flange about an inch wide and inclined slightly downwards so as to penetrate just below the stream bed. The net bag is held in position by a number of 'bulldog' paper clips soldered on to the frame, and is easily detachable. The bag itself consists of three distinct parts:[1]

(i) A front portion made of strong canvas. This may have to withstand considerable friction on sand or stones

(ii) A second bag of fish netting which clips inside the first and extracts the larger animals, also stones and vegetation

(iii) A plankton net joined to the rear part of the canvas and open at the back so that a rubber funnel or unbreakable brass or plastic container can be attached. A clip for the container is fitted to the handle for ease of transport (Plate 3b).

After the larger stones have been removed this type of net can be pushed along a few feet at a time to obtain a fair sample of the complete fauna including that living in the top inch or so of the stream bed.

The sampling of swimming animals presents particular difficulties since a net is not only visible, but tends to set up currents as it is dragged through the water which drive the animals away.

In fish research a present trend is towards the development of electrical methods which aim to stun the animals by passing a discharge through the water. Various types of apparatus have been

[1] Can be purchased ready made from The Freshwater Biological Association, Windermere.

developed in Britain and America but, until recently, all have suffered from the same disadvantages, namely:

(i) They are unwieldly and heavy to carry
(ii) They are effective only against the larger fish.

The nearest approach in this country to a portable electric fish-catcher has recently been developed by W. H. Moore: this gives a random sample of fish down to one inch in length, provided it is used in small volumes of water.[1] It may well be

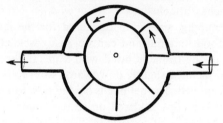

FIG. 26
Diagram to show the principle of the
plankton pump

that, in time, electrical methods will become a valuable aid in sampling communities of the smaller aquatic animals with which the ecologist is generally concerned. The technique is, at present, only in its infancy and there is a big field open for further design and experiment.

Zooplankton is also exceedingly difficult to sample with any degree of precision, and it is doubtful if a method has yet been devised which is both quantitative and does not damage the more fragile organisms. It has been estimated that, using the ordinary types of plankton net (with white bag), the losses in sampling amount to over 75 per cent. No doubt a black bag would improve efficiency, but even so, the effect of the currents set up around the mouth of the net is bound to be appreciable. Fortunately, many elementary studies of plankton are purely qualitative so that these errors do not matter. But for accurate estimates of density

[1] Moore, W. H. (1954). 'A New Type of Electrical Fish-Catcher', *Journal of Animal Ecology*, **23**, 373–5.

there is a demand for an efficient plankton 'pump'. One design developed by the Freshwater Biological Association depends, essentially, on the principle illustrated in Fig. 26. This consists of a chamber fitted with inlet and outlet tubes and housing a wheel with pliable plastic blades. It is pivoted eccentrically so that when rotated by an electric motor, the blades form a tight union with one side of the chamber, thereby setting up an appreciable suction. The apparatus works well but has the disadvantage that it damages some of the smaller organisms. Here, again, there is considerable opportunity for experiment and ingenuity.

(6) *Inhabitants of soil*

It is doubtful if any of the techniques used at present for sampling soil animals achieves a hundred per cent extraction. However, several of them have proved sufficiently reliable to provide good comparative estimates of populations in different localities as well as an approximate idea of the actual density of particular communities.

(a) *Chemical extraction* (Earthworms). A variety of chemicals has been tried for sampling earthworm populations (e.g. derris, potassium permanganate, etc.) but by far the most effective of these is aqueous formalin solution. The concentration required is about a gallon of formalin per square yard, sprayed from a watering can fitted with a rose.[1] Large areas can be marked out with string and sprayed systematically yard by yard, the error due to liquid falling outside being relatively small. For smaller squares it is best to construct quadrats of wood with sides about 2 inches high. These must be placed firmly on the ground and banked up with earth on the outside if necessary, so as to ensure that permanganate does not leak out underneath. A few minutes after treatment the worms will start to appear on the surface. They can then be collected by hand and stored in 4 per cent formalin. No further extraction will normally occur after about half an hour, but the soil should always be dug over in order to include the few individuals that may remain just below the surface. One

[1] The concentration recommended is 25 ml of 40 per cent formalin per gallon of water.

advantage of this technique is that the worms do not retire into the subsoil as they tend to do when a spade is driven into the ground. Furthermore, the different species occurring in samples taken from the same locality are found to exhibit a constant numerical relationship to one another, indicating that the permanganate affects them all to the same extent.

Evans and Guild have made detailed studies of earthworm populations using the method just described[1] and have shown that the size of samples taken from the same soil may be greatly influenced by the temperature and humidity. Moreover, while some species such as *Lumbricus terrestris* remain active throughout the year, others, notably *Allolobophora longa* and *A. nocturna* spend much of the summer in a state of diapause and are therefore largely absent from samples taken during this period.

(b) *Funnel methods* (Arthropods). Many modifications now exist of the original 'Berlese Funnel', first described in 1905. This depends on the simple principle that if soil is heated from above, the various arthropods (particularly Collembola) tend to move away from the hot zone towards the cooler conditions below. Progressive heating of the whole soil sample suspended in a perforated tray over a funnel will therefore drive the animals downwards into a collecting container of preservative underneath.

Modern versions of this apparatus are mostly of the Tullgren pattern, that is, they employ light as well as heat as a means of extraction. A typical example is shown in Fig. 27. This consists of a source of heat and light (40 watt electric light bulb) mounted on a movable rod so that its distance from the soil can be adjusted. A fresh sample of soil is collected and a known volume placed on the wire gauze inside the metal funnel. The dish below contains 70 per cent alcohol. The period of heating required varies with the amount and nature of the soil. Light, dry soils may need only about 24 hours, while heavier, wet ones require 2–3 days. This apparatus, although crude by modern standards, is quite effective for obtaining rough comparisons of the composition of the arthropod populations in different localities. The design of an

[1] Evans, A. C., and Guild, W. J. McL. (1947). 'Studies on the Relationships Between Earthworms and Fertility', *Annals of Applied Biology*, **34**, 307–30.

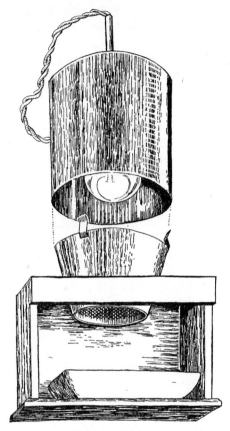

Fig. 27
Tullgren funnel

equipment suitable for more precise work has been discussed by
Macfadyen who has developed a 'high gradient' funnel with
success. Compared with the type just described, its chief im-
provements are:

(i) The use of small funnels in banks of six thus enabling
statistical treatment to be applied to groups of samples

(ii) The avoidance of condensation

(iii) The design of special glass funnels with a narrow included angle (not more than 60°) in order to facilitate the passage of small animals downwards

(iv) A carefully regulated temperature gradient

(v) The soil sample is collected in the container in which it will be heated, thereby avoiding the artificial disturbance of the animals inside.

Detailed consideration of this and similar apparatus is outside the scope of this book but further information may be obtained from the original account.[1]

Various repellent chemicals have been tested in the Tullgren apparatus instead of heat as a means of driving the animals downwards through the soil. These include 'gammexane' (benzene hexachloride), DMP (dimethyl phthalate) and DNOCHP (dinitro-*ortho-cyclo*-hexyl phenol). All have proved to be less efficient than heating for the extraction of mites and spring-tails and it is doubtful whether they are any more effective than flotation methods (described below) in the study of other animal groups.

(c) *Flotation methods* (Small Arthropods and larvae). Many small arthropods and their larvae float readily in liquids whose specific gravity is only slightly greater than that of water. 7 per cent aqueous magnesium sulphate (S.G. 1·07) is often used, but 25 per cent salt solution (S.G. 1·19) seems just as good for many purposes and is much cheaper. A sample of soil or mud (about 150 c.c.) is emptied into a container of approximately 500 c.c. capacity which is then filled with salt solution. White photographic dishes will be found particularly suitable for this purpose. After stirring, many of the arthropods will appear at the surface together with a good deal of plant debris. The animals can now be removed by hand with a small spatula using a hand lens or low power dissecting microscope. All floating plant material should also be inspected at this stage and then taken out. Stirring is now continued until all the large pieces of soil have disintegrated and the liquid assumes a cream-like consistency. By this time it should be

[1] Macfadyen, A. (1953). 'Notes on Methods for the Extraction of Small Soil Arthropods', *Journal of Animal Ecology*, 22, 65–77.

possible to extract from the surface the majority of floating animals larger than 1–1·5 mm. Some species, such as those whose bodies are coated with a layer of mud, also tube-dwelling forms, often refuse to come to the surface. These can generally be detected by decanting the liquid mud into a second dish, using sufficient at a time just to cover the bottom with a thin film. This can be diluted with water if necessary to make it more transparent.

The efficiency of this simple method appears to be very variable. It works well with aphids and many larvae of the Chironomidae (Diptera) for which extraction is generally complete. On the other hand, the difficulty of separating small arthropods from floating debris is undoubtedly an inherent source of error and probably accounts for the low yield of small mites and spring-tails (Collembola).

Salt and Hollick, in their studies of wireworms, have devised a much more elaborate method of extraction which takes place in four phases:

(i) Breaking down the lumps of soil by refrigeration
(ii) Removal of vegetation and other debris by sifting
(iii) Extraction of the animals from the mineral soil by a process of washing
(iv) Separation of the arthropods from the residual fine organic matter at a water-benzene interface.

The procedure, although no doubt more efficient (at least for some species) than that already described, is extremely tedious to perform, and treatment of a single sample requires about 3 days to complete. Full details of the apparatus required and the experimental technique are given in the original account.[1]

Differences of opinion still exist as to the relative merits of hot funnel and flotation techniques. The position is complicated by the fact that no carefully controlled comparisons have yet been made. The truth probably is that while small organisms such as Collembola and mites are best extracted by the Tullgren method, larger forms such as aphids lend themselves more readily

[1] Salt, G. (1952). 'The Arthropod Population of the Soil in some East African Pastures', *Bulletin of Entomological Research*, **43**, 203–20.

to removal by flotation. Clearly, there are great opportunities for further experiment in this field.

MARKING METHODS

One of the main reasons why animal ecology is so much more difficult to study than plant ecology is that animal populations are constantly on the move. Hence, if individuals in a community, once identified, are to be recognized again, it is essential that some means of artificial marking should be employed.

Animals are generally marked for three main reasons:

(i) To distinguish between the members of two or more neighbouring populations. This is particularly necessary in circumstances where several communities, each with a relatively high density, are separated from one another by minor ecological barriers which may not achieve complete isolation.

(ii) In studying their movement. The range of animals varies enormously from migratory journeys of thousands of miles performed by some species of mammals, birds, fishes and insects, to the small local sorties up and down tree trunks characteristic of nocturnal molluscs

(iii) In estimating population numbers by the capture-recapture method (*see* Chapter IV).

(a) *Ringing* (Birds and Mammals). The technique of marking vertebrate animals by attaching light aluminium rings to their legs has been used with conspicuous success in the study of birds. In Britain, a national scheme was initiated by the editorial staff of the magazine *British Birds* in 1909. This was taken over in 1937 by the British Trust for Ornithology which is now responsible for the issue of numbered rings and the keeping of all records connected with British bird ringing. Aluminium rings all look alike at a distance so that the only way of distinguishing between marked individuals of the same species is by trapping them and examining the ring numbers. This limits the value of the scheme as a means of studying local bird movement and behaviour throughout the year. The difficulty has been largely overcome by the introduction of coloured rings[1] which are made of tough celluloid and in the same sizes as the standard rings. Unlike the national marking scheme, the use of coloured rings does not require the sanction of the B.T.O. although a record is kept by the Trust of all individual colour-ringing schemes. This has the obvious advantage of avoiding confusion in areas where several similar studies are going on at once. The types most easily identified are those in single colours (as opposed to stripes) and experience has shown that very little fading occurs over a period of 4–5 years – the maximum life of our smaller birds.

Various types of bird rings are shown in Plate 4b. The B.T.O. ring is aluminium and easily closed by bending; the colour ring is a split celluloid ring and requires a small tool to open it (supplied with the rings). The correct way to hold a bird for ringing is shown in Plate 4a.

The marking of small mammals presents greater difficulty than that of birds. Thin zinc rings were used at first but they tended either to come off, or to be tightened unduly by biting. Aluminium rings of the kind used for birds would therefore be equally unsuitable. A successful type evolved by Chitty[2] for marking field mice and voles is constructed from a rectangular piece of 0·5 mm. pure nickel foil, size 9×3 mm. Numbers can easily be embossed or scratched on the rings but it is advisable to avoid the digit 1 as this tends to cause a line of weakness. The rings are applied with fine-nosed pliers fitted with a strong elastic band to keep them closed. For full details of the ringing and trapping techniques for small mammals, see the references below.

(b) *Fur-clipping* (Mammals). For short-term studies, the clipping of fur down to about $\frac{1}{8}$ inch is a convenient and quick way of marking small mammals. Chitty and Shorten have used this method with success in their study of the Norway Rat[3] and have found that the technique can be much improved by applying a depilatory to the underlying skin. This consists of 7 parts by

[1] Manufactured by The Greenrigg Works, Woodford Green, Essex.

[2] See Chitty, D. (1937). 'A Ringing Technique for Small Mammals', *Journal of Animal Ecology*, 6, 36–53.

[3] Chitty, D., and Shorten, M. (1946). 'Techniques for the Study of the Norway Rat (*Rattus norvegicus*)', *Journal of Mammalogy*, 27, 63–78.

weight barium sulphide, 7 flour, 7 French chalk, 1 Castille soap powder. The mixture is moistened and applied with a spatula; the marks are said to last 2–3 weeks. A simpler method which works well with voles and field mice is to apply a small patch of quickly drying cellulose paint to the tip of the tail. It has been found to last for as long as a month.

(c) *Tagging* (Fishes). Any method of marking which involves the insertion of a metal label into part of the body is inevitably open to certain objections. First, there is always the possibility that the tag may be torn off as the animal moves between stones and through vegetation. Mishaps of this kind are relatively few with the larger fishes. But in small species such as the minnow the use of this method of marking is virtually precluded by difficulties in fixing on the tags and by the ease of their removal. Furthermore, in fish of all sizes, there is always the danger that manipulation in marking may result in unusual behaviour and an abnormally high mortality.

In spite of these objections, tagging has nonetheless been used successfully for some years for marking species such as trout and salmon, both in Britain (by the Freshwater Biological Association) and in America. The type of tag now in general use consists of a short piece of stiff nickel wire bearing a metal label which is attached to the operculum, fin or tail. There is an extensive bibliography on this subject which has been conveniently summarized.[1]

(d) *Paint*. Various types of quickly drying cellulose paint are now obtainable (the solvent is generally amyl- or ethyl acetate). These have proved extremely successful for marking land animals with a hard outer integument, such as arthropods and molluscs. When applied to the wings of butterflies and moths, the drying paint seals the surrounding scales so firmly on to the wing membrane that the coloured mark is retained long after the rest of the scales have been worn away.

The paint is easily applied with any pointed object; the head of a small pin inserted into a wooden handle or a sharpened matchstick have been found suitable for marking small shells and

[1] Rounsefell, G. A., and Kask, J. L. (1943). *Transactions of the American Fishing Society*, 73.

butterflies. The application of this technique to the wings of flying insects, e.g. Lepidoptera, demands a two-man operation – one to hold the wings together with a pair of forceps, the other to apply the paint (this should be on the side of the wing exposed at rest – underside in butterflies). After marking, the animals should be retained for about two minutes before liberation, in order to allow the paint to dry. Remember that many organic acetates are anaesthetics; hence, care must be taken to ensure that, when released after marking, the animals are in a fit state to disperse. This applies particularly to insects which are likely to be kept in small boxes. Some individuals show a decided reluctance to fly on being set free and tend to sit about on the surrounding vegetation. The necessary encouragement to disperse can generally be provided by throwing them into the air from an open pill box. When visiting the releasing site on the next occasion it is important to make sure that all the insects marked previously have in fact flown and that none are still there.

Unfortunately, cellulose paint marks do not last well under water nor will they adhere to wet surfaces. Certain types of ship-fouling paint have, however, been used with success in marking the shells of aquatic molluscs. The proprietary brand 'Necol' (manufactured by Imperial Chemical Industries Ltd.) is particularly suitable on account of its quick drying. The range of colours available is somewhat limited, and it will be found best to purchase the white paint and add dyes to it, as required.

(e) *Intra-vitam stains.* The possibility of using intra-vitam stains for marking small animals such as arthropods has, as yet, hardly been explored at all. Some of these, such as trypan blue, are non-toxic and readily taken up by the body tissues of many arthropods, but it is not known for certain how long the staining lasts.

The possibility of using various dyes for marking fish has recently been investigated by Hamid in America.[1] Experiments with the bluegill (*Lepomis macrochirus*) showed that certain non-toxic stains injected into the fins or operculum could remain fast for at least 90 days without causing any apparent harm to the fish. The stains were applied as 1 per cent aqueous solutions and

[1] Hamid Al-, M. I. (1954). *Progressive Fish Culturist*, **16**.

the following proved the most satisfactory: brilliant vital red, congo red, alizarin red S, chlorazol fast pink B, nigrosine and trypan blue. Experiments with minnows using trypan blue have shown that this method of marking is unsuitable for small fish. Fins and tails seem to lose their colour after about 24 hours, while injection of the operculum is a difficult operation and causes a high mortality. Preliminary trials with trout and grayling suggest that staining may be a suitable means of marking species of larger size.

(f) *Radioactive tracers*. One of the recent trends in the ecological study of animals has been towards an increasing use of radio-active substances as a method of marking small populations. Marked individuals can then be detected, in the wild state if necessary, by a portable Geiger-Müller counter. One obvious limitation of the other methods of marking already described is that they can only be used for one phase of an animal's life cycle, generally the adult. The use of radioactive markers provides a means of overcoming this difficulty. For instance, Kettlewell has found that larvae of the scarlet and garden tiger moths, *Panaxia dominula* and *Arctia caja*, fed on food containing small traces of sulphur-35, were not only themselves radioactive but so also were the resulting adults and their eggs. Such methods open up tremendous possibilities for the study of survival and the operation of natural selection during the different phases of an animal's life.

Isotopes used in this kind of work have to be selected with the greatest care; for their half-life must be long enough to cover the various stages in the life cycle to be studied, yet sufficiently short to avoid quantities of radioactive material remaining in the countryside for an appreciable time. Moreover, they must be substances, like the sulphur series, which are readily absorbed by animal tissues. Obviously, such methods demand expert control, and are outside the scope of the elementary student. They are mentioned here on account of their extensive application in more advanced ecological work and the conspicuous success which many of them have already achieved.[1]

[1] For a concise account of radioactive tracers see Overend, W. G. (1951). *The Use of Tracer Elements in Biology*, Heinemann.

CHAPTER IV

Quantitative Ecology

1. Numerical Studies and their Presentation

There are few kinds of ecological study which do not demand some consideration of the quantitative aspect. An attempt at a numerical approach, no matter how imperfect, is always infinitely preferable to no attempt at all. The important thing is to be aware of the limitations of the various methods available, and to appreciate the circumstances in which each can be most usefully employed.

One of the most frequent needs of the ecologist is a reliable means of determining the density of a population. This is required for such purposes as:

(i) Estimating the extent of the colonization by a species of different kinds of ecological niches

(ii) Studying the economics of a community, for instance, the relationship between numbers and the availability of a particular kind of food

(iii) Determining the selective advantages and disadvantages of the different forms of polymorphic species

(iv) Long-term studies of fluctuations in numbers

(v) Experimental studies of adaptation and evolution in new and changing environments.

Many of these or kindred problems are of a kind with which an elementary student is likely to be faced so that some knowledge of the various methods used for determining animal densities is desirable. So, too, is an appreciation of their limitations.

METHODS OF ESTIMATING DENSITY

(a) Direct counts

Estimating the numbers of a population by direct counting is obviously limited to species of relatively large size in which a high proportion of the individuals is visible at any one moment. Furthermore, movements into and away from the community must be reduced to a minimum if reliable and consistent figures are to be obtained. This method is particularly suitable for birds inhabiting open country or cliffs, and for some of the larger or medium sized mammals such as seals and rabbits. The best time of the year to count a bird population is during the nesting season when movement is restricted. The efficiency of counting can be greatly increased by the use of a number of observers walking in line abreast, each being responsible for the particular section in front of him. All birds seen should be recorded *directly the observation is made*, care being taken to make allowance for those entering and leaving particular sectors while the count is in progress. This procedure is used extensively in determining the populations of game birds such as partridges and, with a little experience, it can yield consistent and reliable results. The problem of counting animal populations in woodland, such as birds and squirrels, is more complex, but the method of line transects used by botanists for some years can be employed successfully for this purpose. Compared with plants, the situation in animals is more complicated because of their mobility, and this necessitates the introduction into the calculation of a number of new variables such as the average rate of movement of the observer also that of the organisms to be counted. However, the procedure involved and the mathematics underlying it are not difficult to understand and deserve further study and trial, for such methods should be useful in a wide range of conditions. The application of the theory of line transects to the study of birds has been developed by Yapp[1] and a summary of his findings is given in Appendix A.

[1] Yapp, W. B. (1957). 'The Theory of Line Transects', *Bird Study*, **3**, 94–104.

(b) *Use of Samples*

Only on rare occasions will it be possible to count a whole population of animals or even an appreciable proportion of one. The estimation of numbers nearly always demands the collection of representative samples which must then be related to the population from which they were withdrawn. The various methods used for collecting animals have already been considered in Chapter III. In general, these are of two kinds:

(i) The collection at random of the animals themselves. In highly mobile species such as fishes and flying insects the areas sampled may be very large extending to hundreds of square yards or even acres. Relatively immobile forms like molluscs and insect larvae can often be sampled effectively by the quadrat method, that is to say by laying down a series of squares of known size at random and counting the animals within them. The area of the quadrat will depend partly on the density of the population to be sampled, and partly on the diversity of the habitat. Thus a six-inch square has proved suitable for sampling colonies of *Gammarus pulex* in parts of the River Itchen while one of a yard side has been used in estimating earthworm populations in cultivated ground by the potassium permanganate method (p. 79).

In most ecological studies it is desirable to make a brief preliminary survey involving the minimum use of special equipment. Approximate estimates of density are often valuable and can generally be obtained quite easily. For instance, in a quick survey of may-fly nymphs in a stream it was decided to count the specimens sheltering underneath ten stones of 'average size' selected at random in each locality sampled. Obviously, such a crude procedure could only provide a rough approximation to the true figures but, nonetheless, it was sufficiently accurate to indicate that the population in one area was about double that in another.

(ii) The removal of samples of the medium with the animals inside it. This is the method often adopted for collecting plankton, e.g. the 'plankton pump' (p. 78) and also for quantifying the populations of small animals inhabiting soil and mud.

A convenient means of counting the larger species of plank-tonic animals such as adult *Daphnia* is to filter a known volume of water through a Büchner funnel attached to a filter-pump. The individuals can be counted quite easily with the aid of a hand lens, particularly if the filter paper is placed on a dark background. With large numbers of animals, it will be found a help to divide the filter paper by pencil lines into about eight equal segments and

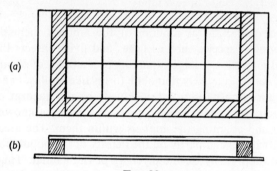

(a)

(b)

FIG. 28
Construction of a Rafter cell to hold 1 c.c. of liquid
1 mm. deep. (a) Surface view (b) Side view (cover
glass in position)

to examine each one in turn. The smaller aquatic organisms are best counted in a Rafter cell which can easily be made in the laboratory and consists of a shallow glass trough containing 1 c.c. of liquid. A microscope slide serves as a good base for the cell and this should be ruled into ten 1-centimetre squares (*see* Fig. 28a). The lines can be made with a diamond and then rubbed over with a blue or black wax pencil (the type used for writing on glass) in order to make them more visible. The sides of the cell are made from strips of microscope slide glass cemented on to the base with Canada Balsam (*see* Fig. 28b). A small volume of the water sample is introduced into the cavity on the slide and a long cover-glass is lowered carefully on top, great care being taken to ensure that no air bubbles are trapped inside. The organisms can then be counted under a microscope square by square, the low power generally providing sufficient magnification. Sometimes it will be a question of counting the individuals of a particular species; on other occasions it may be necessary to discover the relative abundance of different forms. When making estimates of the second kind it is important not to try to count too many species at a time; five is generally quite sufficient. The procedure is to record the number of each form per cm. square until a total of, say, a hundred or more observations have been made. The occurrence of individual species is then expressed as a *percentage frequency*, i.e. as a percentage of the total number of observations made. Since the distribution of plankton in water is practically never uniform, it is essential when estimating its density in a particular locality to obtain counts from as many different samples as possible.

Bulk estimations of the plankton obtained from net samples can be made by determining its dry weight. The animals are killed with 5 per cent formalin and then filtered through a Büchner funnel, the filter paper being previously weighed. This is then heated to constant weight in an evaporating dish on a steam bath and the increase in weight noted. The method is rather crude and takes no account of other matter suspended in the water, such as decomposing organic material. It can only be used when relatively large quantities of plankton are to be collected.

Samples of soil and mud are generally extracted as a 'core' by means of an auger or other similar device. The removal of small animals, mainly arthropods, presents a variety of problems which have already been considered in some detail in Chapter III (pp. 79–84). Suffice it to say here that filtration methods are effective but laborious, several hours being required for the examination of a single small sample. Flotation in magnesium sulphate or sodium chloride solution is a much more rapid process and is particularly suited to the study of mud. Difficulties arise, however, with certain forms such as those species of *Chironomus* (Diptera) whose larvae construct tubes of mud which they are extremely reluctant to vacate. Probably the most effective means of extracting the majority of the smaller species from soil samples is the Tullgren funnel which combines the effects of heat and light in causing the animals to move in the opposite direction. The advantages of this apparatus are that it is not only highly efficient but that it can also be adapted for treating a number of small samples simultaneously. The results obtained thus lend themselves readily to statistical analysis.

(c) *Capture-recapture method*

A particular problem is presented by animals such as flying insects and fishes which are highly mobile and whose numbers cannot therefore be assessed by either of the methods already described. The capture-recapture method has proved useful in such circumstances and is essentially an extension of ordinary sampling procedure. It represents not merely one of the many ways of estimating animal numbers but, with appropriate calculations, it allows deductions of fundamental importance which can be obtained in no other way. Losses from and gains by a population can be assessed over a period, so allowing an estimate of density fluctuations to be made. Moreover, it enables the death rate to be calculated and hence a comparison to be made between different forms in different environments – a real measurement of the effects of natural selection.

Suppose we are studying a colony of butterflies and we catch, say, 50 specimens and mark them by the method already described (p. 86). They are then released into the population once more and given sufficient time (24 hours should be allowed) to assort at random. Next day a further 50 insects are caught, among them 10 which bear marks. We can then calculate the total *flying* population as $(50 \times 50)/10 = 250$. The process of capture and marking can be continued for as long as required, the greater the number of samples taken the more accurate will the estimate of population density become. The record of a period of sampling can be conveniently summarized in the form of a triangular trellis. The example (Fig. 29) shows some results that E. B. Ford and I obtained when studying a small isolated colony of the meadow brown butterfly (*Maniola jurtina*) on Tean, Isles of Scilly in 1946. The dates of the samples run horizontally along the top of the diagram. From the position of each date, lines run downwards south-east and south-west at 45 degrees so as to intersect. The total daily samples are entered at the end of the column running south-west from the date in question, while the total insects released are included at the end of the corresponding column running south-east. In the event of there being no recaptures on a particular day, these two numbers will, of course, be the same except on the rare occasions when an insect is damaged in marking and has to be killed. All recoveries are shown in the body of the

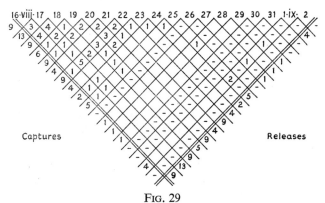

FIG. 29

Results tabulated as a trellis in the capture-recapture method of estimating animal numbers

Heredity: Oliver & Boyd Ltd. (publishers)

table and the number of marks they carry, together with those of insects marked for the first time, represent the total 'marks released' each day. It is not necessary with this method to collect a sample every day. In the table a dash (—) shows that no recaptures were possible on a particular date, either because no insects were caught or because none were released the day before.

Examples will make this method of presentation clear. In Fig. 29 at the extreme left of the table and below the date 16.viii, is the number 9 at the head of the 'Captures' column. A corresponding figure appears under 'Releases' showing that on that date the whole sample was successfully marked for the first time and liberated. On the next day 13 insects were caught, among them 3 captured the day before, each bearing a single mark. These

95

appear on the table in the square to the south-west of the appropriate date. The total insects released was also 13 and this figure appears at the end of the column corresponding to 17th August. Again, the entries for 26th August are all dashes, showing that there was no collecting that day and therefore no recaptures.

Simple direct estimates can be made from the table of the daily flying population. For example, consider the line running south-west from 17th August: out of 9, 6, 9, 4, 9, 4, 2, 5 (total 48) butterflies caught on subsequent dates, 4, 2, 1, 1, 5, 1, 1 (total 15) recaptures belonged to the 13 marked on 17th August. Thus the total number flying on that date can be calculated as approximately $(48 \times 13)/15 = 41$ insects.

The chief requirements for the effective operation of the capture-recapture method are:

(i) The species used must be one in which marked individuals will randomize readily when released. Most mobile forms present little difficulty in this respect, but it is important at the outset of an experiment to determine just how quickly the process of mixing takes place. Tests can easily be made by releasing a number of marked individuals at a central point and judging the time required before recaptures are made with equal frequency throughout the area to be studied.

(ii) Sampling must be entirely at random. The ways of catching invertebrates described in Chapter III are mostly quite suitable and present few problems. The situation among vertebrates is not so satisfactory. The many efficient methods which have been devised for trapping birds, for instance, and the existence of a well established marking scheme, suggest ideal opportunities for estimating the numbers of bird populations by capture-recapture. But, as anyone who has had experience of bird-ringing will know, the samples obtained in traps are anything but random. Some individuals quickly become trap-shy and, once caught, never appear again. Others soon learn to associate a trap with food and it is not uncommon to catch the same blue tit as many as twelve times in a week! Furthermore, there is abundant evidence to show that the appearance during winter of artificial sources of food such as traps and bird tables causes a high proportion of the local population to concentrate in their vicinity and hence to assume an abnormal distribution. These various objections can be overcome to some extent by instituting a number of possible trapping sites dispersed widely in the area to be sampled and keeping all of them permanently baited. The dispositions of the traps are determined by some random process such as drawing numbers out of a hat and their situation is changed regularly, say, once a week. Even so, one major objection remains, namely, that sampling is being carried out in a population whose distribution has been largely determined by external agencies.

The sampling of small mammals such as field mice and voles presents somewhat similar problems to that of birds. In spite of claims that the capture-recapture method is applicable under certain circumstances, it is doubtful if truly random samples are readily obtainable. There is also the additional problem of trapping sufficiently large numbers of animals to provide valid samples since each trap can catch only one individual at a time. Large numbers of traps must therefore be deployed.

(iii) The method of marking must be such as to distinguish between the different dates of capture. This can generally be done by adopting a variety of colours or mark-positions, or by a combination of both. In ecological work on the meadow brown butterfly, for instance, E. B. Ford and I have found that twelve different dots of paint can be applied to the underside of the hind-wings alone; six on each wing.

(iv) The population to be studied must be reasonably stable and not subject to rapid fluctuation in numbers. The simple procedure already described depends for its accuracy on the assumption that the density of a community is virtually constant throughout the period of sampling. This may well be true for a matter of a few days. But in no population of animals do the numbers remain the same for long; immigration and the appearance of young will tend to increase them while emigration and deaths have the opposite effect. In studies of any duration, therefore, the influence of these factors must be taken into account. This is done by comparing the number of recaptures *expected* in a population distributed at random with those actually *obtained*, using as a basis the number of marks existing from day to day. The method of analysis is explained in Appendix B, p. 292.

USES OF STATISTICAL METHODS

We have seen how the difficulty of studying whole populations of animals often necessitates the collection of random samples. The effectiveness of this procedure rests on the answers to three important questions:

(i) To what extent is sampling really random?

(ii) How far are we justified in assuming that the samples withdrawn reflect accurately the conditions in the population as a whole?

(iii) Are the methods of sampling sufficiently sensitive to enable us to compare the situations in two or more different populations?

One of the greatest difficulties in studying living organisms is that they are subject to the influence of such a wide range of variables, many of which are still unknown. As a result, animals and plants seldom conform to the kind of precise, quantitative laws which characterize other branches of science. The solution of quantitative problems in ecology thus demands a kind of mathematical approach which is unlike that employed in elementary physics and chemistry and which is concerned, not with attempting to provide the precise answer 'yes' or 'no', but rather with indicating the *probability* that a particular answer has been obtained by chance. The use of statistical methods demands an arbitrary choice of the point at which the influence of luck may be reasonably excluded. Fortunately, the nature of the mathematical treatments themselves often assists us in making this decision.

Before proceeding to a more detailed discussion of statistical procedure and its uses in analysing ecological results, there is one other important preliminary to be considered – the design of quantitative experiments. Statistics is sometimes regarded by the non-mathematical as a kind of magic tool which can be brought into action when all other methods of analysis have failed. Nothing could be further from the truth. The essence of success in any quantitative experiment is to ask the right questions; in other words, the data collected must be of a kind that can be analysed

in a *pre-determined* way. This is equally important in both short-
and long-term experiments and is a point which organizations
such as school Natural History Societies, which tend to keep
routine records, should always bear in mind. Statistical advice is
now readily obtainable and there is a wealth of good elementary
text-books on the subject (*see* Bibliography). The next chapter
(Chapter v) includes a brief outline of the kinds of method which
are likely to prove useful in elementary animal ecology.

GRAPHICAL PRESENTATION

The first step in the analysis of quantitative data is its assembly
in a form in which it is readily accessible. There are two methods
of presentation:

(i) Tabulation – that is to say, the arrangement of figures in
columns and by categories. This is the method usually adopted in
scientific work and is the most convenient way of presenting data
which require further analysis

(ii) Graphical – this involves the use of diagrams of various
kinds. It is a simple means of displaying, say, the overall results of
sampling or a continuous series of physical measurements, e.g.
temperature records. But it is not as efficient as tabulation for the
summarizing of numerical information.

Four kinds of graphical presentation are commonly used:

(i) *The time-chart.* This is the most suitable way of recording
periodic measurements of physical factors such as temperature
and light (Fig. 30). It is a convention that 'time' should always be
plotted along the *x* axis. When constructing charts of this kind a
question often overlooked is whether successive points should be
joined or not. In ecology, the data likely to be presented in this
way are of two sorts. The quantity measured may be continuous
but erratic such as the variations in light intensity shown in Fig. 30.
There is some justification here for joining the points by straight
lines for this implies a continuity of the variable but ignorance of
its intervening fluctuations. The procedure should be contrasted
with that often used in physics and chemistry when two variables

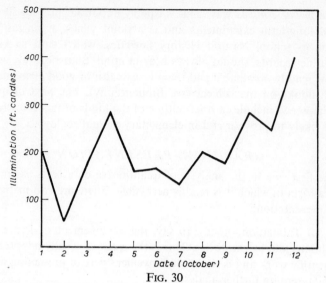

FIG. 30

Time-chart of illumination at the surface of a pond

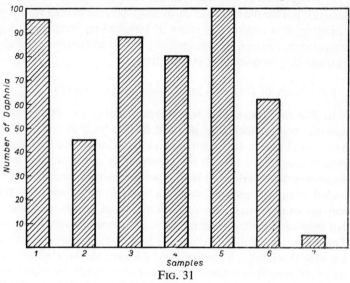

FIG. 31

Bar-chart of numbers of *Daphnia* in successive samples from a pond

are related according to a fixed law, e.g. the solubility of a substance in relation to temperature. Here, the fluctuations between successive readings can be predicted and, in non-linear relationships, the points should be joined by a smooth curve.

When two different factors are being measured at the same time, e.g. the temperature and humidity of the air, it is often helpful to plot them both on the same chart so that any relationship between them can be seen at a glance.

(ii) *The bar-chart*. This is the most convenient way of representing grouped data, e.g. the sizes of successive samples taken from a population (Fig. 31). It is generally quite easy to superimpose a bar-chart on a time-chart if the two quantities being studied are thought to be related. The data shown in Figs. 30–31 were obtained at the same time and place, hence a combination of the two in the way suggested would show at once if any relationship existed between the degree of illumination and the number of *Daphnia* present.

(iii) *The histogram*. In the study of animal and plant populations it is often necessary to analyse a sample in terms of some variable such as size, weight or colour in order to gauge its distribution in the community as a whole. The histogram is the graphical means of representing actual numbers (as opposed to percentages which should be shown by dots joined by straight lines), and is an easy way of determining at a glance if the structure of a population in respect of a particular characteristic is remaining constant or not. A typical example is shown in Fig. 32 which represents the size/frequency distribution in a sample of *Gammarus pulex* from the River Itchen. As a population gets older the proportion of large individuals will tend to increase and the peak of the figure will therefore tend to shift from left to right. On the other hand, the appearance of appreciable numbers of young may well give rise to a second peak among the small individuals.

This simple method of expressing frequency-distribution is of value in many kinds of inquiry. For instance, it is well known that predation on most animal species varies in intensity at different stages of their lives. The histogram provides a ready means of detecting a deficiency in a particular age- or size-group. Again,

101

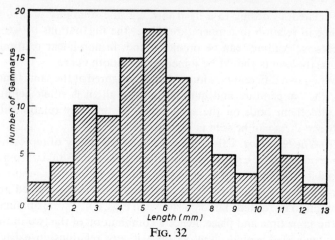

FIG. 32

Frequency histogram showing the size-distribution in a sample
of *Gammarus pulex*

among small animals such as aquatic insects and crustaceans, it is
not always easy to determine when a new brood has appeared,
but if this is of any size it will at once be apparent from a histogram
of the size/frequency distribution.

(iv) *Correlation graphs.* Many elementary ecological problems
are concerned with the simple relationship between a population
and one or more environmental factors, such as temperature or
light. We have already seen what a vast number of variables,
many of them still unknown, interact in a complex way to influence the lives of animals. It is unlikely, therefore, that the effect
of any one will be so potent as to mask that of all the others.
Hence, the type of graph obtained in studies of this kind is not the
straight line or uniform smooth curve characteristic of mathematical functions and of elementary experiments in physics and
chemistry, but rather the sort of diagram shown in Figs. 33–34.
The sampling of certain species of may-fly nymphs in a stream
(Fig. 33) shows clearly that, in general, an increase in the speed
of the current is accompanied by a rise in the density of animals.
We are thus justified in drawing an ideal straight line midway
between the scatter of points, indicating a positive association

102

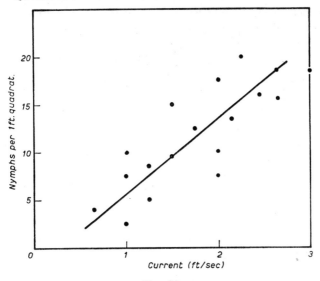

FIG. 33

Graph showing positive correlation between the speed of a current and the distribution of may-fly nymphs in a stream

between the two variables observed. The wide divergence of some of the readings will be due to a variety of causes the chief, no doubt, being errors in sampling, for in areas as small as one square foot it is certain that many of the samples collected will be far from random. Nonetheless, the measure of agreement obtained indicates strongly the desirability of using such methods however crude they may be.

Sometimes the association between two variables is negative, that is to say, an increase in one brings about a corresponding decrease in the other. In such negative linear correlations the line always runs in a direction from north-west to south-east; in positive correlations the slope is in the opposite direction. Fig. 34 shows how an increase in the speed of the current is associated with a decrease in the population density of the small aquatic snail *Hydrobia jenkinsi*. The number of snails in the stream was large but the rate of flow of the water was so variable that only a six-inch quadrat could be used. However, the results show that the use of this rather inadequate means of sampling was fully justified in the circumstances.

Obviously, it is an advantage if, in addition to the methods of

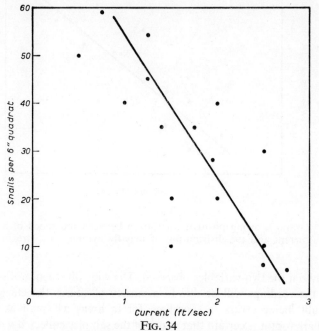

FIG. 34

Graph showing negative correlation between the speed of a current and the distribution of the snail *Hydrobia jenkinsi* in a stream

graphical representation outlined above, some more precise mathematical measure can be used to denote both the degree and the size (positive or negative) of the linear association between the variables. A simple coefficient employed by statisticians for this purpose is the *correlation coefficient*. Methods of calculating it are outside the scope of this book but will be found in most works on statistics (*see* Bibliography).

Quantitative Ecology

2. Statistical Methods

Much has been said in the previous chapter about samples and sampling procedure. It now remains to consider a few of the ways in which statistical methods can help in the analysis of ecological data once it has been accumulated. No attempt will be made here at a mathematical derivation of the various formulae used. For the great majority of biologists, statistics serve merely as a valuable tool. The most important thing, therefore, is to know not how the tool is constructed, but rather how it can be employed to the best effect.

AVERAGES

One of the commonest needs in quantitative ecology is a way of deriving information from a series of comparable samples. The obvious method is to determine their mathematical average or *mean* which can then be compared, if required, with that of similar groups of samples from other localities. Problems arise here which can best be illustrated by an example.

A class was studying the density of populations of the small Gastropod *Hydrobia jenkinsi* living in a Hampshire chalk stream. Samples of the snails were collected from the surface of the mud in two different localities using a 1-foot quadrat. Some of the results are shown on page 106.

Judged on the basis of their means, there would appear to be an appreciable difference between the two groups. If we examine the size of the various samples, however, we find that one set of readings is much more consistent than the other. In those from Locality A, the maximum is 120 and the minimum 65 snails (difference=55); while in Locality B the maximum is 170 and the minimum 54 (difference=116). The magnitude of the difference between the largest and smallest numbers in a series of samples is a measure of the scatter or range of the observations. Obviously, scatter alone is not a reliable index of the homogeneity of sampling since it depends on two values only instead of on all the available information. Nonetheless, the reliability of the average of a number of samples, all of which lie closely about their mean, is bound to be greater than one which is in the midst of a widely dispersed series.

Locality A		*Locality B*	
Sample No.	*No. of snails*	*Sample No.*	*No. of snails*
1	80	1	170
2	120	2	95
3	65	3	54
4	74	4	123
5	89	5	88
	Total 428		Total 530
	Mean=86		Mean=106

In order to make a valid comparison of the means of two or more series of samples, two further pieces of information are, thus, required:

(i) The number of samples taken
(ii) The range of the observations within each group.

These two factors together determine the magnitude of the sampling error.

STANDARD DEVIATION

The simplest and most useful measure of the sampling error is the *standard deviation*. This is the square root of the average of the deviations of the samples squared from their arithmetic mean: or, stated as an equation,

$$\text{S.D.} = \sqrt{\frac{\Sigma(x-\bar{x})^2}{N}},$$

where $x =$ number of each sample,

$\bar{x} =$ the mean,

$N =$ number of samples,

$\Sigma =$ sum.

It is now possible to carry the analysis of the data from the two snail populations (p. 106) a stage further.

For Locality A we have:

Sample No.	x	$x-\bar{x}$	$(x-\bar{x})^2$
1	80	−6	36
2	120	34	1156
3	65	−21	441
4	74	−12	144
5	89	3	9

Mean $(\bar{x}) = 86$ $\qquad\qquad \Sigma = 1786$

$$\text{S.D.} = \sqrt{\frac{1786}{5}} = 18\cdot9.$$

$\therefore$ True mean $= 86 \pm 18\cdot9$.

Similar treatment of samples from Locality B gives:

Sample No.	x	$x-\bar{x}$	$(x-\bar{x})^2$
1	170	64	4096
2	95	−11	121
3	54	−52	2704
4	123	17	289
5	88	−18	324

Mean $(\bar{x}) = 106$ $\qquad\qquad \Sigma = 7534$

$$\text{S.D.} = \sqrt{\frac{7534}{5}} = 38\cdot8.$$

$\therefore$ True mean $= 106 \pm 38\cdot8$.

Once their standard deviations have been calculated, we can

gain a much clearer idea of the value of our samples than we could have from their means alone. In this example, the difference between the averages from the two localities was only 20. But we now see that while the true mean for Locality A lies within the range 108–70, that for Locality B is 145–67.

We are thus faced with the problem of deciding whether the differences between these two groups of samples can reasonably be ascribed to luck, or whether they should be regarded as indicating the existence of two distinct populations.

STANDARD ERROR

One of the commonest needs in quantitative biology is a way of determining whether there is a significant difference between two observed means, or not. Provided the numbers are reasonably large (30 or more), the question can be answered by calculating the *standard error* of the differences between these means. This indicates the probability that a given result shall be equalled or surpassed by chance. We are then left with the arbitrary decision as to the point at which statistical significance has been achieved. The differences between two quantities is generally judged to be significant when it equals or exceeds *twice* the standard error; that is to say, when the odds are roughly 20 : 1 against the result being due to chance.

The reason for taking $2 \times$ S.E. (Standard Error) as the point at which a difference begins to attain significance can most easily be explained by the following table:

The probability of a difference exceeding
$$\begin{cases} \text{S.E.} \times 1 \text{ by chance is 1 in 3,} \\ \text{S.E.} \times 2 \text{ by chance is 1 in 22,} \\ \text{S.E.} \times 3 \text{ by chance is 1 in 370,} \\ \text{S.E.} \times 4 \text{ by chance is 1 in 17,000.} \end{cases}$$

Thus, S.E. $\times 2$ stands, as it were, at the point where the curve of probability starts to become very steep, so that only a slight excess over it means that the chance of obtaining the result by luck is really quite small.

Provided two variables are independent and uncorrelated, as in the previous example, the standard error of the difference between their means is given by the formula:

$$\text{S.E.} = \sqrt{\frac{\sigma_1^2}{N_1} + \frac{\sigma_2^2}{N_2}},$$

where σ_1 and σ_2 = the Standard Deviations,
N_1 and N_2 = the number of samples in each group.

Returning to the original example (p. 106) the data required for calculating the standard error are as follows:

	Locality A	Locality B
Number of samples	5	5
Mean	86	106
Standard Deviation	18·9	38·8,

$$\therefore \text{ S.E. of difference} = \sqrt{\frac{18 \cdot 9^2}{5} + \frac{38 \cdot 8^2}{5}} = 19 \cdot 3.$$

The observed difference between the two means (20) is less than $2 \times$ S.E. (38·6). Thus, judging from the small number of samples taken, there is no indication of a difference in density.

The erratic type of sampling used here as an example is just the kind which is likely to be encountered in elementary work and great care must be taken in interpreting the results. In this instance, it may well be that the density of the population in Locality B was, in fact, greater than that of Locality A but the method of sampling was not sufficiently sensitive to show it. A further series of readings was therefore indicated. If the erratic fluctuations persisted, the next step would have been to use a smaller quadrat (say 6 inch) in order to determine their true value.

No matter how imperfect the sampling methods may be, exercises of this kind are useful in giving students an idea of the meaning of significance and of the value of simple statistical tests.

The standard error can also be used in ecology for a variety of other purposes. Since the calculations involved are so very quick and easy, it is worth mentioning a few further applications.

(i) *Standard Error of a Percentage.* One of the most convenient ways of expressing the relationship between two variables is as a percentage. Suppose we collect a sample of animals and find the proportion exhibiting a particular characteristic, how can we relate the condition in our sample to that of the population from which it was taken? A typical example is as follows.

The seasonal breeding activity of *Gammarus pulex* can be gauged by the number of adult females bearing eggs or young in the brood pouch. In a sample of 136 females taken in the autumn, 31 (22·8 per cent) were found to be breeding. What is the situation in the population as a whole?

The standard error of a percentage is given by the formula,

$$S.E. = \sqrt{\frac{p(100 - p)}{N}},$$

where $p =$ the percentage,
$N =$ the number in the sample.

For the sample of *G. pulex*

$$S.E. = \sqrt{\frac{22·8 \times 77·2}{136}} = 3·6.$$

We can now write the proportion of breeding females in our *sample* as $22·8 \pm 3·6$ per cent. Furthermore, the chances are approximately $20:1$ that their percentage in the *population as a whole* lies within the range $22·8 \pm (S.E. \times 2)$, i.e. 30 to 15·6 per cent. In order to obtain a more precise result than this, it is clear that a much larger sample would have had to be taken.

(ii) *Comparison of expected and observed Percentages.* Sometimes we are justified in expecting a particular result such as a 50 per cent sex-ratio, and we wish to know whether the conditions in a sample conform with expectation, or not.

In a random sample of 120 meadow brown butterflies, 44 per cent were males. Does this represent a significant departure from sex-equality?

Since we are expecting a 50 per cent ratio, we must calculate the standard error on that assumption, i.e.

$$\text{S.E.} = \sqrt{\frac{50 \times 50}{120}} = 4 \cdot 6.$$

The departure from expectation in the sample is $50-44=6$ per cent. This is less than $2 \times \text{S.E.}$ ($=9 \cdot 2$). We can therefore conclude that our observed result gives no indication of a divergence from the expected sex-ratio.

In the field, it is often helpful to apply a quick check to see if two quantities differ significantly from *equality*. Perhaps samples are being collected and it is desirable to know whether more animals are required, or not. A rough test can be made as follows. Find the difference between the two numbers and subtract 1 from it; square the result and divide this by the sum. Significance is achieved when the resulting figure is greater than 4. This can be represented in the form of an equation as:

$$\frac{(D-1)^2}{N} > 4 \text{ (for significance),}$$

where $D =$ difference between two numbers,

$N =$ their sum.

It is emphasized that this method is only approximate and, for more accurate results, the standard error should always be calculated as already described.

(iii) *Comparison of two observed Percentages.* Percentages, like any other standards, mean little when used alone: the ecologist constantly needs to compare them. Once the standard errors of two unrelated quantities are known, that of the difference between those quantities can be calculated from the formula,

$$\text{S.E.} = \sqrt{(A^2 + B^2)},$$

where A and B are the standard errors of the two variables.

To return to the study of breeding frequency in *G. pulex* already discussed (p. 110). A further sample of 160 females taken the following spring was found to contain 62 (38·8 per cent) breeding individuals. Is the difference between the two samples a real one in the sense that it suggests the influence of changing climatic factors in controlling reproduction? The relevant data are:

	Autumn	*Spring*
No. in sample	136	160
No. breeding	31 (22·8 per cent)	62 (38·8 per cent)
Standard Error	3·6	3·9

$$\text{S.E. of difference} = \sqrt{(3\cdot6^2 + 3\cdot9^2)} = 5\cdot3.$$

The observed difference in the percentages breeding is $38\cdot8 - 22\cdot8 = 16$. Since this is more than 3 times the standard error, we are justified in concluding that the divergence is significant and not just due to luck in sampling.

SMALL SAMPLES

The previous calculations have depended on the assumption that, with relatively large numbers, the distribution of individuals is normal (i.e. at random) or approximately so. Obviously, the smaller a population becomes, the more will its distribution tend to deviate from normality. The extent of this deviation is shown by the so-called t-distribution, which enables us to determine the significance of the difference between means of a series of small samples, in a way analogous to that already used for larger quantities. The t test can, of course, be applied equally well to large samples as to small ones, but as the numbers increase the t-distribution approaches the normal distribution more and more closely so that the rather laborious calculations involved become no longer worth while.

The formula can conveniently be expressed as,

$$t = \frac{(\bar{x}_1 - \bar{x}_2)\ \sqrt{\dfrac{I}{N'}}}{\sqrt{\Sigma(x_1^2) - \dfrac{[\Sigma(x_1)]^2}{N_1} + \Sigma(x_2^2) - \dfrac{[\Sigma(x_2)]^2}{N_2}}},$$

where $\Sigma(x_1)$ and $\Sigma(x_2)=$ the sums of the two series of samples,
$\bar{x}_1$ and $\bar{x}_2=$ their means,
N_1 and $N_2=$ the number of samples in each group.

$$\sqrt{\frac{1}{N'}}=\sqrt{\frac{N_1 \cdot N_2(N_1+N_2-2)}{N_1+N_2}}.$$

The following type of problem demands this kind of treatment. A comparative study was made of the earthworm populations in two small neighbouring plots of ground, one of which had recently been manured while the other had not. Sampling was done by the potassium permanganate method (*see* p. 79) using quadrats of 3-foot side. The following results were obtained by a class of students:

Plot 1 (with manure)		*Plot 2 (no manure)*	
Sample No.	*No. of earthworms*	*Sample No.*	*No. of earthworms*
1	5	1	4
2	9	2	3
3	12	3	6
4	9	4	8
5	10	5	5
6	7	6	3
7	5	7	4
8	8	8	5
9	4		
	Total 69		Total 38
	Mean $(\bar{x}_1)=7\cdot67$		Mean $(\bar{x}_2)=4\cdot75$

Do the samples reveal any significant difference between the densities of the two populations?

For Plot 1	*For Plot 2*
$N_1=9$	$N_2=8$
$\Sigma(x_1)=69$	$\Sigma(x_2)=38$
$\Sigma(x_1)^2=585$	$\Sigma(x_2)^2=200$
$\bar{x}_1=7\cdot67$	$\bar{x}_2=4\cdot75$

Thus $\bar{x}_1 - \bar{x}_2 = 2 \cdot 92$ (disregarding the sign).

$$\sqrt{\frac{I}{N'}} = \sqrt{\frac{9 \times 8 \times 15}{17}} = 7 \cdot 97.$$

$$\Sigma(x_1{}^2) - \left[\frac{\Sigma(x_1)}{N_1}\right]^2 + \Sigma(x_2{}^2) - \left[\frac{\Sigma(x_2)}{N_2}\right]^2$$

$$= 585 - \frac{69^2}{9} + 200 - \frac{38^2}{8} = 75 \cdot 5.$$

$\therefore$ by the formula

$$t = \frac{2 \cdot 92 \times 7 \cdot 97}{\sqrt{75 \cdot 5}} = 2 \cdot 68.$$

The next step is to determine the number of degrees of freedom (N). This is defined as the least number of independent variables which must be given values before the state of a system can be completely determined. The figure can be quickly obtained from the formula:

$$N = N_1 + N_2 - 2 (= 15 \text{ in this example}).\ \textit{See also p. 121.}$$

Reference must now be made to Table 3 which shows the values of t for different numbers of degrees of freedom corresponding to a probability P. It will be seen that for $N=15$, the value of $t=2 \cdot 13$ for a probability of $0 \cdot 05$ (i.e. 1 in 20). Our calculated estimate ($2 \cdot 68$) exceeds this (P=nearly $0 \cdot 02$); hence, the difference between the two means can be judged significant, indicating a 'real' divergence in the densities of the two earthworm populations.

In the example chosen there was no doubt about the meaning of the result. Occasions may arise, however, in which the calculated value of t closely approaches or equals a probability of $0 \cdot 05$. Caution should be exercised in interpreting situations of this kind and it is always wise, if possible, to obtain further comparable samples before drawing conclusions.

χ^2 DISTRIBUTION

We have seen (p. 108) how a calculation of the standard error may prove useful when a distribution is normal, or nearly so, and when

TABLE 3

Table of t

N	0·90	0·80	0·70	0·50	Probability 0·30	0·20	0·10	0·05	0·02	0·01	0·001
1	0·16	0·33	0·51	1·00	1·96	3·08	6·31	12·71	31·82	63·66	636·62
2	0·14	0·29	0·45	0·82	1·39	1·89	2·92	4·30	6·97	9·93	31·60
3	0·14	0·28	0·42	0·77	1·25	1·64	2·35	3·18	4·54	5·84	12·94
4	0·13	0·27	0·41	0·74	1·19	1·53	2·13	2·78	3·75	4·60	8·61
5	0·13	0·27	0·41	0·73	1·16	1·48	2·02	2·57	3·37	4·03	6·86
6	0·13	0·27	0·40	0·72	1·13	1·44	1·94	2·45	3·14	3·71	5·96
7	0·13	0·26	0·40	0·71	1·12	1·42	1·90	2·37	3·00	3·50	5·41
8	0·13	0·26	0·40	0·71	1·11	1·40	1·86	2·31	2·90	3·36	5·04
9	0·13	0·26	0·40	0·70	1·10	1·38	1·83	2·26	2·82	3·25	4·78
10	0·13	0·26	0·40	0·70	1·09	1·37	1·81	2·23	2·76	3·17	4·59
11	0·13	0·26	0·40	0·70	1·09	1·36	1·80	2·20	2·72	3·11	4·44
12	0·13	0·26	0·40	0·70	1·08	1·36	1·78	2·18	2·68	3·06	4·32
13	0·13	0·26	0·39	0·69	1·08	1·35	1·77	2·16	2·65	3·01	4·22
14	0·13	0·26	0·39	0·69	1·08	1·35	1·76	2·15	2·62	2·98	4·14
15	0·13	0·26	0·39	0·69	1·07	1·34	1·75	2·13	2·60	2·95	4·07
16	0·13	0·26	0·39	0·69	1·07	1·34	1·75	2·12	2·58	2·92	4·02
17	0·13	0·26	0·39	0·69	1·07	1·33	1·74	2·11	2·57	2·90	3·97
18	0·13	0·26	0·39	0·69	1·07	1·33	1·73	2·10	2·55	2·88	3·92
19	0·13	0·26	0·39	0·69	1·07	1·33	1·73	2·09	2·54	2·86	3·88
20	0·13	0·26	0·39	0·69	1·06	1·33	1·73	2·09	2·53	2·85	3·85
22	0·13	0·26	0·39	0·69	1·06	1·32	1·72	2·07	2·51	2·82	3·79
24	0·13	0·26	0·39	0·69	1·06	1·32	1·71	2·06	2·49	2·80	3·75
26	0·13	0·26	0·39	0·68	1·06	1·32	1·71	2·06	2·48	2·78	3·71
28	0·13	0·26	0·39	0·68	1·06	1·31	1·70	2·05	2·47	2·76	3·67
30	0·13	0·26	0·39	0·68	1·06	1·31	1·70	2·04	2·46	2·75	3·65

When *N* is greater than 30, *t* may be treated as a normal deviate without serious inaccuracy resulting.

(Abridged from *Statistical Tables for Biological, Agricultural and Medical Research* by R. A. FISHER and F. YATES, with the kind permission of the authors and publishers, MESSRS. OLIVER AND BOYD.)

no more than two variables are involved (i.e. there is 1 degree of freedom.) But it often happens in biology that we know nothing about the distribution of a group of organisms, the only quantitative data available being the number of individuals falling into a series of catagories, e.g. the size-groups of animals belonging to different populations. In such circumstances, the methods already

TABLE 4

Table of χ^2

N	0·90	0·80	0·70	0·50	Probability 0·30	0·20	0·10	0·05	0·02	0·01	0·001
1	0·016	0·064	0·15	0·46	1·07	1·64	2·71	3·84	5·41	6·64	10·83
2	0·21	0·45	0·71	1·39	2·41	3·22	4·61	5·99	7·82	9·21	13·82
3	0·58	1·01	1·42	2·37	3·67	4·64	6·25	7·82	9·84	11·34	16·27
4	1·06	1·65	2·20	3·36	4·88	5·99	7·78	9·49	11·67	13·28	18·47
5	1·61	2·34	3·00	4·35	6·06	7·29	9·24	11·07	13·39	15·09	20·52
6	2·20	3·07	3·83	5·35	7·23	8·56	10·65	12·59	15·03	16·81	22·46
7	2·83	3·82	4·67	6·35	8·38	9·80	12·02	14·07	16·62	18·48	24·32
8	3·49	4·59	5·53	7·34	9·52	11·03	13·36	15·51	18·17	20·09	26·13
9	4·17	5·38	6·39	8·34	10·66	12·24	14·68	16·92	19·68	21·67	27·88
10	4·87	6·18	7·27	9·34	11·78	13·44	15·99	18·31	21·16	23·21	29·59
11	5·58	6·99	8·15	10·34	12·90	14·63	17·28	19·68	22·62	24·73	31·26
12	6·30	7·81	9·03	11·34	14·01	15·81	18·55	21·03	24·05	26·22	32·91
13	7·04	8·63	9·93	12·34	15·12	16·99	19·81	22·36	25·47	27·69	34·53
14	7·79	9·47	10·82	13·34	16·22	18·15	21·06	23·69	26·87	29·14	36·12
15	8·55	10·31	11·72	14·34	17·32	19·31	22·31	25·00	28·26	30·58	37·70
16	9·31	11·15	12·62	15·34	18·42	20·47	23·54	26·30	29·63	32·00	39·25
17	10·09	12·00	13·53	16·34	19·51	21·62	24·77	27·59	31·00	33·41	40·79
18	10·87	12·86	14·44	17·34	20·60	22·76	25·99	28·87	32·35	34·81	42·31
19	11·65	13·72	15·35	18·34	21·69	23·90	27·20	30·14	33·69	36·19	43·82
20	12·44	14·58	16·27	19·34	22·78	25·04	28·41	31·41	35·02	37·57	45·32
22	14·04	16·31	18·10	21·34	24·94	27·30	30·81	33·92	37·66	40·29	48·27
24	15·66	18·06	19·94	23·34	27·10	29·55	33·20	36·42	40·27	42·98	51·18
26	17·29	19·82	21·79	25·34	29·25	31·80	35·56	38·89	42·86	45·64	54·05
28	18·94	21·59	23·65	27·34	31·39	34·03	37·92	41·34	45·42	48·28	56·89
30	20·60	23·36	25·51	29·34	33·53	36·25	40·26	43·77	47·96	50·89	59·70

When N is greater than 30, use $\sqrt{2\chi^2} - \sqrt{2n-1}$ as a normal deviate.

(Abridged from *Statistical Tables for Biological, Agricultural and Medical Research* by R. A. FISHER and F. YATES, with the kind permission of the authors and publishers, MESSRS. OLIVER AND BOYD.)

described are often inappropriate and it is necessary to make use of a statistic known as χ^2. The distribution of χ^2 has been calculated and is shown in Table 4. This gives the values of χ^2 corresponding to particular probabilities (P) and varying numbers of degrees of freedom (N).

The χ^2 calculations provide some of the most useful tests in biology and although they vary somewhat in detail, all are based on the following simple principle. If O is the *observed* frequency of any one variable and E the frequency that would be *expected* as a result of some hypothesis, then χ^2 is obtained by dividing the square of the difference between O and E by E and summing these quotients for each category into which the variable falls. Thus,

$$\chi^2 = \Sigma \left[\frac{(O-E)^2}{E} \right].$$

In certain types of investigation we are justified in expecting a particular result, for instance, when testing a suspected Mendelian ratio or sex-equality. However, in ecology, such instances are rare and there are seldom any grounds for predicting that a particular relationship between two or more variables will be achieved. One of the features of χ^2 calculations is that it is possible in such circumstances to generate one's own expectation based on the data available; the method of doing so will be clear from the examples which follow.

The use of χ^2 really necessitates our making an assumption in advance. Thus in Contingency Tables (2×2, $n \times n$, etc. – *see* p. 120 *et seq.*) where it appears at first sight as if we had no expectation, we are actually saying 'let us assume that the various values, relative to their classes and frequencies, are distributed so as to be homogeneous. Do the results differ from this assumption, or not?'

Having found χ^2 we must determine the number of degrees of freedom (*see* p. 121) before we can make use of the tables. The rules for doing this will be explained with each example. The fact that this quantity can take on any value from 1 upwards is an indication of the wide scope of the test compared with that of the standard error. The tables show the probability (P) of a calculated value being exceeded by chance. If this probability is *less* than 1 in 20 (0·05), then there is evidence that the observed data depart significantly from the hypothesis being examined. This hypothesis may assume one of two forms, either that a variable has a particular kind of distribution or that there is no association between the variables. The second is the commonest situation in ecology and is known as a *null hypothesis* since it assumes that the variables are not related. Obviously, if we can disprove a null hypothesis, it follows that the variables must be associated with one another.

Two variables (*with expectation*)

Situations of this kind are relatively rare in ecology and are mainly concerned with such problems as the testing of sex-ratios. Data involving only one degree of freedom can, of course, be analysed by determining the standard error (*see* p. 108); the χ^2 test is, however, a more sensitive and only slightly more laborious method of achieving the same end. It may be instructive here to re-analyse the data used in the example on p. 110. These were,

No of butterflies in sample	Males	Females
120	53 (44 per cent)	67 (56 per cent)

Is there a significant departure from sex equality?

The calculation is most conveniently presented in the form of a table:

	Males	Females	Total
Observed (O)	53	67	120
Expected (E)	60	60	120
$O-E$	-7	7	
$(O-E)^2$	49	49	
$\Sigma\left[\dfrac{(O-E)^2}{E}\right]$	0·82	$+0·82$	

∴ $\chi^2 = 1·64$. The number of degrees of freedom (N)=1 (generally written as $\chi^2_{(1)}$).

From the table, $P=0·2$. This is well above the level of significance (0·05) and there is therefore no evidence of a departure from the expected 50 per cent ratio.

The sensitivity of the χ^2 test is illustrated by the following example. Suppose that, in our study of butterfly sex-ratios, the data had turned out to be:

No of butterflies in sample	Males	Females
120	49 (41 per cent)	71 (59 per cent)

Calculation of the standard error is as follows:

$$\text{S.E.} = \sqrt{\frac{41 \times 59}{120}} = 4\cdot49.$$

Departure from expectation of 50 per cent $= 9$
$$2 \times \text{S.E.} = 8\cdot98.$$

We are hardly justified in assuming a divergence from sex-equality from such a close result.

Determining χ^2, as before, we get:

	Males	Females	Total
O	49	71	120
E	60	60	120
$O-E$	-11	11	
$(O-E)^2$	121	121	
$\sum\left[\dfrac{(O-E)^2}{E}\right]$	$2\cdot02$	$+2\cdot02$	

$$\therefore \chi^2_{(1)} = 4\cdot04; \; P = \text{between } 0\cdot05 \text{ and } 0\cdot02$$

showing that, in fact, a significant departure from a 50 per cent ratio had taken place. This could be detected by χ^2 but not by the less sensitive standard error test.

Two variables (no expectation). 2×2 table

A common situation in ecology is when two variables are being studied and both are dichotomous; that is to say, each can be divided into two classes. A typical example is as follows.

Two colonies of the crustacean *Gammarus pulex* were being studied, one in a swiftly flowing stream, the other in almost still water. It was noticed that both colonies were subject to a certain amount of parasitism on the gills by the protozoan *Dendrocometes*, but that those living in the current appeared to be less affected than the others. The numbers of *Gammarus* collected were:

	Parasitized	Not parasitized	Totals
Slowly flowing	52	37	89
Swiftly flowing	24	40	64
	76	77	153

Was the degree of parasitism significantly different in the two localities?

The method of presentation is known as a table of contingency. In this instance, each of the two variables is divisible into two categories only, hence we speak of a 2×2 table. Before proceeding further, a check should be made of the totals of the vertical and horizontal columns. Both should, of course, add up to the grand total (153, in this example).

Theoretically, the next step should be to deduce the values *expected* since we have no right to assume that any particular relationship exists between the number of parasitized and non-parasitized individuals. In fact, a simplified method of calculation avoids this procedure in a 2×2 table. This is best explained by rewriting the table using letters:

	x_1	x_2	Totals
y_1	a	b	Σy_1
y_2	c	d	Σy_2
	Σx_1	Σx_2	T

$$\chi^2 = \frac{(ad-bc)^2 T}{(\Sigma x_1)(\Sigma x_2)(\Sigma y_1)(\Sigma y_2)},$$

where $T = \Sigma y_1 + \Sigma y_2$.

In our example, $\chi^2 = \dfrac{[(52 \times 40)-(37 \times 24)]^2 153}{76 \times 77 \times 89 \times 64} = 6 \cdot 52$.

We now need to find the number of degrees of freedom, that is to say, the number of classes among the data with a fixed total to which quantities can be assigned arbitrarily. Like the value of χ^2, they are strictly additive. In a 2×2 table there are, clearly, three degrees of freedom but only *one* is available for the kind of comparison we are making here. Owing to their additive nature, the other two are used up in the two remaining comparisons that can be made from such a table. These are Σx_1 and Σx_2 (2 classes with a fixed total, so they add up to one degree of freedom), and Σy_1 and Σy_2. Thus, when we come to compare the homogeneity of the whole set of figures, only one of the three degrees of freedom remains available.

In any contingency table, the number of degrees of freedom *remaining available* for a comparison of homogeneity is given by the formula $(c-1) \times (r-1)$ where c and r are columns and rows respectively.

It follows that the number of degrees of freedom (N) in a 2×2 table must always be 1.

Thus $\chi^2_{(1)} = 6.52$; for which $P =$ nearly 0.01 (from table).

Evidently there is a significant association between the speed of the current and the degree of parasitism.

More than two variables (with expectation)

Circumstances will frequently arise in ecology in which two or more variables are to be studied each being divisible into more than two classes. Very rarely, however, will there be any grounds for expecting a particular ratio. Calculations of this kind are confined in biology almost exclusively to the testing of genetic ratios and need not be considered further here. Suffice it to say that the procedure is similar to that already outlined for verifying a sex-ratio (p. 119) except that the number of degrees of freedom will be increased.

More than two variables (no expectation)

(i) $2 \times n$ *Tables*. There are many kinds of ecological problems in which it is necessary to investigate the relationship between two variables, one of which is dichotomous while the other is divisible into more than two classes (say, n). A typical example is provided from a study of the size of the minnow, *Phoxinus laevis*, in the River Itchen.

Two samples were collected on the same day, one in a slowly flowing stream, the other in a static backwater adjoining it. The lengths of the minnows were measured and classified into size-groups as in the table. Is there a significant difference in the size-distribution characteristic of the two localities?

Size groups (mm.)

	10–15	15–20	20–25	25–30	30–35	35–40	*Totals*
Current	5	16	34	6	31	7	99
No current	2	37	30	14	42	3	128
	7	53	64	20	73	10	227

A table of this kind is known as a $2 \times n$ table, and the method of calculating χ^2 from it can best be explained by substituting letters for numbers.

	x_1	x_2	x_3	x_4	x_5	x_6	*Totals*
y_1	a_1	a_2	a_3	a_4	a_5	a_6	Σy_1
y_2	b_1	b_2	b_3	b_4	b_5	b_6	Σy_2
	Σx_1	Σx_2	Σx_3	Σx_4	Σx_5	Σx_6	T

Assuming a and b to be any comparable pair of observed frequencies, we can now calculate a series of values of χ^2 from the equation,

$$\chi^2 = \frac{[(\Sigma y_2 \times a_1) - (\Sigma y_1 \times b_1)]^2}{(\Sigma x_1)(\Sigma y_1)(\Sigma y_2)}.$$

The sum of these expressions will give the total value of χ^2.

Thus, in the example we have:

$$\frac{[(128 \times 5)-(99 \times 2)]^2}{7 \times 99 \times 128} = 2 \cdot 20$$

$$\frac{[(128 \times 16)-(99 \times 37)]^2}{53 \times 99 \times 128} = 3 \cdot 88$$

$$\frac{[(128 \times 34)-(99 \times 30)]^2}{64 \times 99 \times 128} = 2 \cdot 35$$

$$\frac{[(128 \times 6)-(99 \times 14)]^2}{20 \times 99 \times 128} = 1 \cdot 51$$

$$\frac{[(128 \times 31)-(99 \times 42)]^2}{73 \times 99 \times 128} = 0 \cdot 04$$

$$\frac{[(128 \times 7)-(99 \times 3)]^2}{10 \times 99 \times 128} = 2 \cdot 83$$

$$\text{Total } \chi^2 = 12 \cdot 81$$

The number of degrees of freedom in a $2 \times n$ table is $(c-1) \times (r-1)$, as explained on p. 121. In this instance the number of columns (c) is 6 and the number of rows (r) is 2. Hence $N=5$. We can thus write $\chi^2_{(5)}=12 \cdot 81$, for which P lies between $0 \cdot 05$ and $0 \cdot 02$. The difference has clearly reached the level of significance, and there are evidently good grounds for assuming the minnow populations in the two localities to be different as regards size-distribution.

It will sometimes happen in a $2 \times n$ table that certain values are small or missing. In such circumstances the procedure is the same as in an $n \times n$ table (*see* below).

(ii) $n \times n$ *Tables*. Sometimes we are faced with a slightly more complicated situation in which two variables are each divisible into more than two catagories. A typical example is provided by data for the number of spots (ranging from 0 to 5) on the underside of each hindwing in the female meadow brown butterfly (*Maniola jurtina*). The results of sampling four neighbouring localities in Southern England are summarized on p. 124, and we wish to know whether the communities concerned can be judged to exhibit the same spot-distribution.

Localities

Spot Numbers	A	B	C	D	Totals
0	37	26	24	63	150
1	12	10	11	21	54
2	4	6	10	17	37
3	1	1	4	4	10
4	—	2	1	—	3
5	—	—	—	1	1
	54	45	50	106	255

The first point to notice is that there are missing values in the last two rows. These must, therefore, be accumulated with the row above. It is also important to avoid small numbers and values less than 5 should be accumulated, if possible. The resulting table is generally known as an $n \times n$ table. In order to explain the method of working, we can rewrite it in the form of letters as follows.

	x_1	x_2	x_3	x_4	Totals
y_1	a_1	a_2	a_3	a_4	Σy_1
y_2	b_1	b_2	b_3	b_4	Σy_2
y_3	c_1	c_2	c_3	c_4	Σy_3
y_4	d_1	d_2	d_3	d_4	Σy_4
	Σx_1	Σx_2	Σx_3	Σx_4	T

No short method is known of calculating χ^2 from an $n \times n$ table. Our first step must, therefore, be to find the *expected* value for each observed frequency. This is obtained by multiplying the total for the appropriate column by that of the corresponding row and dividing by T. Thus, the expected frequency for the top left-hand cell will be

$$\frac{(\Sigma x_1)(\Sigma y_1)}{T}.$$

Similarly, that of the bottom right-hand cell is

$$\frac{(\Sigma x_4)(\Sigma y_4)}{T}.$$

The figures so obtained are now inserted, each in the appropriate cell, and enclosed in brackets to distinguish them from the observed frequencies. The χ^2 for each cell is now calculated in the usual way according to the formula:

$$\frac{(O-E)^2}{E} \ (see \ \text{p. 117}).$$

The sum of these values will give the total χ^2 for the table. The number of degrees of freedom (N) for a table of contingency having c columns and r rows is given by

$$N=(c-1)\times(r-1) \ (see \ \text{p. 121}).$$

Our data can now be rewritten in the following form with the last two rows accumulated:

Locality

Spot Numbers	A	B	C	D	Totals
0	37 (31·76)	26 (26·47)	24 (29·42)	63 (62·35)	150
1	12 (11·43)	10 (9·53)	11 (10·59)	21 (22·45)	54
2	4 (7·84)	6 (6·53)	10 (7·25)	17 (15·38)	37
3–5	1 (2·97)	3 (2·47)	5 (2·74)	5 (5·82)	14
	54	45	50	106	255

A quick check on the working can be made at this stage, for the totals of columns and rows both for observed and expected values should be the same.

The calculated figures for χ^2 can be tabulated as follows:

Spots	A	B	C	D	Totals
0	0·86	0·08	1·00	0·07	2·01
1	0·28	0·23	0·16	0·09	0·76
2	1·88	0·43	1·04	0·17	3·52
3–5	1·31	1·14	1·86	1·16	5·47

11·76=Total χ^2

There are 4 rows and 4 columns.

$\therefore$ $N=9$, i.e. $\chi^2_{(9)}=11\cdot76$, for which P is between 0·3 and 0·2.

This is well above the level of significance and there is, therefore, no indication of any divergence in spot-distribution between the four colonies of butterflies.

Although somewhat tedious to calculate, the $n \times n$ table can be invaluable in ecological work both as a means of testing the relationship between two comparable sets of variables, and also for establishing whether a series of data are homogeneous or not. Used in this way, χ^2 provides us with an answer to the question that is often so difficult to resolve by inspection alone, namely, to what extent are we justified in adding together the results of a number of related samples which appear superficially to resemble one another?

CHAPTER VI

Measurement of Edaphic Factors

Of all the natural media that can support life, soil is undoubtedly the most complex and difficult to study. Not only does its composition vary enormously in different parts of the world, but the nature of its constituents may change appreciably even over a distance of a few yards. Such variations frequently bring about corresponding changes in the nature and density of the animal populations. Some soils are capable of supporting huge numbers of small animals. For instance, it has been estimated that a single gram of fertile loam may contain as many as 1,000,000,000 protozoans. On the other hand, the acid conditions prevailing in peat bogs almost preclude animal life altogether.

The many ecological factors operating in soil (*edaphic factors*) are still only incompletely understood. Nonetheless, certain of them undoubtedly play a major part in determining the distribution of soil animals and it is with these that we shall be concerned in this chapter.

COMPOSITION OF SOIL

The solid constituents of soil are largely derived from the rocks which form the earth's crust. The process of 'weathering', mainly by the action of wind and rain, results in the gradual erosion of the rock surface and its breakdown into pieces of varying size. Some rocks, such as granite, are hard and therefore tend to erode slowly, forming large particles. Others, like sandstone, are much softer and therefore wear away more readily.

Particle-size plays a large part in determining the ecological characteristics of a soil and is the criterion used in classifying most of its solid constituents. The usual categories are as follows:

Solid constituent	Diameter of particles (mm.)
Gravel (grit)	>2
Coarse sand	2—0·2
Fine sand	0·2—0·02
Silt	0·02—0·002
Clay	<0·002

The artificial separation of these various solid components is known as mechanical analysis. Gravel and sand can be conveniently removed by passing dried soil through sieves of standard mesh (Fig. 35). These are obtainable from many biological

FIG. 35
Pocket soil sieve showing the various parts, including three gauzes
P. K. Dutt & Co. Ltd.

dealers. The fineness of silt and clay preclude the use of this simple procedure and for their removal recourse must be had to more elaborate techniques. These are described in the standard works on agricultural chemistry (*see* Bibliography). The ecologist will seldom be concerned with the detailed analysis of the particles in a particular soil but rather with their combined effect in contributing to the environment as a whole.

Another solid constituent of soil is *humus* – the rotting remains of plant and animal material.[1] Its composition inevitably varies a great deal, both in its chemical nature and in the physical properties of its particles.

A fertile soil must always contain adequate quantities of such organic matter because:

(i) In providing a suitable environment for the activity of

[1] The term humus may be used in a variety of senses. Throughout this book it will be assumed to refer to all organic matter contributing to the colloidal nature of soil.

PLATE 5

(*a*) Oakwood clearing. An area of great contrasts in illumination. (Crab Wood, near Winchester)

(*b*) Drainage ditch in *Glyceria* fenland. (Winchester College Nature Reserve)

PLATE 6

Some British Moths with Industrial Melanic Forms ($\times \frac{3}{4}$ approx.)

1. Peppered moth (*Biston betularia*)—Typical
2. Peppered moth (*Biston betularia carbonaria*)—Melanic
3. Peppered moth (*Biston betularia insularia*)—Melanic
4. Scalloped hazel (*Gonodontis bidentata*)—Typical
5. Scalloped hazel (*Gonodontis bidentata*)—Melanic
6. Waved umber (*Hemerophila abruptaria*)—Typical
7. Waved umber (*Hemerophila abruptaria*)—Melanic

nitrifying bacteria, it is promoting the return of valuable inorganic minerals to the soil

(ii) The capacity of humus for absorbing water lessens the danger of drought resulting from excessive evaporation or too rapid drainage.

All soils contain a certain amount of water but the quantity they can hold without becoming waterlogged varies greatly. This depends mainly on the proportion of humus and clay present. Clay particles have the capacity of imbibing water (*hygroscopic water*) which causes them to swell and adhere together forming a slimy, glutinous surface so characteristic of many parts of the West Country during periods of rain. When drought occurs the particles give up their water and contract in size. This is the cause of the cracks which sometimes occur in clayey soils during hot weather. In a well-drained soil much of the water falling on the surface as rain will be carried away into the parent rock material below. During this process the soil particles themselves become invested in a covering of water which adheres to their outer surface (*capillary water*). In periods of drought, water reaches the top-soil from below by welling up between the particles by the process of capillary action.

Soil water contains a great number of minerals in dilute solution many of which are of vital importance for the growth of plants. Also suspended in it are a variety of colloidal particles. Some are organic; others are simple inorganic compounds such as the basic oxides of iron which occur widely in acid soils.

---

8. Nut-tree tussock (*Colocasia coryli*)—Typical
9. Nut-tree tussock (*Colocasia coryli*)—Melanic
10. Willow beauty (*Cleora rhomboidaria*)—Typical
11. Willow beauty (*Cleora rhomboidaria*)—Melanic
    (Rural in England; industrial in Germany)
12. Mottled beauty (*Cleora repandata*)—Typical
13. Mottled beauty (*Cleora repandata*)—Melanic
14. Tawny-barred angle (*Semiothisa liturata*)—Typical
15. Tawny-barred angle (*Semiothisa liturata*)—Melanic

Classification of soil types

The mechanical analysis of soil provides a ready means of distinguishing one type of soil from another. In practice, the position is complicated by the fact that different systems of classification are used in Britain and America. Not only are there two distinct gradings of particle size, but also the grouping of soils according to the relative proportions of their constituents differs too. This is not the place for a detailed discussion of this problem; for further information reference should be made to one of the standard agricultural text-books (*see* Bibliography).

The commonest types of soil can be arranged roughly in five categories:

(i) Sandy loam
(ii) Clay loam
(iii) Loam
(iv) Chalky
(v) Peaty.

A typical analysis of these soils is shown in Table 5.

	Sandy loam	*Clay loam*	*Loam*	*Chalky*	*Peaty*
Water	2·4	4·4	2·4	2·4 ·	8·4
Humus	4·0	6·4	14·3	6·9	32·8
Coarse sand	10·3	3·9	0·1	20·2	26·6
Fine sand	67·0	30·1	53·3	21·9	14·2
Clay and silt	16·3	55·2	29·7	9·6[1]	18·0

[1] Also 39 per cent calcium carbonate.

TABLE 5. Approximate mechanical analysis (per cent) of various soils. (*Modified after Hall.*)

No method of naming soils can do more than give an approximate idea of their composition. Should ecological requirements demand, the only really satisfactory way of determining the true nature of a soil is by a detailed quantitative analysis of a series of representative samples.

Zonation of soil

It has already been pointed out that the nature of soil tends to vary greatly over quite short distances. Still more marked changes can be seen, even within a few inches, if we examine a vertical section (soil profile). In any natural or cultivated land, the top eight inches or so are generally soft, dark in colour and easy to manipulate (*surface soil*). Below this layer the soil rapidly becomes lighter in colour and much harder to dig (*sub-soil*). A count of the number of small arthropods in samples from the two levels will confirm the marked difference existing between them, the population at the surface being far more numerous than that further down. A comparison of some typical examples of surface and sub-soils is given in Table 6.

	Water		Humus		Coarse sand		Fine sand		Clay and Silt	
	Soil	Sub-soil	Soil	Sub-soil	Soil	Sub-soil	Soil	Sub-soil	Soil	Sub-soil
Sandy Loam	2·4	1·7	4·0	3·0	10·3	9·7	67·0	68·6	16·3	17·0
Clay Loam	4·4	5·5	6·4	4·4	3·9	0·8	30·1	16·0	55·2	73·3
Loam	2·4	4·6	14·3	8·1	0·1	0	53·3	47·5	29·7	39·8

TABLE 6. Approximate mechanical analysis (per cent) of various surface and sub-soils. (*Modified after Hall.*)

As might be expected, the organic content of the top-soil is in every instance higher than that of the sub-soil and this largely accounts for the big numerical difference in the animals occupying the two zones, most of which are humus feeders.

Sometimes the soil profile presents a much more complex picture than that outlined above, and the relative position and extent of the various zones may play an integral part in determining the distribution of plant and animal colonists. Sandy soils often overlie a parent substance such as gravel which is highly porous and therefore easily drained. In areas of heavy rainfall, the continuous irrigation of the soil from above inevitably results in many important minerals, particularly the basic compounds of calcium and iron, being washed out of the surface layers altogether. A soil of this kind is said to be leached and is known as a *podsol*.

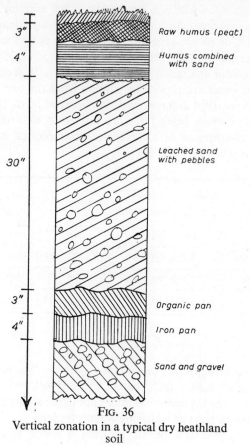

3"   Raw humus (peat)

4"   Humus combined with sand

30" Leached sand with pebbles

3"   Organic pan

4"   Iron pan

     Sand and gravel

Fig. 36

Vertical zonation in a typical dry heathland soil

Bacterial activity in the upper humus layer generally results in the production of various acids which cannot be neutralized by the limited bases available. In such circumstances the breakdown of dead plant remains is only incomplete and a layer of peat is the result. This may vary in thickness from a few inches to several feet. Below it is generally a zone of grey, leached sand overlying a much narrower band of black, rock-like substance. This is known as *organic pan* and represents the accumulation of small particles of humus which have been washed down from above. Sandy soils are frequently rich in iron compounds and these often occur in the colloidal state. In general the particles are smaller than those of organic pan and, if they accumulate at all, they always tend to do so at a slightly lower level, forming *iron pan*. Below this region again will be parent substance, e.g. gravel, virtually unaltered except for a certain amount of leaching.

The resulting zonation is shown in Fig. 36 and this is characteristic of dry heathland such as occurs widely in the New Forest area. Most of the plants and practically the whole of the animal community are associated with the peat layer. Some of the larger plants such as pine and birch are able to penetrate the lower levels but they owe their survival to the association of their roots with various soil Fungi (*mycorrhiza*).

Sampling of soils

The ecological study of soil generally involves taking series of representative samples in different localities. We have seen how vertical zonation plays a large part in determining the composition of such samples, hence it is important that any sampling device should be capable of extracting soil accurately from a known depth. The use of a spade or trowel has obvious limitations and by far the most efficient device is the soil auger (*see* Fig. 37). This consists of a steel tube about 2 inches in diameter and 18 inches long. The rim at one end is sharpened and at the other, two holes are bored through which can pass a quarter-inch metal rod to act as a lever. To one end of this rod is fixed a cylindrical piece of wood slightly narrower in diameter than the bore of the tube. Thus the handle also serves as a ramrod for removing the core of earth which will remain inside the auger after sampling. The provision of a series of graduations cut on the outside of the auger at about 2-inch intervals will enable samples to be taken at particular depths.

After extraction from the auger, the soil is laid out in a shallow tray or dish and, if required for analysis, is allowed to dry in the air for a day or so. It is then passed through a 2-mm. sieve (Fig. 35) which removes most of the gravel and larger plant

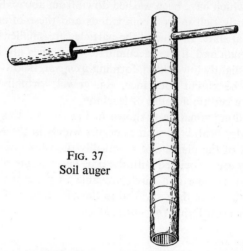

FIG. 37
Soil auger

remains. The residue is now transferred to a mortar, rubbed with a *wooden* pestle[1] and, finally, sieved once more. The result is sometimes known as 'fine earth'.

Water content

Humidity is one of the principal edaphic factors which influence the distribution of animals. A good example of its importance is provided by earthworms which demand an 'optimum humidity range'; they are seldom found in the driest soils or in those that are permanently waterlogged.

In plant ecology and agriculture it is often useful to estimate the water content of soil in a number of different ways. For instance, its *saturation capacity* denotes the percentage of water held against the force of gravity by a soil in which the pores are completely filled with water. Methods of making such measurements are described in the relevant text-books (*see* Bibliography),

[1] The use of a metal or earthenware pestle is inadvisable as this is likely to break up many of the small stones which will still be present.

but they will not normally be needed in studies of soil animals whose activities and distribution are largely influenced by the *absolute water content*. This is naturally a variable quantity rising to a maximum after heavy rain and falling rapidly during periods of hot weather. Single estimates will obviously mean very little, but a series of samples collected *at the same time* in different places can provide a useful and reliable comparison. Sampling should not be attempted immediately after heavy rainfall as the soil is almost certain to be saturated. If possible, a period of about 24 hours should be allowed for the excess water to drain away.

A convenient weight (about 10 gm.) of air-dry fine earth (*see* p. 134), is heated in an evaporating dish on a steam bath or in an oven at about 105° C., until the weight is constant. Soils containing large amounts of clay or organic material will take longer to dry than lighter ones. Cooling must take place in a desiccator. The loss in weight (conveniently expressed as a percentage) represents the moisture derived from the hygroscopic water and some of the capillary water. Provided the various samples are subjected to the same amount of preliminary air-drying, the final figures obtained will provide a valid comparison of the humidity of the different soils.

Organic matter

The organic component of fine earth will be very largely colloidal and hence can be regarded as humus for all practical purposes. Accurate estimation is difficult, but the loss in weight on ignition gives a reasonable estimate of organic content and provides a reliable means of comparing different soil samples.

About 5 gm. of oven-dried soil (this must have been cooled and stored in a desiccator to avoid uptake of moisture) are weighed in a crucible and heated to red heat for about half an hour. Cool in a desiccator, weigh and reheat until the weight is constant. The loss in weight (expressed as a percentage) will be a reliable guide to the amount of oxidizable organic matter present. One of the chief sources of error in this met hodis the decomposition of inorganic minerals, particularly carbonates. The necessary correction can be made by adding a little ammonium carbonate solution to the cooled solid and then heating on a water bath or in an oven at about 105°C. to drive off the excess. Cool and reweigh; the gain in weight will represent the amount of CO_2 lost by the carbonates during the initial heating.

Temperature

The composition of soil determines to a large extent the rate at which its temperature varies, also the magnitude of the thermoclines existing within it. We shall see (p. 213) how temperature gradients in water have a surprising effect on the vertical distribution of aquatic organisms. A comparable situation exists in soil but is far less well known. Heavy soils, i.e. those containing large amounts of clay and humus, by virtue of their capacity for retaining water, tend to heat up and cool down slowly. Sandy soils, on the other hand, are exceedingly porous and permit a rapid movement by convection of the gases which comprise the soil atmosphere. Hence they are subject to rapid fluctuations in temperature.

The resistance thermometer described in Chapter II (p. 30) is an ideal instrument for studying temperature changes in soil. Thermistors are very robust and can remain buried in the ground with their leads projecting above the surface for considerable periods of time. The chief limiting factor appears to be the durability of the insulating material on the leads rather than that of the thermistor itself. When taking readings it is only necessary to attach the wires to the terminals of the portable Wheatstone Bridge.

The soil atmosphere

Surprisingly little is known about the nature of the atmosphere below soil level, nor is it clear to what extent the fluctuations in its composition, which undoubtedly occur, influence the distribution and activity of the animal community. One thing seems certain, namely, that the composition of soil air and atmospheric air is never the same.

In their studies of the Fungi inhabiting the litter layer of beech woods, Harley and Brierley[1] have devised an ingenious method of obtaining samples of the soil atmosphere in this zone. The procedure is applicable to the study of surface soils in general and provides a ready means of analysing the microclimate in which such animals as woodlice, centipedes and millipedes exist.

The apparatus (Fig. 38) consists of a piece of polyvinyl chloride (PVC) tubing about 30 cm. long and 3 cm. in diameter.[2]

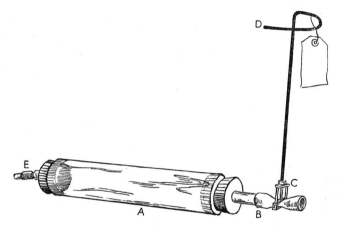

FIG. 38

Plastic tube apparatus for sampling the soil atmosphere

This is sufficiently large to provide two 25 c.c. gas samples for analysis. Each end is fitted with a rubber bung, one carrying a small piece of capillary tubing and the other a short length of wider glass tubing. The capillary tube is fitted with a stopper consisting of a piece of glass rod inside a short rubber tube. The wider tube (nozzle) is also supplied with a short length of rubber

[1] Harley, J. L., and Brierley, J. K. (1953). 'A Method of Estimation of Oxygen and Carbon Dioxide Concentrations in the Litter Layer of Beech Woods', *Journal of Ecology* **41**, 385–7.

Brierley, J. K. (1955). 'Seasonal Fluctuations in the Oxygen and Carbon Dioxide Concentrations in Beech Litter with Reference to the Salt Uptake of Beech Mycorrhizas', *Journal of Ecology*, **43**, 404–8.

[2] Obtainable from BX Plastics Ltd., Higham Station Avenue, Chingford, London, E.4.

tubing and a well greased screw clip, with a length of strong wire soldered on to the clamping screw. Before use, the apparatus should be carefully tested for leaks by closing both ends and squeezing under water.

It is best to use the tubes in pairs so as to provide a check on the results obtained in a particular locality. They are buried in the surface soil or litter layer with the wire projecting upwards and bearing the date (as in Fig. 38). This process inevitably disturbs the soil and temporarily upsets the equilibrium between the soil atmosphere and that outside. Hence, it is important that the nozzles of the tubes should remain *closed* for a day or so until the normal soil conditions have been restored. They are then opened by turning the wire handles, whereupon gaseous diffusion takes place from the tubes into the soil atmosphere and vice versa. Experience has shown that equilibrium is generally established after 24 hours, but it is advisable to allow about a week in order to ensure that soil conditions are quite stable. The period of a month suggested by Harley and Brierley appears to be excessive, except, perhaps, for very heavy soils with a relatively low permeability. It is important to remember to tighten the screw clip on the nozzle before removing a tube from the soil.

Estimation of oxygen and carbon dioxide

The principal constituents of the soil atmosphere are nitrogen, oxygen and carbon dioxide together with small, variable amounts of other gases. The oxygen and carbon dioxide content of a gas sample are best estimated by means of a Barcroft-Haldane apparatus (Fig. 39) in which the oxygen is absorbed by alkaline pyrogallol (in tube O) and the carbon dioxide by caustic soda solution in tube C. The plastic tube container described above is particularly suitable for feeding a gas sample into the apparatus at I since it can be squeezed easily. A detailed account of the analysis procedure is outside the scope of this book but a full description is given elsewhere.[1] It is unnecessary to purchase the complete Barcroft-Haldane apparatus which is rather expensive

[1] See Peters and Van Slyke (1956): *Quantitative Clinical Chemistry Methods*, Vol. 2, Williams and Wilkins, Baltimore.

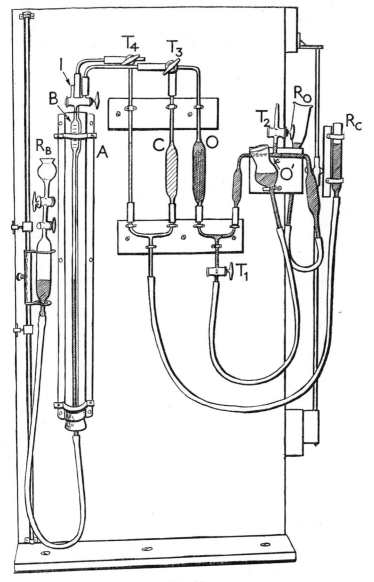

FIG. 39
Barcroft-Haldane gas analysis apparatus

when supplied by dealers. The critical part is an accurately calibrated 25 c.c. gas burette (B) which costs about five pounds. Once this has been obtained the rest of the equipment can be constructed without much difficulty in a laboratory workshop.

The sampling of gases in mud presents a special problem since they are almost exclusively dissolved in water. The following technique has been found to work well on the soft bottom of ponds and in slowly flowing streams and rivers. A series of porous pots is attached to a wooden framework (Fig. 40) at intervals corresponding to the depths at which samples are to be taken. Each pot is supplied with a tightly fitting cork in which is inserted a small length of narrow bore glass tubing with short pieces of rubber tubing at the end. The pots are filled with water (this is most conveniently done at the place where the sample is to be taken) and the corks carefully inserted. Any excess water passes up the glass and rubber tube; the latter is then clipped so as to ensure that no air bubbles enter the pot. The apparatus is now lowered to the appropriate depth and secured in position, e.g. by suspending it from a horizontal pole. Equilibrium is established between the gases inside and outside the pots in a matter of a few hours, but it is advisable to allow at least a day in order to enable the mud to recover from the temporary upset in vertical zonation which must inevitably have occurred. The oxygen and carbon dioxide content of the water inside the pots can then be estimated in the usual way (*see* Chapter II, pp. 45–52).

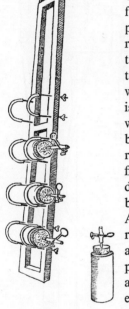

FIG. 40

Porous pot apparatus for sampling gases in mud

The efficient working of this method depends on the effectiveness of the porous surface of the pots. These should be scrubbed regularly after use and left to soak for a few hours in distilled water before being allowed to dry.

Hydrogen-ion concentration (pH)

The colorimetric methods of estimating the pH of water already described (Chapter II, pp. 52–53) are equally applicable to the study of soil and are sufficiently accurate for all ordinary purposes. Most soils are well buffered, hence they can be diluted considerably without any appreciable alteration in the pH. Moreover, in applying a colorimetric test, it is not necessary to use any particular quantity of unknown. Water shaken with soil containing an appreciable amount of clay will remain murky for a considerable time and the colour of the multiple indicator will therefore be obscured. This difficulty can be overcome by taking equal quantities of soil and precipitated barium sulphate which will result in all colloidal particles settling at the bottom of the test tube leaving a clear liquid above. The colour of this, after addition of the indicator, is matched against the chart of standards in the usual way. The British Drug Houses Ltd. have produced a compact soil pH-testing outfit containing all the necessary equipment including a bottle for distilled water and an ample supply of graduated test tubes. This costs about three pounds and will be found invaluable in field studies. For more accurate estimates of pH a B.D.H. capillator is convenient and easy to use (see p. 52).

Soil Minerals

Although not directly related to animal distribution, the simple inorganic minerals dissolved in soil water play a vital part in influencing the growth of plants and hence the distribution of the animals dependent upon them. Similarly, in natural waters, the periodic rise and fall in the numbers of minute planktonic Algae can be closely correlated with changes in the mineral content and with variations in the density of small herbivores such as water fleas. Some knowledge of the fluctuating concentration of the common minerals is thus desirable for a reasonably complete picture of the physical environment.

Many methods are used in the chemical analysis of soil and

water (the same methods are generally applicable to both) and they are described in detail in the appropriate text-books (*see* Bibliography). For general simplicity, speed and reasonable accuracy, colorimetric tests are to be preferred and the following will be found suitable in elementary ecological work.

Preparation of a soil extract

An essential preliminary in the mineral analysis of soil is the preparation of an aqueous extract containing the solutes required for test. This is obtained as follows. A fresh sample of soil is dried immediately on a steam bath or in an oven at about 105°C. in order to stop further bacterial action. It is then allowed to cool and stored in a desiccator. Transfer about 250 gm. of this dry soil into a Büchner funnel[1] and wash with 1 litre of hot distilled water. This should be sufficient to dissolve out most of the soluble minerals present. Allow the filtrate to cool and make up to 1 litre in a volumetric flask.

If the resulting liquid is cloudy or distinctly coloured it should be treated with aluminium hydroxide as follows. Dissolve 125 gm. potassium or ammonium alum in a litre of distilled water. Add ammonium hydroxide until no more precipitate of alumina appears. Wash this precipitate well and then mix the solid with distilled water making up to a litre. Add a little of this mixture to the soil extract to be tested at the rate of about 1 c.c. per 150 c.c. of sample. Shake well, allow to settle, and filter if necessary.

The sample is now ready for analysis by any of the methods to be described. All of these have been used extensively, and found to work well. Although included here as ways of studying soil, they are equally suitable for the estimation of minerals in natural waters.

The most time-consuming part of colorimetric analysis is the preparation of the various reagents and standards. Once these are available, the tests themselves can generally be carried out quite quickly. It is important to remember that we are dealing with concentrations of minerals, often amounting to only a few parts

[1] A wide porcelain funnel pierced with numerous holes and used in conjunction with a filter pump and vacuum flask.

per million.[1] Hence, if accurate and consistent results are to be achieved, it is essential that all glassware, particularly volumetric flasks and their stoppers, should be kept scrupulously clean.

(a) *Estimation of total inorganic nitrogen.* Inorganic nitrogenous substances are present in soil and natural waters mainly in the form of nitrate, nitrite and ammonium compounds. An overall estimate of the total nitrogen (most conveniently estimated as ammonia) will thus provide a good idea of the general fertility.

The following reagents are required:

A. Nessler's Solution. Dissolve 10 gm. potassium iodide in 10 c.c. distilled water. Add a saturated solution of mercuric chloride until a slight permanent precipitate is formed. Now add 80 c.c. of 9 M potassium hydroxide solution (504 gm. per litre) and make up to 200 c.c. with distilled water. Allow to stand for 24 hours and then filter.

B. Zinc-copper couple. This is prepared by allowing granulated zinc to stand in dilute copper sulphate solution for a few minutes until the zinc is well coated with copper. Wash and allow to dry. N.B. – Zinc-copper couple does not keep well and a fresh supply should always be made as required.

C. Concentrated hydrochloric acid and dilute caustic soda solution. Both of these must be tested with Nessler's solution to make sure that no ammonium compounds are present.

Take about 250 c.c. of soil filtrate (or natural water) and filter to remove all suspended matter. This is best done with a Büchner funnel and filter pump. Extract two 100 c.c. samples and to each add about 5 gm. zinc-copper couple and 5 drops of concentrated hydrochloric acid. Stir well and incubate at 35°–40° C. for 6 hours. Reduction of the nitrogen present will now be complete. Add enough caustic soda solution to make the liquid alkaline and

[1] The extraction of the last traces of soluble material is an exceedingly difficult matter, and the rather crude method suggested here makes no claim to complete efficiency. Elementary soil studies are nearly always comparative and the important thing is to adopt a standardized procedure. Details of more elaborate methods of mineral extraction can be found in the standard text-books of Agricultural Chemistry (*see* Bibliography).

distil for at least 15 minutes, collecting the distillate in about 100 c.c. of cold distilled water. After this time test a few drops of the liquid coming over with Nessler's solution. If no orange-yellow colour appears all the ammonia must have been removed. Make up the distillate to a convenient volume, say, 200 c.c. Transfer 45 c.c. of this to a 50 c.c. Nessler Tube[1] and add 5 c.c. Nessler's solution. A clear orange-brown colour indicates the presence of ammonia. The formation of a brown precipitate shows that considerable quantities of nitrogen are present and the solution must be diluted accordingly if an accurate result is to be obtained.

A standard for comparison is made by dissolving 3·82 gm. of dry, freshly sublimed ammonium chloride in a litre of distilled water. This will give a stock solution containing 1000 parts of nitrogen per million which can be diluted as required. The nitrogen content of soil is very variable but most natural waters contain less than 10 parts of nitrogen per 1,000,000 (average 1–3 parts).

The colours of the unknown and standard solutions are now compared by standing the tubes on a white surface and looking *down* on to the surface of the liquid. Remember the degree of dilution of the distillate in calculating the concentration of nitrogen in the original 100 c.c. sample. With a little practice the method will be found to be quite sensitive and capable of detecting variations of half a part of nitrogen in a million of water (i.e. 0·5 mg. per litre). As in all colorimetric methods, a more rapid comparison can be made by using a Lovibond Comparator[2] (or similar colorimeter) for which a series of coloured discs is provided corresponding to the tints produced in Nessler's solution by different concentrations of ammonia. This dispenses with the necessity of preparing standard solutions for comparison, although the colours of the glass filters require checking from time to time.

The above method can, of course, be used for estimating ammonia only, in which case the reduction with zinc-copper couple is omitted.

---

[1] A flat-bottomed tube of standard dimensions with a graduation at the 45 c.c. mark.
[2] Manufactured by the British Drug Houses Ltd.

PLATE 7

(a)

(b)

Seasonal change in an animal habitat. (Fenland ditch in Winchester College Nature Reserve.) (a) Spring (early May); Marsh Marigold (*Caltha palustris*) in flower. (b) Summer (mid-July). A dense growth of sedges, grasses and meadow-sweet (*Filipendula ulmaria*) has obscured the water

PLATE 8

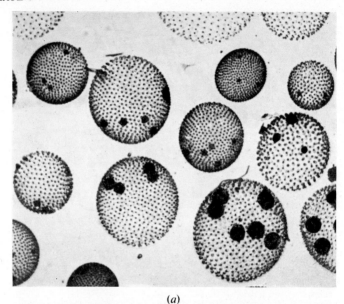

(a)

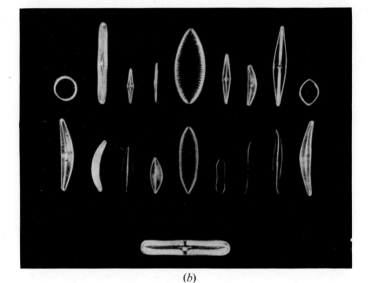

(b)

Common constituents of plant plankton in fresh water. (a) Coenobiate alga *Volvox* (×75). (b) Diatoms (×100). 1st row: *Melosira, Pinnularia, Stauroneis, Rhopaloidia, Surirella, Stauroneis, Cymbella, Stauroneis, Cymatopleura.* 2nd row: *Cymbella, Epithemia, Navicula, Cymbella, Surirella, Cymatopleura, Pleurosigma, Pleurosigma, Cymbella.* Bottom: *Pinnularia*

When using this method of nitrogen analysis the following points are worth noting:

(i) Nessler's solution should always be added *slowly* and in the *cold*. Warming produces a yellowish precipitate and no colour comparison is then possible.

(ii) A similar precipitate is formed in the presence of certain ions, notably chlorine. It is therefore important that when the distillate is collected it should be dissolved in water and not hydrochloric acid.

(iii) All glassware must be scrupulously clean. Corks used in the distillation apparatus should be covered with tinfoil or, better still, glass stoppers should be used.

(iv) Two similar samples should be tested together as a check on accuracy.

(v) The orange-yellow liquid formed in the Nessler reaction does not keep well (little longer than a day). A fresh series of standards should therefore be prepared on each occasion from the various stock solutions of ammonium chloride, which keep indefinitely.

(vi) Sometimes the addition of Nessler's solution produces a cloudiness which upsets the colour match. The following will often be found an effective remedy. Dissolve 50 gm. sodium potassium tartrate in 100 c.c. distilled water and filter. Now add 5 c.c. Nessler's solution, allow to stand for a few days and then filter off any brown precipitate. Add an equal quantity of this solution to Nessler's reagent just before use. The resulting fluid is unstable and must be prepared afresh as required.

(b) *Estimation of nitrate.* It is often desirable to estimate the quantities of certain specific nitrogenous compounds present in a sample. A typical instance is in the study of the effect of fertilizers on plant and animal life in both soil and natural waters. The Sprengel method is quick and reliable, and gives an accurate determination of nitrate, provided the amount of chloride present does not exceed 30 parts per million (otherwise the result obtained will be too small). In most soils and inland waters this difficulty does not arise, but in the sea and in estuaries the total chloride present must first be estimated (*see* p. 53) and then neutralized as follows. To a convenient volume of soil extract or water add dilute sulphuric acid until neutralization is nearly complete. Now treat with an appropriate quantity of standardized silver sulphate solution[1] so as to precipitate all but a trace (about 10 parts per million) of the chloride present. Filter well.

The following reagents are required for the estimation of nitrate:

A. Phenol-sulphonic acid. This can either be purchased ready made or prepared as follows. Add 18 gm. of pure phenol to 9 c.c. of distilled water in a 250 c.c. evaporating dish. Now run in 111 c.c. of pure sulphuric acid and heat on a water bath at 100°C. for about 8 hours. This is a stock solution and it keeps well provided it is in the dark.

B. Potassium or sodium hydroxide solution. About 12N., e.g. dissolve 240 gm. caustic soda in 500 c.c. distilled water.

C. Potassium nitrate solution (for use as a standard). Dissolve 0·722 gm. pure potassium nitrate in 1 litre of distilled water. 100 c.c. of this solution diluted to 1 litre will give a concentration of 10 parts of nitrate per million (i.e. 1 c.c. of solution $\equiv$ 0·00001 gm. nitric nitrogen).

D. Aluminium sulphate – 10 per cent solution in water.

E. Concentrated ammonia.

10 c.c. of soil extract (or more if the amount of nitrate present proves to be small) are evaporated on a water bath until dry. Do not use a flame for this purpose as the minerals present may be partially decomposed. Allow to cool, then add 1 c.c. phenol-sulphonic acid and 1 c.c. of distilled water. Mix well, warm on a water bath for a further 10 minutes and add about 2 c.c. aluminium sulphate solution and just enough ammonia to make the liquid alkaline. Dilute with distilled water to 100 c.c. The object of adding aluminium hydroxide is to remove any final traces of colouring matter that might interfere with the colour match.

Transfer 50 c.c. to a Nessler tube and compare the yellow

[1] This can be prepared by dissolving 4·397 gm. pure, dry silver sulphate in 1 litre of distilled water. 1 c.c.$\equiv$0·001 gm. chlorine.

colour obtained with that derived from 10 c.c. of standard solution treated in the same way.

This method appears to be most accurate over a range of nitrate concentrations between 1 and 10 parts per million. Beyond these limits colour matching becomes rather difficult and appropriate concentration or dilution is desirable. These coloured solutions, unfortunately, do not keep and have to be made anew for each series of tests unless they are performed within a few hours of each other. This difficulty can be overcome once the first series of standards has been made, by using suitable concentrations of picric acid solution. These keep permanently and will be found to give good results. As in the previous test for total nitrogen, the Lovibond Comparator contributes greatly to speed, and a standard series of appropriately coloured discs is available. These should, however, be matched against actual standards from time to time.

(c) *Estimation of nitrite*. Nitrites seldom occur in appreciable quantities in natural waters but they may be found in certain types of soil containing much decaying material. Colorimetric estimation is easily carried out by the Griess-Ilosva method, which is extremely sensitive. The following reagents are required:

A. Sulphanilic acid solution. Dissolve 1 gm. of pure acid in 60 c.c. glacial acetic acid and 240 c.c. distilled water.

B. α-Naphthylamine solution. Dissolve 0·2 gm. in 60 c.c. glacial acetic acid and 240 c.c. distilled water.

C. Stock nitrite solution (standard). Dissolve 1·1 gm. silver nitrite in distilled water and precipitate the silver with NaCl. Dilute to 1 litre. Further dilute 5 c.c. of this solution to 1 litre (i.e. $\times 200$); add about 1 c.c. of chloroform as a preservative. The concentration is now 0·5 mg. nitrogen per litre.

Thus 1 c.c. $\equiv 0·0005$ mg. N $\equiv 0·00164$ mg. NO_2.

Take a 100 c.c. sample of water or soil extract in a Nessler tube and add 1 c.c. of each of the solutions A and B. Allow to stand for 10 minutes; the appearance of a pink colour shows that nitrite is present. This is matched against the tints derived from different concentrations of the standard nitrite solution which have been treated in the same way. It is important that the time allowed after the addition of the reagents should always be the same, as the colour gradually deepens on standing. The necessity for preparing a fresh series of standards at each test can be overcome by using dilute aqueous solutions of the red stain basic fuchsin. These must be made up with distilled water (*not* tap water) as the traces of chlorine often present in main water gradually bleach the dye on standing. If stored in a dark place, the colours should remain fast for a considerable time.

(d) *Estimation of phosphate.* Next to nitrate, the phosphates in soil and water are the most important minerals influencing plant and animal growth. They normally occur in small quantities (less than 1 part per million of water) but, nonetheless, their determination may be important in the study of a rapidly changing environment. The 'molybdenum blue' test provides a ready means of colorimetric estimation involving the minimum of time and apparatus.

The following reagents are required:

A. Standard Phosphate solution. Weigh out 0·4263 gm. pure ammonium monohydrogen phosphate $[(NH_4)_2HPO_4]$ and make up to a litre with distilled water (1 c.c. $\equiv$ 0·1 mg. phosphorus). Add one crystal of potassium permanganate as a preservative. A suitable stock solution can be made by diluting 100 c.c. of this solution to 1 litre (1 part of phosphorus per million).

B. Molybdate-sulphuric acid reagent. Add 100 c.c. of 10 per cent ammonium molybdate solution to 300 c.c. of 50 per cent (by volume) sulphuric acid. This should be stored in a dark bottle as the reagent is rapidly decomposed in the light.

C. 2·5 per cent stannous chloride prepared by dissolving 2·5 gm. in 10 c.c. concentrated HCl. Make up to 100 c.c. with distilled water, filter and store in small stoppered bottles, each containing a piece of pure tin.

Transfer 100 c.c. of sample to a Nessler tube and add 1 c.c. of solution B followed by about 5 drops of C. Mix well and allow to stand for 10 minutes. If phosphorus is present, a blue colour will appear and this is then matched against comparable standards made up from solution A and treated in the same way. 'Molybdenum blue' is unstable, but the necessity for preparing subsequent standards can be avoided by the use of aqueous solutions of various common blue stains, e.g. methylene blue. These keep well provided they are not exposed to excessive light. Alternatively, a Lovibond Comparator can be used with a series of coloured filters.

The results of the test can then be expressed as parts of phosphorus per million or, more usually in agricultural practice, as 'available phosphate' (P_2O_5).

CHAPTER VII

The Study of Soil Communities

We have already seen in Chapter VI that soil is a highly complex and variable mixture. Yet, in spite of its complexity, the study of its ecology at an elementary level is both practicable and well worth while. In the following chapter some ways will be suggested in which such studies may be carried out.

The composition of the surface soil often changes appreciably even within a few yards and, for this reason, it is advisable to select several small areas for examination (say, 10 square yards or less) rather than one large locality. Useful comparisons can then be made of different soils and their associated fauna.

Before beginning a soil survey, it is desirable to know something of the geology of the district. The Geological Survey Office now publishes two kinds of map covering most parts of Britain. One of them shows the 'solid' geology and includes the stratified rocks, but omits the superficial deposits such as glacial sands and gravels which overlie them. The other is concerned with 'drift' geology and includes only the recent surface deposits. It is this kind that we require as a guide to soil-structure.

Once a site has been selected, the next step is to prepare a map of the area and mark on it the positions where samples have been taken. Bearing in mind the variability of soil, it is important that the map should be as accurate as possible. Plants are often a reliable indicator of soil conditions, particularly where the presence or absence of calcium is involved. Some species such as traveller's joy (*Clematis vitalba*), wayfaring tree (*Viburnum lantana*), spindle tree (*Euonymus europaeus*) and rock-rose (*Helianthemum nummularium*) habitually colonize chalk and lime-stone soils. These are known as *calcicoles*. The colonists of acid conditions, such as exist in heaths and bogs, are said to be *calcifuge* and their distribution is restricted to lime-free localities.

Typical examples are the various heathers (*Erica*), ling (*Calluna vulgaris*) and gorse (*Ulex europaeus*).

EDAPHIC FACTORS

When studying the ecology of an animal and plant community, it is important to know something of the physical environment in which the organisms live. The various methods of measuring edaphic factors have already been considered in Chapter VI. In the following pages some suggestions will be made as to how they can be usefully employed in elementary field-work.

Soil composition

Soil samples can conveniently be extracted for mechanical analysis with an auger such as that already described (p. 133). A quick but only approximate way of finding the proportions of the

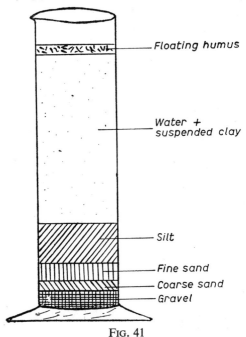

FIG. 41
Constituents of soil separated by shaking with water

151

solid constituents, is to shake a quantity of fresh soil with water in a tall vessel, such as a large measuring cylinder, and then allow it to settle. A typical result is shown in Fig. 41. The various zones will be arranged in order of particle-size, the coarsest constituent (gravel) being at the bottom. Their thicknesses will, thus, be proportional to their abundance. The only exceptions to this rule are clay, which forms a murky suspension in water that may take some time to settle, and humus which floats on the surface. Incidentally, the clay particles can be made to flocculate quite quickly by the addition of a solution of a calcium compound such as lime water. This is one of the chief reasons for adding lime to clayey soils, for the precipitation of clay makes the ground more porous and improves drainage.

The only accurate means of mechanical soil analysis is by the use of sieves and other quantitative methods described in Chapter VI.

Vertical zonation

Soils are never of uniform composition; they are always divisible vertically into at least two zones – the top-soil and the sub-soil. Generally, the situation is more complex than this, for instance in the podsols of heathland (often known as mor) which we have already considered (p. 132). The zonation of a soil plays an important part in controlling the number of animals that live in it and their distribution. Two of the chief factors concerned are the amount of organic material present and the supply of water; these are generally related. A striking example is provided by the work of P. W. Murphy on the distribution of Acarina (mites) in heathland soils. Fig. 42 (a) shows the condition found in natural heathland where no less than 96 per cent of the total arthropod population is concentrated in the top $2\frac{1}{4}$ inches – the zone of high organic content. Fig. 42 (b) represents a vertical section through a heathland soil which has been planted artificially with conifers. The formation of a secondary litter layer on the surface has resulted in a partial evening out of the Acarine distribution but two large peaks are evident in the zones containing the maximum organic matter.

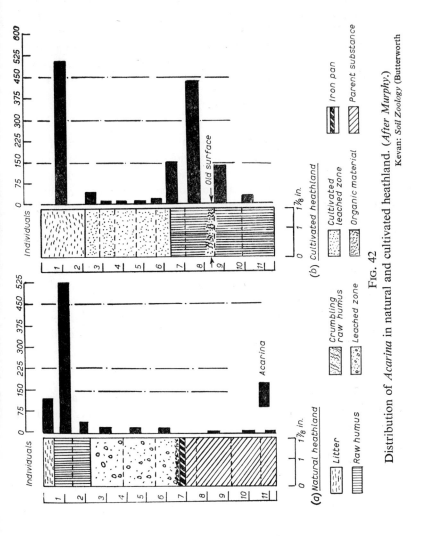

FIG. 42

Distribution of *Acarina* in natural and cultivated heathland. (*After Murphy.*)
Kevan: *Soil Zoology* (Butterworth

(a) *Natural heathland*

(b) *Cultivated heathland*

Litter

Crumbling raw humus

Iron pan

Raw humus

Leached zone

Cultivated leached zone

Parent substance

Organic material

Acarina

Old surface

Individuals

These findings are typical of the variations likely to be encountered in studies of the distribution of soil animals. Hence, as a preliminary to such studies, it is important that careful charts of soil zonation should be prepared such as that shown in Fig. 36. The necessary information can be obtained either by digging a small trench or by extracting a soil core with an auger. Preferably, both methods should be employed where possible, one as a check on the other.

Soil water

One of the main reasons why such a vast host of animals has colonized the soil is because it provides an insurance against the danger of desiccation. Few soil species can live above ground for long and those that do so have to adopt some means of protecting themselves during dry weather such as hiding in rotting tree trunks or among fallen leaves. It is a significant fact that sandy soils never support as many animals as those containing a high proportion of humus and some clay.

Thus, the water content of a soil and the amount of organic matter present, together provide a reliable index for predicting the density of animal colonization.

Methods of measuring soil water have been described in Chapter VI and some of these should form part of any study of edaphic factors.

Organic matter

The humus content of soils varies greatly but in the majority it ranges between 5 and 15 per cent (wet weight). However, in peaty soils, such as occur in heathland, it may exceed 30 per cent. We have already seen how the presence of organic matter influences the water-holding capacity of soils. This is clear from the analyses in Tables 5 and 6 (pp. 130–131).

A second equally important role of humus is to provide food for the countless numbers of organisms, both animal and plant, which can feed upon nothing else. We shall be concerned later with the animals when we consider the biotic factors which influence their distribution. By far the most numerous plants are the Bacteria, Fungi and Algae, most of which feed saprophytically. By their activities, complex organic materials are broken down into their constituent parts and finally into simple manurial salts which serve to enrich the soil once more. The nitrogen cycle in soil is dependent largely on this sequence of events.

The quantity of organic matter present is, thus, an index of soil fertility and another item which should be taken into account when making a preliminary survey of edaphic factors.

Temperature

Fluctuations in temperature occur constantly in soil just as they do above ground but the variations are never as great as in air nor do they take place so rapidly. We have already seen how the magnitude of temperature changes is related to soil composition; sandy soils, being porous, tend to heat up and cool down quickly while in heavy soils fluctuation is much less marked.

Soil temperature is not an easy thing to measure accurately for once a thermometer or similar device has been thrust into the ground, the natural equilibrium is disturbed and this may take some time to restore. Moreover, all soils exhibit a marked vertical thermocline which may extend to a depth of several feet. Undoubtedly the best way of measuring this thermocline is to insert a series of thermistors at different depths leaving them for a period of several days before any temperature readings are taken. The method of doing this has already been described (p. 136).

The effects of temperature variations on the lives of soil animals are still far from clear. It has been suggested, for instance, that the water-balance of the invertebrate body may be influenced to an appreciable extent by periodic heating and cooling. The soil atmosphere is normally saturated with water vapour but at night, when the temperature drops, much of this water will be converted into dew. The inhabitants of the upper soil layers must thus be subjected regularly to flooding once daily. What effect, if any, this has on their distribution and vertical movement is not known.

Heat undoubtedly plays an important part in influencing nocturnal activity at the soil surface. Thus, among Carabid

155

beetles, it is found that on warm summer nights the numbers active on the surface of sandy and loam fields are about twice as high as in day-time. On cold nights, however, activity in loam soils is only about the same as by day while on sandy soils it is reduced to approximately half this amount.

The temperature characteristics of different kinds of soil are also known to affect breeding activity. Several species of beetles (Carabidae) inhabiting light soils raise two generations a year while most of those in loam fields have only one.

Soil atmosphere

It has been stated (Tischler, 1955) that the composition by volume of an 'ideal soil' should be 50 per cent solid matter, 25 per cent air and 25 per cent water. Obviously, this is nothing more than a rough generalization but it gives an idea of the proportions of the three constituents occurring in the average loam.

As far as soil air is concerned, very little is known about either its composition or the extent to which this fluctuates. Still less is it clear what effect, if any, such fluctuations exert on the distribution and activities of animals which habitually occupy the air-filled cavities between the soil particles, such as mites and spring-tails. Air is normally present in all soils except those that are water-logged (e.g. certain types of fenland), and it is probably true to say that the percentage of oxygen, although always slightly less than that of the atmosphere, is sufficient to satisfy the rather modest requirements of the multitudinous arthropods which inhabit it. The situation as regards carbon dioxide is quite different for this is constantly being produced in large quantities by the respiratory activity of the whole living community. Some will dissolve in the soil water or combine with calcium compounds to form bicarbonate. But the greater part is present as gas. How the bulk of this is removed is not clear. No doubt a good deal escapes by passive diffusion through the pores of the soil, temporary fluctuations in atmospheric pressure presumably bringing about a constant interchange of soil air and outer air. But some carbon dioxide undoubtedly manages to accumulate, its concentration varying with the depth, the nature of the soil and the time of year; to mention only a few of the factors concerned.

Here is a field which would undoubtedly repay further investigation. Unfortunately, any procedure which involves the collection and analysis of gas samples is bound to be time-consuming and to demand the use of specialized equipment. This is not, therefore, a subject for study as classwork but it could profitably be pursued as an individual project. A great deal has still to be learnt about the use of the technique described in Chapter VI, which has already proved successful in the study of litter-layers and promises to be equally suitable for the investigation of surface soils in general.

Hydrogen-ion concentration (pH)

A general trend in the development of any soil is towards a condition of increasing acidity due to the formation of carbon dioxide by living organisms and to the accumulation of various organic acids as a result of bacterial activity. Such tendencies are normally offset by the natural occurrence of bases or by the artificial addition of lime, when these are deficient. Most animals tend to shun regions of high acidity and this accounts for their absence from localities such as peat bogs. Carbonic and other acids in the soil water can be neutralized to some extent by the secretions of the calciferous glands which are found in the bodies of many species such as woodlice, centipedes, millipedes and earthworms. But there must obviously be some source of calcium nearby if adequate replenishment of these glands is to be effected.

Earthworms are particularly sensitive to variations in pH and the requirements of different species have been studied extensively on account of their economic importance in the soil. Thus the genus *Allolobophora* (which includes several of the larger species) is intolerant of acid and is seldom found in conditions where the pH is below 5. The genus *Lumbricus*, on the other hand, appears to be ubiquitous and can tolerate a pH as low as 3·7. Both these genera are abundantly represented in neutral and alkaline soils. A few species such as *Bimastus eiseni* and *Dendrobaena octaedra* are acid tolerant and restricted to a range of pH of about 3·7–4·6.

157

Some typical results obtained by sampling earthworm populations in soils with different pH values are shown in Table 7.

pH (upper 10 cm.)	Sites examined	% with Bimastus eiseni (acidophile)	% with Lumbricus rubellus (ubiquitous)	% with Allolobophora sp.(acidophobe)
Below 4·5	22	82	45	0
Over 5·0	13	8	77	92

TABLE 7. Occurrence of earthworms in Lake District woodland soils. (*After Satchell.*)

These figures show clearly the important part played by pH preferences in determining the distribution of the various forms.

The pH of a soil varies surprisingly both on the surface and at different depths. For this reason, when edaphic factors are being studied, it is essential to make a thorough survey of the area selected. This applies particularly when studying the kinds of animals mentioned in this section. The colorimetric method of pH determination described in Chapters II and VI will be found sufficiently accurate for ordinary classwork. It is inexpensive, quick to use and can be readily employed on the spot. For more precise work, an electric meter is required. This is rather costly and can only be used in the laboratory.

Soil minerals

The influence on animals of the many minerals dissolved in soil water is mostly indirect, in that they supply the vital manurial salts on which plant growth depends. We have already seen (p. 154) that a proportion of organic matter is necessary in soil, not only as a source of animal food, but also as the medium in which bacterial activity, such as that involved in the nitrogen cycle, can take place. It is therefore not surprising to find that, in cultivated ground, the values for carbon and nitrogen are closely related. Estimates at Rothamsted have shown the C/N ratio to be normally about 12 : 1, thus suggesting that nitrogen content may be a fair index of the amount of organic matter present in a soil.

The element whose effects on animals are most evident and easily demonstrable is calcium. There is now much evidence to show that its presence in soil is one of the prime factors influencing colonization by such forms as centipedes, millipedes and earthworms, most of the detailed information available having been derived from studies of the latter group.

Calcium probably exerts its influence on soil-inhabiting species in three distinct ways:

(i) By controlling pH. We have already seen (p. 157) how many animals are sensitive to quite small changes in pH and that the most acid soils are largely devoid of a resident fauna. Earthworms, for instance, may be classified into groups according to their pH preference, although there is still some doubt as to why these preferences should exist. Are they due to the adverse effects of acidity itself, or is the principal factor a lack of calcium with which a low pH is generally associated? The answer may be complex, but the fact that certain species such as *Bimastus eiseni* and *Dendrobaena octaedra* habitually colonize land with a pH range of 3·7–4·6, strongly suggests that the concentration of hydrogen ions itself must be a determining factor in some instances.

(ii) As an essential item in the diet. The role of calcium in the metabolism of soil animals is still far from clear. Several of the larger forms such as centipedes, millipedes and earthworms possess calciferous glands, and in calcareous soils it can be shown that earthworms add calcium to the soil which they defaecate as casts. It is reasonable to suppose that the effective functioning of these glands is vital to the lives of such species; in which case, it is essential that they should be able to replenish the calcium supplies which they are constantly losing to the outside. In this connection it is interesting to note the observations of Lydford (1943) that certain millipedes, such as *Cylindroiulus londinensis*, tend to select for their food those leaves which have the highest calcium content. The role of calcium in the lives of the smaller species is more dubious and little is known about it. But the fact that calcareous soils usually support the largest microfauna, strongly suggests that its beneficial effects may be almost universal.

(iii) By its effects on the permeability of body tissues. The

159

influence of calcium ions in controlling the passage of solutes through living membranes is well known. Thus, cell layers which may be impermeable to certain substances when calcium is present become permeable to them in its absence. This fact may be of importance in arthropods such as millipedes which periodically lose their outer cuticle when moulting. The presence of adequate supplies of calcium will have the beneficial effect of reducing permeability and hence of limiting the rate of water uptake by osmosis.

Methods of determining the mineral content of soils have been described in Chapter VI. Unfortunately, these are apt to take rather a long time to carry out and so may not be suitable for class use. However, they may well prove valuable in the study of individual problems at an elementary level. Estimations of calcium content are likely to prove particularly revealing as the foregoing account shows, for these can be related directly to the density and distribution of a number of the larger animals, particularly earthworms. Incidentally, an interesting comparison can be made of the mineral content of a soil and that of the worm casts on its surface, particularly as regards the quantities of calcium compounds and organic material present in each.

DISTRIBUTION OF SOIL ANIMALS

It is not easy to state precisely what animals constitute the true soil fauna for there are many species whose associations with soil are of only a temporary or erratic kind. In the following account the term 'soil' will be used in its widest sense to include both the various zones of earth and the litter layer above. The numerous species permanently resident in these regions thus constitute the true soil community, while periodic visitors such as the garden snail (*Helix aspersa*), and animals which pass their young stages in soil (cysts, eggs, larvae, pupae, etc.) or use it only for overwintering, must be regarded as only temporary inhabitants.

One of the main difficulties facing the student of soil is the superabundance of organisms which it supports. Among the animals, for instance, there are huge numbers of arthropods, many of which belong to groups not normally encountered in elementary work. The problem of identification thus appears to be insuperable. But the situation is not as bad as it seems. In the first place, the individual species within a genus frequently exhibit much the same kind of ecological characteristics and requirements. Identification down to genus (or, even, as far as the order) is often quite sufficient for a satisfactory study if only a general picture is required. The recent advent of numerous keys for the identification of different groups has also greatly eased the problem facing the elementary ecologist. References to some of these are given in the Bibliography. Outstanding among them is a masterly summary by Kevan[1] covering the whole fauna of soil and the litter layer. This will be found invaluable for classwork.

In the following account of the distribution of soil animals, the number of species considered has purposely been reduced to a minimum. The only forms treated in detail are those which are relatively easy to study and which are useful in illustrating certain general ecological principles.

INHABITANTS OF THE LITTER LAYER

Significance of moisture. How to avoid desiccation is one of the principal problems of survival facing all living organisms. In the course of their evolution animals have attempted to overcome this difficulty in one of two ways – either by developing a relatively impervious outer covering or by restricting their activities to permanently humid conditions. It is with the second category that we are concerned when studying the occupants of the litter layer. The distinction between these two groups is clearly shown in Fig. 43, where representative rates of water-loss in dry air are compared for corresponding saturation deficiencies. Thus in the woodlouse (*Porcellio*) and millipede (*Oxidus*) (both typical inhabitants of the litter layer) the rate of desiccation varies throughout the temperature range and is proportional to the saturation deficiency of the atmosphere. But in characteristic open-air forms such as the spider (*Lycosa*) and insect (larva of *Pieris*) the waxy

[1] Kevan, D. K. McE. (1955). 'Identification of Soil and Litter Inhabiting Animals', *Soil Zoology* (Proceedings of the University of Nottingham Second Easter School in Agricultural Science, 1955). Butterworth.

layer of the cuticle ceases to be porous at about 40°C. with the result that no appreciable water-loss takes place below this temperature.

Moisture is, thus, the prime factor influencing the distribution of animals in the litter layer and constitutes the background against which a picture of the fauna must be built up. Oddly enough, in spite of the importance of water in their lives, there

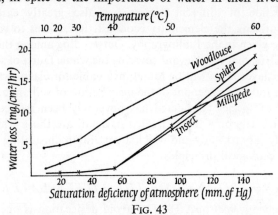

FIG. 43

Graphs showing rate of water-loss of certain arthropods in relation to atmospheric humidity.
(*From Cloudsley-Thompson*)
Science News 36 (Penguin Books, Ltd.)

appears to be little or no development of the power of positive hydrotaxis among such forms as woodlice, centipedes and millipedes. Instead, their response is the curiously negative one of being repelled by drought. This seems to be remarkably effective in preventing the animals from wandering far from their normal habitats and often results in local aggregations of large, isolated colonies. In woodlice, and no doubt in other forms too, the habit of congregating in damp places is enhanced by the fact that a moist atmosphere tends to reduce activity and hence the degree of mobility. It has also been shown that such animals, when on the move, seem to turn more frequently in wet paces than in dry ones.

A consideration of the effects of varying humidity is thus an important part of any investigation of the fauna inhabiting the litter layer. One of the failings of past studies of the subject is that they have been almost entirely qualitative. There are thus considerable opportunities for adding to existing knowledge in this field. The water content of samples of the litter layer can generally be estimated by methods similar to those described for soil, while the wet and dry thermistor technique (p. 35) is well suited to the determination of relative humidity in many types of microhabitat.

A set of responses complementary to those just considered, are the varying reactions of the litter fauna to changes in light intensity. As might be expected, all species show marked negative phototaxis but in woodlice, at least, the sensitivity of the response is closely related to the humidity of the surroundings. Thus an increase in moisture is associated with a decrease of light-sensitivity. Animals of the litter layer are invariably active after dark when the atmospheric temperature is reasonably low and relative humidity high. Even so, in leaving their moist day-time abode, many species are forced to risk partial desiccation. An increase in their negative response to light is thus of value in ensuring a safe return before dawn. It has been shown that different species vary greatly in their degree of drought tolerance and their ability to withstand atmospheric conditions can be related to modifications in structure and behaviour. Thus, among woodlice, the most tolerant species belong to the genus *Armadillidium* – so-called on account of their capacity for rolling into a ball like a miniature armadillo. But even these can only venture into dry places for relatively short periods. Nonetheless, it is probably true to say that all litter layer animals become photo-positive in dry air so that if their daytime haunt should dry up they will tend to wander about in the open until they either find a more suitable abode or perish in the attempt.

Study of distribution

From the previous account it will be clear that a general study of litter layer animals falls naturally into two parts – the examination of daytime distribution and an assessment of nocturnal activity. On theoretical grounds we would expect the overriding influence

163

of humidity to result in a discontinuous distribution of species with localized aggregations in regions of high organic content. Such a situation can be clearly illustrated in any garden or wood. With the onset of nocturnal activity this discontinuity must be largely broken down with the formation of intermingling populations of various species. Experience with millipedes, however, suggests that the differences in distribution by day and by night are not as great as might be supposed. Even allowing for the influence of the more obvious factors such as the availability of food, the impression remains that certain types of ecological barrier exist about which little or nothing is known at present, but whose effect on distribution is considerable.

Thus, the first step in the study of animals of the litter layer is to gain a general idea of their diurnal and nocturnal distribution within a limited area. This is best recorded on a large-scale map. Successive observations should be made over a period of time, particularly during changeable weather conditions, in order to judge the extent to which distribution varies. An entertaining and instructive variation can be introduced at this point by establishing one or more artificial habitats such as small heaps of wet peat or rotten wood underneath upturned flower pots in which the drainage holes have been blocked with corks. This will provide some idea of the preferences of different species and also of the speed with which the various forms can find and colonize a new locality.

One of the most interesting aspects of such studies is the extent of movement within a particular zone. Are the various colonies subject to a good deal of isolation or is a constant interchange taking place between them? The apparent existence of effective ecological barriers at least suggests that movement may not be as unrestricted as is sometimes assumed. The method of marking animals with cellulose paint (p. 86) is well suited to the study of larger forms such as woodlice and beetles, but very little work has so far been carried out in this field. In a few investigations, centipedes and millipedes have been marked by the removal of various legs, but methods involving some degree of mutilation are open to many obvious objections and are best avoided as a general rule.

The various factors influencing the distribution of animals in the litter zone also exert important long-term effects. We have seen how a moist environment is the overriding need of all these communities, a condition favouring the evolution of localized aggregations in restricted areas. One obvious disadvantage of this situation is that it tends inevitably to restrict dispersal and hence to lessen the potentiality for colonizing new localities. How this difficulty is overcome is not altogether clear, but studies of woodlice suggest that two features of their behaviour contribute to the solution of the problem which may well be characteristic of other groups as well. The first is the fact, already discussed, that the desiccation of a habitat results in a lessening of the urge to move towards moisture with the result that the animals tend to wander about in dry air as long as their power of water-retention permits. This 'do or die' policy presumably achieves a certain degree of successful dispersal. A second contributory feature is the incidence of fluctuation in numbers. Like most animal populations, those of woodlice have often been observed to increase and decrease periodically. Occasional outbursts in numbers have been recorded in woodlice, centipedes and millipedes and these are often associated with remarkable swarming movements. Instances are recorded in which the passage of a horde across a railway line has held up a train, the wheels of the engine skidding on the squashed bodies of the animals underneath. Unlike similar irruptions among mammals such as lemmings, these erratic journeys of arthropods are not just a means of reducing the pressure on food supply and living-space, but they may also result in a permanent extension of range if suitable new habitats happen to be available.

A problem which is bound to arise in the study of any group of organisms is that of identification. Fortunately, there are concise works covering most of the common animals likely to be found in litter layers and these are summarized in the Bibliography.

Population density

The various studies considered so far have been largely of a subjective kind. As an inquiry proceeds and the amount of data begins to accumulate it should become possible to employ a more precise and quantitative approach. This applies particularly to the estimation of numbers. We shall be concerned here only with the larger species which can be counted easily by eye such as wood-lice, beetles, centipedes and millipedes. The determination of density in minute forms demands the use of special techniques which will be considered fully in the next section.

Small colonies of the larger animals can often be counted successfully by eye. Moreover, if a system of paint marking is employed, some estimate can be made of the rate of turnover in a localized community. The problems of determining density become more complex, however, when large numbers are involved. Here, it would seem, is a good opportunity for employing the capture-recapture method (p. 94) which has been used hardly at all in these circumstances. Such studies as have been made so far seem to suggest that, in isolated habitats, randomization of marked individuals takes place quite quickly and the collection of representative samples therefore presents little difficulty. This is evidently a field where good opportunities exist for further experiment at quite an elementary level.

INHABITANTS OF THE SOIL

In the following pages the soil fauna is assumed to include all those animals whose complete life cycle is passed underground irrespective of whether or not they appear periodically at the surface. Judged on this basis, the animal colonists of the soil can be grouped for convenience into three categories:

(1) *The burrowers*. In Britain these are represented by a few vertebrates such as the mole, earthworms and various arthropods, particularly beetles.

(2) *Inhabitants of the soil water*. These include the vast fauna resident in the capillary water occupying spaces within the soil and the water-film enveloping the particles themselves. Protozoa predominate, particularly the innumerable flagellates, and their study is a highly specialized branch of soil science. In a neutral manured soil at Rothamsted it has been estimated that they may reach the astonishing density of 1,000,000 per gram of soil, being distributed roughly in the proportions of amoebae 280,000, flagellates

770,000 and ciliates 1,000. Such numbers, incidentally, are a mere trifle when compared with the density of the micro-flora in similar circumstances. Thus, a single gram of soil may contain as many as 5,000,000,000 bacteria which corresponds to a weight of more than 4 tons of bacterial protoplasm per acre.

Many other minute members of the water fauna also occur in great numbers; these include the Turbellaria (flatworms), Nematoda (roundworms), Rotifera (wheel animalcules) and Tardigrada ('water-bears'), to mention only a few.

(3) *Occupants of the air spaces.* This is a varied group of organisms, ranging from minute forms permanently committed to an existence inside the soil to those which appear periodically at the surface, generally after dark. The predominant factor governing their lives is the water supply, and their varying ability to exist in the open air is determined almost entirely by the extent to which they are able to avoid the danger of desiccation. The lower their drought resistance, the more intimate is the association of such species with the soil. Most of this soil-air fauna are arthropods (the majority are insects), typical members being the Acarina (mites), Pauropoda (pauropods), Collembola (springtails), and Coleoptera (beetles). Other competitors for the habitat include many insect larvae, mostly belonging to the Diptera ('flies'), but these cannot be regarded as permanent residents since the adult phase is spent above ground.

1. *Burrowing animals*

The principal burrowers in soil belong to three groups, the mammals, annelids and arthropods. A great deal has been written about their activities and some references to the literature are included in the Bibliography. A short survey of this kind can obviously make no pretence of treating exhaustively such a vast subject as the soil fauna; nor would an attempt to do so be of much value to the elementary student. The most useful compromise would seem to be to select a few typical organisms and to consider their ecology from the point of view of practical study.

Earthworms provide a convenient example of burrowing forms, for the number of species occurring in Britain is not great and the larger kinds can be identified fairly easily by reference to a good key.[1] Moreover, the use of potassium permanganate solution provides a convenient and fairly reliable means of collecting samples (see p. 79).

Methods of studying burrowing forms. The general principles governing the study of earthworm distribution are much the same as those already outlined for the occupants of the litter layer. It is important to remember that the composition of soil may vary greatly within short distances and for this reason the areas chosen for examination should be as small as possible.

While it is true to say that all earthworms are burrowers, the depths to which they penetrate are exceedingly variable depending on the species and the nature of the soil. A few forms such as *Lumbricus rubellus* are shallow workers among the loose organic material and plant roots. They seldom penetrate to a depth of more than about three inches below the surface. At the other extreme *Allolobophora nocturna* and *Lumbricus terrestris* are frequently found at depths of eight feet and even deeper. The nature of the burrow systems also varies greatly; so, too, does the speed with which tunnels are made.

A detailed study of earthworm distribution in a particular locality therefore involves:

(i) Sampling of small areas in order to obtain estimates of density

(ii) The construction of a vertical profile by deep digging to show the distribution of the different species

(iii) The construction in the laboratory of a vermarium (a box with glass sides) in which different species can be kept in order to study their mode of burrow-formation. The results can then be related to those obtained at different depths under natural conditions.

The sampling of earthworm populations presents considerable difficulties and no really successful method has yet been devised.

[1] See Černosvitov, L., and Evans, A. C. (1947). 'Lumbricidae', *Synopsis of the British Fauna No. 6* (Linnean Society, London).

Dilute formalin solution works well but seldom penetrates to a depth of more than about three feet. Its use should, therefore, always be supplemented by digging if a reliable estimate of the deeper burrowing species is to be obtained. The details of burrow systems are also often difficult to unravel particularly in light soils which are apt to crumble if disturbed. When constructing vermaria, this problem can be overcome to some extent by using well compacted soil to which has been added a certain amount of clay to bind it. The vermarium must, of course, be kept dark.

The density of earthworms is another aspect of their ecology which is comparatively easy to study and is of particular value at an elementary level, since variations can often be related to the influence of a few factors which are clearcut and readily quantified. Once again, extensive sampling of populations is required by the methods already outlined.

Charles Darwin estimated that an average earthworm population, mainly *Lumbricus terrestris*, numbers about 50,000 per acre. Recent investigations have shown the distribution of the various species to be much more complex than Darwin supposed, and of the twenty-five or so found in Britain, as many as twelve have been identified in a single field. Populations of 500,000 per acre are now known to be quite common, while in highly cultivated soils containing abundant organic matter and with a favourable mineral balance, the numbers may attain double this figure. Darwin's estimate represents the size of a worm population likely to be encountered under unfavourable conditions such as in acid pasture and scrubland. Although convention demands that earthworm densities should be expressed as numbers per acre, in fact these figures mean little when applied to small areas where appreciable fluctuations may occur even within a few yards (Fig. 44). The various factors influencing density and activity are still far from clear but organic matter, acidity, minerals and soil texture are some of the chief ones. Local aggregations must also occur during the breeding season and how long these take to disperse in the different species is not known for certain. The truth of the matter is almost certainly that the influence of specific

169

factors on earthworm distribution varies with the circumstances, and this makes the whole problem of their ecology the more fascinating to study.

One other important aspect of earthworm ecology which should

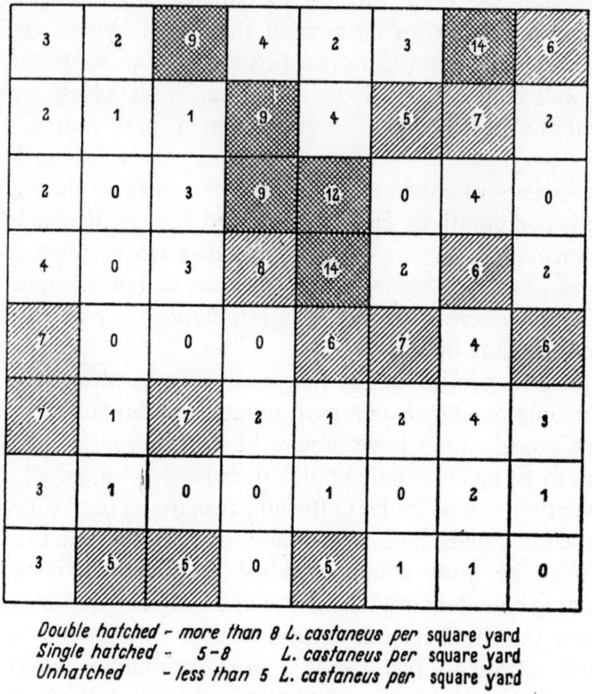
3 2 9 4 2 3 14 6
2 1 1 9 4 5 7 2
2 0 3 9 12 0 4 0
4 0 3 8 14 2 6 2
7 0 0 0 6 7 4 6
7 1 7 2 1 2 4 3
3 1 0 0 1 0 2 1
3 5 5 0 5 1 1 0
Double hatched - more than 8 L. castaneus per square yard
Single hatched - 5-8 L. castaneus per square yard
Unhatched - less than 5 L. castaneus per square yard

FIG. 44
Distribution of the worm *Lumbricus castaneus* in an eight yard quadrat. (*After Satchell.*)

Kevan: *Soil Zoology* (Butterworth)

be studied is their influence upon the environment in which they live. The annual turnover of soil resulting from casting alone is prodigious and is variously estimated at between 2 and 35 tons per acre. In some tropical and sub-tropical countries the figure is said to exceed 100 tons per acre. In fact, the true amounts involved must be much greater than these, particularly in cultivated soils where large quantities of cast material will be required to line the burrows and to fill up the many soil interstices.

The principal results of earthworm colonization and activity in soil can be summarized as follows:

(i) An improvement in drainage properties of the intact soil on account of burrowing

(ii) A reduction in pore space due to fine division of the soil particles

(iii) An increase in the water-retaining capacity of the soil without waterlogging. The reasons for this are not clear but the addition of organic matter is insufficient to account for the change

(iv) A rise in the amount of colloidal material present

(v) An increase in the percentage of organic matter when this is low

(vi) An increase in the amount of minerals, particularly calcium

(vii) The formation of coarser soil aggregates. Thus, Guild found that while 90 per cent of a dried soil passed through a 30-mesh sieve, only 10 per cent passed after being worked for six months by *Lumbricus terrestris*.

The collection and examination of worm-casts can thus provide much useful information concerning the physical and chemical changes going on in the ground as well as the magnitude of soil turnover.

2. *Inhabitants of the soil water*

The water fauna of soil differs markedly from the burrowers and the occupants of the air spaces. Practically all its members are microscopic, the majority being Protozoa. Their study is a highly specialized branch of soil science and is not within the scope of the elementary student. One interesting aspect of the animals themselves is that many appear to be dwarf forms of species commonly found in fresh water. For instance, the ciliate *Colpoda steini* often reaches a size of 30–60 μ in fresh water but its counterpart in soil seldom exceeds 18 μ. The various Rhizopoda such as *Amoeba limax* are well suited to this kind of existence since, by changing their shape, they are able to squeeze into minute crevices which cannot be colonized by other forms.

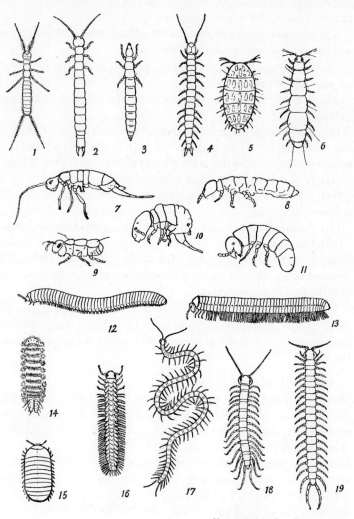

Kevan: *Soil Zoology* (Butterworth)

Fig. 45

Comparatively little is known about the influence of environmental factors on these animals. Changes in temperature appear to exert little direct effect and the only major requirement in their lives is an adequate supply of water. For those species which live near the surface the danger of desiccation lurks as a constant threat, and it is not surprising to find that many of them have evolved the power of forming protective cysts. These are an advantage not only in periods of drought but also under the adverse conditions of winter as well.

3. *Occupants of air spaces*

The non-burrowing terrestrial fauna exhibit a great diversity of form and modes of life. The majority are arthropods, notably the Isopoda (Crustacea), mites (Arachnida), spring-tails and beetles (Insecta), to mention only a few (Fig. 45). In some highly organic soils the mites (Acarina) and spring-tails (Collembola) constitute as much as 90 per cent of the total resident population.

FIG. 45

Some typical soil arthropods: 1, 2, Diplura; 3, Protura; 4, Symphyla; 5, 6, 9, Pauropoda; 7, 8, 10, Collembola; 11–16, Diplopoda; 17–19 Chilopoda (not to same scale)

1 Campodeid (*Campodea*)
2 Japygid (*Japyx*)
3 Proturan (*Eosentomon*)
4 Symphylid (*Scutigerella*)
5 Broad pauropod (*Eurypauropus*)
6 Typical pauropod (*Pauropus*)
7 Entomobryomorph spring-tail (*Mydonius*)
8 Poduromorph spring-tail (*Onychiurus*)
9 Hexapod larva of pauropod (*Pauropus*)
10 Round spring-tail (*Megalothorax*)
11 Hexapod larva of snake millipede (*Iulus*)
12 Colobognath millipede (*Polyzonium*)
13 Snake millipede (considerably shortened for purposes of illustration) (*Cylindroiulus*)
14 Tufted millipede (*Polyxenus*)
15 Pill millipede (legs not normally visible from above) (*Glomeris*)
16 Flat-back millipede (*Polydesmus*)
17 Geophilomorph centipede (*Geophilus*)
18 Lithobiomorph centipede (*Lithobius*)
19 Scolopendromorph centipede (*Scolopendra*)

Once again, humidity is the primary factor influencing the distribution of these forms. Unlike the previous group, liquid water is not required, but in order to survive successfully all species need an atmosphere which is virtually saturated with water vapour. Their resistance to desiccation is very variable, those forms with the greatest tolerance being able to colonize the zones nearest the surface while the less well adapted are permanently committed to the deeper layers where conditions remain more constant. Hence, a feature of distribution among the inhabitants of the air spaces is a well marked and characteristic vertical zonation.

The density of small arthropods in fertile soils is often enormous. For instance, an estimate of the animals in a square metre of compost sampled to a depth of 10 cm. included 130,000 spring-tails, 83,000 other insects and their larvae, more than 300,000 mites and several millions of nematodes.

CHAPTER VIII

The Study of Terrestrial Habitats

A striking feature of the terrestrial habitats of animals is their great diversity. They range from woods of all kinds, through shrub areas characterized by such plants as bramble, hawthorn and dogwood, to low-growing field layers of ever varying composition. Their vegetation is determined by many ecological factors the chief of which are their geographical and topographical position, the nature of the soil and the relationships of the plants, both with one another, and with the animals which depend upon them.

When studying soil communities we saw how desirable it was to concentrate on small areas at a time. This principle applies even more to land habitats. The selection of a site will often be determined by local conditions, but for elementary classwork it is a good plan, if possible, to choose a locality which offers sharp contrasts. A hedge with north and south aspects is ideal; so, too, is part of a wood with brightly illuminated and heavily shaded portions. The difficulty in elucidating the various physical factors influencing plant and animal distribution is that nearly always, several of them operate together to produce a combined effect. Nonetheless, it is true to say that in the sort of conditions we are considering, one or two factors generally play a predominant part and their detailed study is therefore well worth while.

Once a site has been selected the next question to decide is the extent of the mapping to be undertaken. This is a time-consuming operation and should be reduced to a minimum. On the other hand it is important to record the nature of the ground and the distribution of the principal vegetation, as this is bound to play some part in determining the constitution of the animal population. The most useful kind of map is generally a simple plan such as that shown in Fig. 46. On occasions, the influence of shade may be important, as in the study of a hedgerow, so that a line

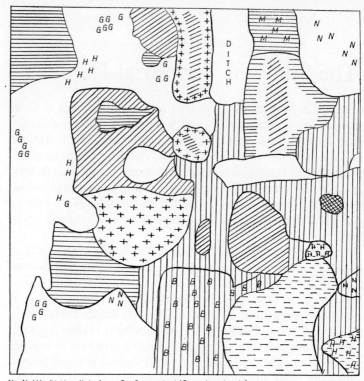

N = Nettle (Urtica dioica)   G = Groundsel (Senecio vulgaris)   H = Hogweed (Heracleum sphondylium)   M = Meadowsweet (Filipendula ulmaria)   B = Bindweed (Convolvulus arvensis)

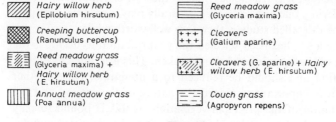

Hairy willow herb (Epilobium hirsutum)	Reed meadow grass (Glyceria maxima)
Creeping buttercup (Ranunculus repens)	Cleavers (Galium aparine)
Reed meadow grass (Glyceria maxima) + Hairy willow herb (E. hirsutum)	Cleavers (G. aparine) + Hairy willow herb (E. hirsutum)
Annual meadow grass (Poa annua)	Couch grass (Agropyron repens)

FIG. 46

Plan of a portion of fenland (Winchester College Nature Reserve)

PLATE 9

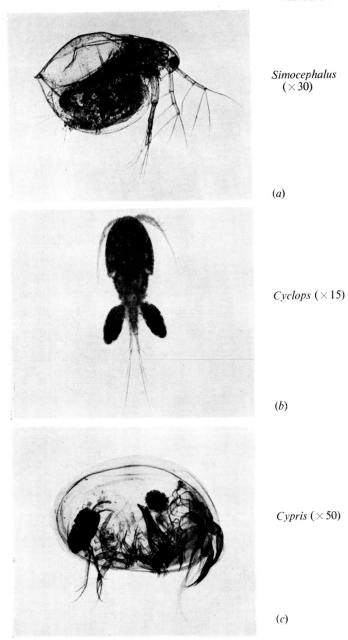

Simocephalus
(×30)

(*a*)

Cyclops (×15)

(*b*)

Cypris (×50)

(*c*)

Small herbivorous Crustacea which are common constituents of animal
plankton in fresh water

PLATE 10

(*a*)

(*b*)

The Great Diving beetle (*Dytiscus margi-nalis*); a ferocious carnivore inhabiting static fresh water. (*a*) larva. (*b*) adult female

transect (*see* Fig. 47) will be valuable in representing the relative heights of the various plant zones. The construction of accurate maps is a particularly important preliminary to any long-term study, for many plants and animals are sensitive to quite small

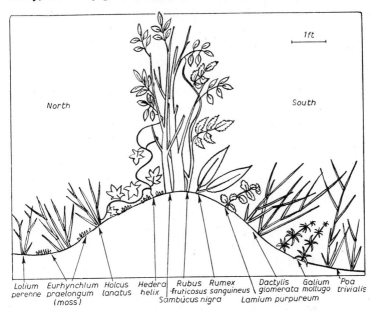

1 ft

North

South

Lolium | Eurhynchium | Holcus | Hedera | Rubus | Rumex | Dactylis | Galium | Poa
perenne | praelongum | lanatus | helix | fruticosus | sanguineus | glomerata | mollugo | trivialis
| (moss) | | | Sambucus nigra | Lamium purpureum

FIG. 47

Transect through a hedge to show varying heights of vegetation and the difference between plant species colonizing the North and South aspects

environmental changes and are often subject to marked fluctuations in range and density from one season to the next.

Various methods of measuring climatic factors have already been considered in Chapter II; these will be found suitable for the kind of studies to be described in this Section. It should be borne in mind that factors such as light intensity vary from one moment to the next and the value of studying them lies, not so much in the individual measurements as in range of variation which they represent.

STUDY OF CLIMATIC FACTORS

Light

Sunlight exerts an influence on animal communities in two principal ways. The first is an indirect one, namely, its effect on plant growth. This is obvious enough from an examination of the undergrowth at the brightly illuminated edge of a beech wood and towards the inside. Secondly, the degree of illumination determines the extent to which animals can see and be seen.

For comparisons of light intensity, readings should be taken in quick succession preferably when the sky is uniformly clear or overcast. The following measurements taken in an oak wood clearing (Plate 5a) during October show the kind of results to be expected:

   (i) Open daylight 800 ft/candles
   (ii) Below tree canopy (birch) 260 ft/candles
   (iii) Under shrub layer (bramble) 45 ft/candles
   (iv) Under bracken 5 ft/candles. There was practically no plant growth in this zone except creeping cinquefoil (*Potentilla reptans*) and heath bedstraw (*Galium saxatile*).

Temperature

Observations in woodland will show that flying insects, such as certain species of butterflies, tend invariably to concentrate in patches of sunshine and to avoid deep shade. No doubt there are several reasons for this but one of them is undoubtedly that a lack of sun is always associated with a lowering of temperature. Thus the insects, being cold-blooded (poikilothermous) are unable to obtain sufficient heat from the air around them for the maintenance of active flight.

A series of readings taken with a resistance thermometer (*see* p. 30) in light and shade will provide an accurate idea of the diversity of an animal's environment. For instance, the difference in temperature between the middle and the outside of a thick hawthorn hedge at noon in early July was found to be as much as 12°C. But, while conditions outside changed rapidly towards evening, those inside remained much more constant in the comparative absence of circulating air currents. Thus, when the temperature outside the hedge had fallen 10°C. that inside had only dropped by 4°C.

The majority of animals are cold blooded and by far the most important influence of temperature upon them is in controlling their metabolic rate. The activities of many kinds of insect larvae provide good evidence of this. For example, the caterpillars of moths such as the scarlet tiger (*Panaxia dominula*) and mullein shark (*Cucullia verbasci*) can often be found sunning themselves on their food plants, while in cloudy or rainy conditions they invariably remain deep down among the vegetation. Not much is known as yet about the climatic conditions which exist in microhabitats such as thick vegetation and clumps of grass. There seems little doubt that atmospheric conditions in these places are very different from those of the air above. This applies particularly to temperature changes which, as we have already seen, take place more slowly when the free circulation of air is restricted. Here is an aspect of animal ecology which would repay further study and which could be investigated quite easily with the type of homemade equipment already described. Systematic measurements made in a variety of microhabitats might well enable us to relate more closely the climatic changes to the behaviour and activities of the animals themselves.

The onset of winter presents particular problems for coldblooded forms whose rate of metabolism is greatly slowed down as a result of the reduced temperature. Many species hibernate in the larval or adult state deep down among the vegetation or in crevices in the bark of trees. Others overwinter in an inert resting stage such as an egg or pupa. Although quantitative records are difficult to obtain, there is much evidence to suggest that the mortality among hibernating invertebrates due to such causes as parasites, predators and adverse weather conditions is extremely high. Judging by the relative abundance of larval and adult stages in common insects such as the small white butterfly, *Pieris rapae* (which overwinters as a pupa), the rate of elimination must often reach 75 per cent and may frequently be higher than that. It is extraordinary, however, how well some forms are adapted to hibernation even though not in an inert stage. The larvae of the scarlet tiger moth (*Panaxia dominula*) seem to suffer hardly any loss during winter. The great mortality occurs in nature, also in the laboratory, just before pupation after a considerable period of feeding in the spring.

Among the warm-blooded (homiothermous) animals, small mammals such as the pygmy shrew, *Sorex minutus*, are at a disadvantage in cold weather on account of their relatively large surface area which promotes a rapid loss of heat. Even during the summer such forms have to spend much of their time underground while in winter they have no alternative but to hibernate.

Humidity

The moisture present in the atmosphere of an animal habitat is a difficult quantity to gauge because it is constantly changing. It depends on a variety of other factors the chief of which are the rainfall, temperature and wind. Humidity thus tends to remain most constant in patches of thick vegetation and regions of deep shade. Measurements made with an atmometer (p. 38) at a number of places on the outside and inside of a dense beech wood on a hot summer's day, showed that the average rate of evaporation in the shade was only 18 per cent of that in the sun.

The influence of humidity on animals is of three main kinds:

(i) It has an indirect effect in determining the composition of plant communities. These are much more sensitive than most animals to changes in atmospheric moisture, on account of their greater liability to desiccation.

(ii) It plays a significant part in controlling their temperature. A cold, damp atmosphere promotes a rapid loss of heat by conduction from the surface of the body, a deficiency which a poikilothermous animal or a small homiothermous one must find hard to make good by its metabolism alone. On the other hand, moist conditions in summer tend to reduce heat loss due to the evaporation of water.

(iii) The avoidance of desiccation is another problem which many small animals have to face. This applies particularly to

180

'thin-skinned' forms such as insect larvae which tend to live among dense vegetation such as the leaves of trees or in tufts of grass. A relatively high humidity is characteristic of such conditions which are somewhat comparable with those in the litter layer above the soil, described in Chapter VII.

Collecting in terrestrial habitats

Once an area has been selected and mapped and preliminary measurements of the chief climatic factors have been made, the process of collecting can begin. It will soon be obvious, even from the most superficial study, that the distribution of animals is far from uniform. Slowly moving forms such as beetles and snails are frequently associated with a single species of plant while even the highly mobile mammals, birds and flying insects invariably show preference for some localities rather than others. Three principal considerations determine the extent to which animal colonists are restricted to particular habitats.

(i) The climatic conditions and the magnitude of their variations

(ii) The amount of protection available both against adverse weather and from predators

(iii) The presence of the right kinds of food.

Some species, by virtue of a restricted diet or a narrow tolerance of climatic change, come to occupy a particular kind of micro-habitat. Extreme examples are internal parasites which are often restricted to a single species of host. But the majority of free-living animals have achieved varying degrees of adaptability and are able to withstand a fairly wide range of environmental variation.

Considerations of this kind serve to underline the difficulty of studying a terrestrial community with any degree of precision. This is particularly true where classwork is involved.

The first step in an ecological survey is to determine the principal plant microhabitats available, e.g. trees, shrubs, field layer. These must often be subdivided further into distinct species, for each may be associated with a characteristic fauna. More-over, a single plant such as a tree will generally support a variety of small communities on the undersides of its leaves, in the crevices of the bark and elsewhere. In an elementary study it will clearly be impossible to sample all these colonies and an arbitrary decision will therefore have to be made as to which should take priority. The more restricted and uniform the area chosen, the easier will this decision become. The various microhabitats must be collected separately. Slowly moving species will generally form distinct communities while mobile forms, such as flying insects, may appear in a variety of places.

If possible, collecting should be carried out both by day and by night in order to show the marked changes in distribution that are brought about with the onset of darkness. The influence of seasonal change is equally striking and winter collecting will provide a completely different picture of the animal communities from that obtained in summer.

BIOTIC FACTORS

Feeding and food relationships

The classification of animals on the basis of their feeding into herbivores, carnivores and scavengers, although somewhat

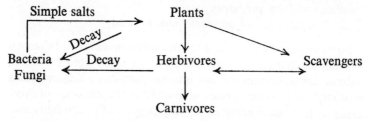

FIG. 48. Generalized food cycle in a land community

arbitrary, provides a convenient means of drawing up a preliminary plan of the food relationships in any community. Such a scheme is shown in Fig. 48.

The study of animal foods and feeding methods is a difficult and time-consuming procedure but, with careful observation, a great deal of useful information can be accumulated in the course of general collecting. The main classes of evidence which contribute to our knowledge of the feeding activities of animals are as follows:

(i) The association of a species with a particular microhabitat. For instance, defoliators like caterpillars, snails and slugs generally confine their attention to specific kinds of plants, so do gall-formers such as certain wasps and midges. Similarly, small predators seldom live far away from their prey, e.g. ladybird beetles prey upon aphids which are always to be found associated with young plant growths.

(ii) A study of feeding behaviour. Many of the larger and more mobile animals such as birds and mammals select certain favoured localities in which to devour their food which are not necessarily situated in close proximity to its original source. Typical examples are the anvil stones selected by thrushes for cracking snail shells. Careful observation of such areas will provide evidence, both of the species preyed upon and numbers taken each day. Furthermore, marking of living snails with cellulose paint can often give a useful indication of the source of the food if the number of suitable habitats in the vicinity is small. Here is a wide field for elementary experiment. It should be borne in mind that a bird always attacks a mollusc on the dorsal side in the region of the visceral hump; the paint marks must, therefore, be applied underneath where they are both invisible to the predator and unlikely to be destroyed.

Observations of this kind conducted at different times of the year and in varying localities enabled Cain and Sheppard to show that the song thrush is the principal agent responsible for controlling the colour and degree of banding in shells of the brown-lipped snail, *Cepaea nemoralis* (Fig. 49). The selective value of a particular kind of shell coloration depends upon the environment in which it happens to exist. Light colours are an advantage in uniform localities such as open downland but become conspicuous in woodland where the proportion of dark-banded shells is high. Seasonal change also affects the proportions of the different colours. Thus the advent of spring brings about a marked drop in the selection of yellow shells in open country as the background becomes greener and conceals them more effectively.

(iii) An examination of mouth parts, such as the cutting mandibles of leaf-eating insects and the sap-sucking proboscis of aphids which are quite easily seen. So, too, are the predatory jaws of centipedes. Among mammals, the herbivorous dentition of the rabbit and squirrel is quite distinct from that of carnivores such as the fox and hedgehog.

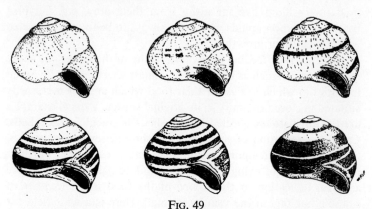

FIG. 49

Variation in shells of the brown-lipped snail, *Cepaea nemoralis*

Dowdeswell: *Mechanism of Evolution* (Heinemann)

(iv) An analysis of stomach contents and food remains. This is a laborious process and is generally worthwhile only in the larger animals. However, a prolonged study of a particular form, e.g. a species of bird, is the only way of gaining a really accurate idea of its food. Excreta will seldom provide much useful evidence but regurgitated material, such as the pellets dropped by owls, are a well-known and reliable source of information on foods with a large indigestible portion such as the cuticles of arthropods and the bones and hair of vertebrates.

The diet of the majority of animals is far more diverse than is commonly believed; moreover, it is subject to considerable variation at different times of the year as the availability of food changes.

(v) A study of the species in captivity. The use of this method for carnivores has obvious limitations, but it can be of value with small organisms such as insects and molluscs which frequently devour a variety of plant foods. In teaching, this is a convenient way of introducing the idea of food preferences which are just as strong among animals as they are in human beings. Most species seem to know 'what is good for them'; thus, herbivores normally restrict their diet to plants which are non-poisonous. But the

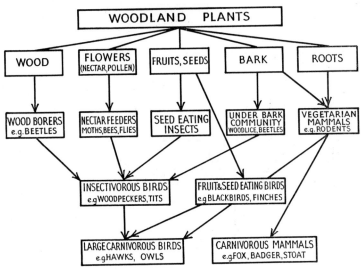

FIG. 50

Food chains in woodland based on parts of plants other than their leaves

Neal: *Woodland Ecology* (Heinemann)

larva of the scarce hook-tip moth, *Drepana harpagula* will eat either the small-leaved lime *Tilia cordata*, or the large-leaved *T. platyphylla* though the latter kills it.

One outcome of the study of diet among the species in a particular habitat is the realization that the various forms depend upon one another in a most complex way. The food economy of a community can be represented conveniently by a series of *food chains*; the more diverse the feeding habits of the animals, the more complicated do these chains become. E. G. Neal has made an admirable study of a piece of woodland and has summarized the principal food chains in a concise form. Fig. 50 shows some of the animals which depend upon the various parts of a plant, other than its leaves.

Fig. 51 is concerned with a more restricted microhabitat being based on plant leaves only. In both diagrams it will be noted that the feeding habits of the animals are grouped in relation to their

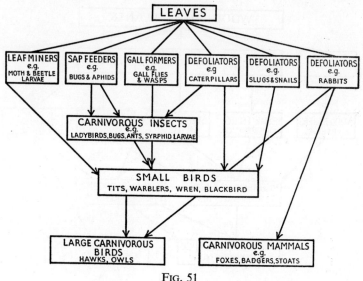

FIG. 51

Food chains in woodland based on plant leaves

Neal: *Woodland Ecology* (Heinemann)

particular diet. Thus, in Fig. 51, the various herbivores include leaf-miners, sap-feeders, gall-formers, and defoliators. The classification of feeding habits has given rise to the idea of the *ecological niche* – an economic concept which denotes the availability of a particular sort of food and facilitates a more accurate assessment of the amount of competition likely to occur in particular circumstances between different species with the same requirements. For instance, the defoliators will include insects with biting mouth parts such as caterpillars and molluscs which feed by means of a rasping radula, like slugs and snails. In general, insect larvae tend to be restricted in their diet while snails devour a great variety of vegetation. As a result, the two will only come into conflict when plants are scarce and confined to a few species.

Certain general conclusions can be drawn from the study of food chains in any kind of animal habitat.

(i) Plants, by virtue of their ability to photosynthesize (autotrophic nutrition), form the basis of all animal life.

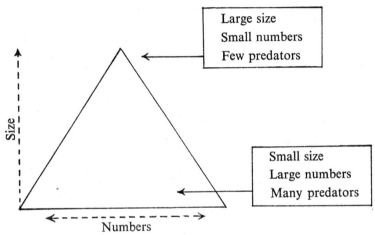

FIG. 52. Diagram illustrating the pyramid of numbers in an animal community

(ii) The variety of foods consumed by a particular species is often very great. Furthermore, it generally varies with circumstances such as the age of the animal and the time of year. All food chains are consequently complex and fluctuating in their composition.

(iii) As we follow along a food chain from herbivores to carnivores, the size of the animals progressively increases until a point is reached at which the individuals are large enough to be free from predators altogether. Reference to Figs. 50 and 51, will show that this stage is attained in a maximum of five links, the average being three.

(iv) The two ends of a food chain represent not only a divergence in animal size, but also a difference in numbers. Thus, the small herbivores exist in huge numbers and support many predators. As we descend the scale the rate of reproduction progressively decreases with increasing size, terminating in the largest carnivores. These are relatively rare and free from predation. Represented graphically, the density-size relationships of a community assume a triangular form (Fig. 52) which is sometimes known as the *pyramid of numbers*.

Population density

Subjective estimates of whether an animal is common or rare are easy to obtain in the course of ordinary collecting. Although purely relative, such records should always be kept as they provide useful evidence of the larger variations in density occurring in different places. Moreover, such studies are an essential preliminary to a more quantitative approach.

The various methods at present available for estimating the density of animal populations have already been considered in Chapter IV. All of them find application to varying degrees in the extremely diverse situations existing in terrestrial habitats.

Direct counts are the only means of determining populations of the larger animals such as badgers and foxes. Their mobility, coupled with the fact that they are largely nocturnal, necessitates finding their homes and counting them as they emerge and return. Such counts demand much patience and expenditure of time, but they can be most useful in providing information on density, and also on behaviour and breeding habits as well. Anyone doubting the feasibility and value of watching a badger set systematically should read E. G. Neal's admirable work on the subject.[1]

Similar methods can be used by day for counting birds, but these are of limited value unless the locality is small or a large number of observers are employed. More accurate counts of the larger mobile species such as birds and squirrels can be made by the line transect method, details of which are given in Appendix A. Out of the breeding season, bird trapping and ringing can also be used in relatively small areas as a means of determining density by

[1] Neal, E. G. (1948). *The Badger*. Collins.

means of the capture-recapture method. In order to avoid up-setting the natural distribution of the bird population as a result of introducing new sources of food, it is important that:

(a) A large number of traps should be employed at the same time

(b) Their location should be changed regularly in a random manner

(c) If only a few traps are available, bait should be put down at a number of other points within the locality.

Marking and recapture can also be used in small mammals such as field mice as a means of estimating their density. The Long-worth trap (*see* p. 71) will be found the most suitable type and the various methods of marking are described in Chapter IV. The use of capture-recapture in invertebrates depends largely on whether they can be marked effectively without damaging them and on their readiness to randomize within the population once they are released. So far, the application of this procedure has been explored in only a few groups and good opportunities exist for further experimental work.

From his studies of woodland, Neal concluded that there was no accurate means of determining the density of species inhabit-ing, say, the parts of a tree, other than the rather crude procedure of beating or counting the numbers per leaf. Such methods have obvious limitations and can give no more than a very generalized idea of the population present. The development of the mercury vapour moth trap (p. 62) has made a small contribution in pro-viding a means of estimating the relative occurrence of different species in a particular community. But it provides little informa-tion about the different microhabitats occupied and its use is limited to a single order of insects.

Special possibilities for study are provided by those animals with a distinct diurnal rhythm of behaviour. Woodlice, for instance, tend to congregate by day in large aggregations among litter and in rotten wood. As darkness falls these temporary colonies disperse and roam about the surface of the ground and vegetation in search of food. By dawn they have concentrated once more but not necessarily in the locations from which they emerged. Counting by day and marking with cellulose paint can thus yield evidence of local density, dispersal and of the daily turnover taking place in each microhabitat.

ENVIRONMENTAL CHANGE

The superficial appearance of stability exhibited by a locality at first sight can be most misleading. We have already seen how the environment in which plants and animals live represents a complex balance of different factors whose relative influence is in a continual state of flux. All living organisms possess varying degrees of adaptability and it is their power of adaptation which largely determines the success with which they can colonize and thrive in a particular place. Provided environmental fluctuations remain within normal limits there is a good chance that species once established in a habitat will be able to maintain themselves there. But in the event of changes becoming more extreme, such forms will be faced with the prospect of extinction unless they are able to undergo sufficient reorganization to cope with the new situation. Progressive modification in an organism which takes place in response to environmental changes is known as microevolution. Some species are remarkably sensitive to such variations and evolve appreciably in a short time. Among butterflies, E. B. Ford and I have detected significant alterations in populations of the meadow brown, *Maniola jurtina* after only a single generation when their habitat has undergone a marked change.

Short-term variations

The extremes included under this heading are those normally associated with seasonal change and are, therefore, well within the range of tolerance of most species. Such short-term changes can be classified for convenience into several categories.

(i) *Erratic changes.* These are mostly of a physical kind such as variations in illumination, and take place constantly from one moment to the next. The larger animals such as birds are independent of their direct effects although they may be influenced indirectly; for instance, by the fluctuating behaviour of their insect foods. The more exposed the habitat the more extreme do these climatic changes become. Secluded microhabitats, on the other hand, present a much more stable environment. This is well shown by the measurements of temperature made by Overgaard and Macfadyen in moss cushions about 3 cm. thick on the north- and south-facing sides of a thatched roof during a hot summer's day (Table 8).

| Layer | South-facing (°C.) | | | North-facing (°C.) | | |
	Max.	Min.	Mean	Max.	Min.	Mean
Surface	46	7	25	43	9	22
Under moss	40	12	25	30	11	18
5 cm. below thatch surface	30	15	22	26	13	18

TABLE 8. Temperatures (°C.) in and near moss cushions on a thatched roof. (*After Macfadyen.*)

It will be noted that conditions out of the sun were more uniform than those in it, the range of temperature variation at each period being considerably less. We still know surprisingly little about the kinds of microclimate in which animals live and this is a side of ecology in which the elementary student can make many useful contributions. The apparatus required is not difficult to construct and various types are described in Chapter II.

(ii) *Diurnal and nocturnal changes.* The transition from day to night brings about marked changes in animal distribution and activity. Among flying species, for instance, moths, owls, nightjars and bats replace the characteristic daylight forms. Indeed, it is true to say that all communities are divisible into clear-cut day and night components, the one half being active while the other rests. Clearly, it is important to study both of them if a complete picture of an animal habitat is to be built up. The physical changes involved in the transition concern chiefly illumination, temperature and humidity. The influence of some of these on such forms as nocturnal arthropods has already been discussed in Chapter VII.

191

(iii) *Seasonal changes.* Factors associated with the onset of winter which exert a profound influence on the lives of terrestrial animals are a drop in temperature and changes in plant form and activity. The response of animal communities to cold conditions and the methods available for overwintering have already been considered in an earlier part of this chapter. Suffice it here to stress once more the importance of examining an animal colony in both its summer and winter aspects in order to gain a true appreciation of the substantial changes involved.

Leaf-fall in deciduous trees and the dying back of herbaceous plants present particular problems for the animals which formerly relied upon them for their food and shelter. Many species hibernate either as adults or in a resting stage, while others, such as the bean aphid (*Aphis fabae*) have to turn their attention to different hosts notably the guelder rose (*Viburnum opulus*) and spindle tree (*Euonymus europaeus*) whose young buds provide food for the first brood which hatches in early spring from eggs laid in the preceding autumn. The difficulties are no less severe for the predators on these small herbivores which either have to change their location or the nature of their diet.

Long-term variations

Anyone who has kept annual records of the animals or plants in a particular locality must have noticed the striking natural changes which often take place. Such long-term studies are not the subject of this book, but it is appropriate to mention them here because, as yet, we know so little about the mode of action of the many factors involved. Useful information of this kind can often be accumulated gradually and without any extra trouble as a result of a succession of short-term studies made in the same area.

Three of the principal causes of long-term ecological changes are worth brief consideration.

(i) *Plant succession.* The process by which successive colonists replace one another in a plant habitat is well known. Annuals are followed by herbaceous perennials which are themselves succeeded by woody perennials until, eventually, a climax vegetation is achieved. Given the right conditions, such as an open piece of

PLATE 11

(a) Sector of a gently sloping rocky shore near Lyme Regis (Dorset)

(b) Shanny (*Blennius pholis*), out of water on a rock ($\times \frac{3}{4}$)

PLATE 12

(*a*) Flat top-shells (*Gibbula umbilicalis*), at low tide ($\times\frac{1}{2}$)

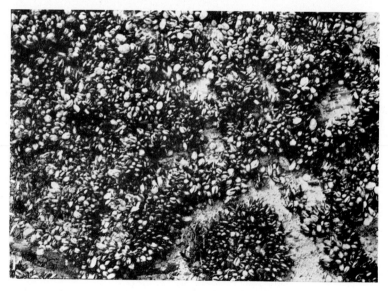

(*b*) Young mussels (*Mytilus edulis*), forming a dense mass on a rock surface ($\times\frac{1}{4}$)

fertile soil, the process of plant succession can proceed at a surprising speed. A famous example is part of the Broadback wheat field at Rothamsted which was left unharvested in 1882 and has not been touched since. Records show that it soon became a dense thicket and it is now a fully grown oak wood. Associated with this change are corresponding alterations in the animal population. For instance, the area now supports a typical woodland community of insects.

(ii) *Human influence.* Under natural conditions plant successions of all kinds take place relatively slowly but, aided by man, they can proceed at a surprising rate. Thus, certain parts of an area of fenland in the valley of the River Itchen were formerly overgrown by nettles. After three years' treatment with sodium chlorate solution all the nettle beds had been exterminated and their place taken by a dense growth of reed meadow grass (*Glyceria maxima*) and comfrey (*Symphytum officinale*). The large colony of the small tortoiseshell butterfly (*Aglais urticae*) which had formerly subsisted upon the nettles declined sharply while a tiny population of the scarlet tiger moth (*Panaxia dominula*) previously confined to a patch of comfrey in one corner of the area increased greatly in numbers and became quite common.

At the other extreme, human interference may exert important influences of a much more delayed kind. Many areas of our woodland much frequented by the public, such as Epping Forest, are suffering severely from a lack of young regenerating seedlings of trees like beech and hornbeam. This is not due to any lack of natural seed but human trampling has been shown to be largely responsible for the failure of the young trees. In areas where brushwood enclosures have been constructed and human access restricted, such difficulties have been successfully overcome.

(iii) *Influence of animal colonists.* The everyday activities of the larger animals, like those of man, sometimes exert profound changes on the natural environment. This is obvious enough from an examination of an area formerly colonized by rabbits and subsequently freed of them by myxomatosis. Thus, it is no coincidence that badger sets are often to be found in the midst of elder thickets, for elder is one of the few trees which, as a young sapling, can withstand the depredations of badgers and continue growth until it finally reaches a stage when it is immune to further damage.

PROTECTIVE ADAPTATIONS

One of the main purposes in the life of animals is self-preservation. We have seen in the previous pages how terrestrial habitats exhibit a greater variety of conditions than any others and it is, therefore, not surprising to find that the methods of protection adopted by land species are equally numerous and varied.

Animal protective devices have often been described and no useful purpose would be served in further theoretical discussion here. Some references to the appropriate literature will be found in the Bibliography. Such adaptations can be classified for all practical purposes under the following headings.

(i) *Adaptations for concealment.* These include the use of special colours, tones, patterns, shapes and postures. In addition, the effectiveness of these devices depends almost always on an ability to remain quite still. Examples among terrestrial species are innumerable and one has only to enter an oak wood to find numerous Geometrid moths settled on the bark of trees or their larvae ('stick caterpillars') perched precariously on stems and leaves.

The degree of elaboration of these concealing devices varies enormously. Among moths, the adult oak beauty (*Biston strataria*) possesses a pattern and tone of coloration which blend beautifully with the bark of trees on which it rests by day. In some species, such resemblances are restricted to one sex only as in the common mottled umber (*Erannis defoliaria*), where the male is cryptically coloured but the female is wingless and relies upon her small size to hide in cracks and crevices. At the other extreme, most birds and mammals exhibit little more than a general resemblance to their surroundings and some of them rely on their ability to 'freeze' in a state of immobility when sudden danger approaches and they are unable to get away in time.

The practical study of such adaptations is of two kinds. First, there must be a series of observations accompanied by descriptive records of examples seen. This is a necessary preliminary to the second stage – a more objective analysis of the efficiency of such methods. It should be borne in mind that no device gives perfect protection; all are fallible to varying degrees. For instance, an individual may settle in unsuitable surroundings, or it may fail to orientate itself on a tree trunk in conformity with its pattern and hence be easily seen. Again, it may move at a critical moment when a potential predator is near.

There is, at present, a great dearth of experimental evidence concerning the selective value of different protective devices in animals and this is a field in which the amateur can make valuable contributions. The recent work of Kettlewell and others on the peppered moth, *Biston betularia*, provides an admirable example of how such studies can be carried out. The species is well known as providing the most sensational example of rapid evolution yet witnessed in any living organism; for, within a period of little more than 100 years, whole populations inhabiting the industrial midlands of England have changed from the normal speckled form to a black variety, *carbonaria*. A second dark form also occurs which is somewhat intermediate in appearance between the other two. This is known as *insularia* and is usually the rarest of the three (*see* Plate 6). Kettlewell's experiments were carried out in a small wood near Birmingham – an area subject to heavy industrial pollution. It had long been suspected that the spread of these black forms (melanics) was due, at least in part, to the advantage they gained in matching their soot-blackened surroundings. But precise evidence was lacking both as to the extent of the advantage, if any, and also the kind of selective agents (predators) involved.

Some 651 marked *betularia* were released at a number of points in the proportions 171 normal : 416 *carbonaria* : 64 *insularia*. The natural population of the wood comprised about 90 per cent melanics. The moths were then 'scored' in relation to their backgrounds. It was found that a range of 2 yards was sufficient to tell invariably whether an insect was conspicuous or inconspicuous against its surroundings. Having made the initial decision, the observer then walked away until the moth was just no longer visible. In this way the following series of arbitrary 'scores' of divergence or similarity were constructed, all observations being made in the shade and in 'average daylight'.

'*Conspicuous*' insects (on incorrect background):
Visible at 30 yards and over   −3
Visible at 20–30 yards   −2
Visible at 10–20 yards   −1

'*Inconspicuous*' insects (on correct background)
Invisible at 2 yards   +3
Invisible at 5 yards   +2
Invisible at 10 yards +1

By the use of this comparatively simple method the following results were obtained (Table 9).

Score	+3	+2	+1	−1	−2	−3	No. of inconspicuous insects		No. of conspicuous insects		Total releases	Average score per insect
Typical								%		%		
on oak	3	5	9	7	44	86	17	11	137	89	154 ⎱ 171	−2·11
on birch	10	6	1	0	0	0	17	100	0	0	17 ⎰	+2·53
Carbonaria												
on oak	184	127	47	7	1	0	358	98	80	2	366 ⎱ 416	+2·33
on birch	8	8	5	4	7	18	21	42	29	58	50 ⎰	−0·54
Insularia												
on oak	21	5	10	8	9	3	36	64	20	36	56 ⎱ 64	+0·857
on birch	5	2	1	0	0	0	8	100	0	0	8 ⎰	+2·50

TABLE 9

The conclusions to be drawn from these figures are clear. On oaks with a uniform sooty bark, *carbonaria* is well protected while typical *betularia* is conspicuous. The mottled dark and light patches of birch offer a variety of surroundings suitable to all three forms but less so to *carbonaria*. All backgrounds seem to suit *insularia* but its concealment is less perfect than that of *carbonaria* on dark trunks. Kettlewell was subsequently able to relate conspicuousness to survival in males of the three forms and showed the percentage survival per day in *carbonaria* to be 16·8 per cent higher than that of *betularia*, while *insularia* possessed an 11·4 per cent advantage over the normal form.

Two classes of evidence contributed to these findings.

(i) The use of mercury vapour lamps to attract the moths at night (mostly males) combined with the capture-recapture method of estimating survival.

(ii) Direct observation of predators at work by day. This revealed the interesting fact that birds such as the robin and hedge sparrow habitually prey selectively upon moths resting on tree trunks and branches, but their actions are so quickly performed that they had previously been overlooked by ornithologists and entomologists who both strongly denied that such an occurrence took place, even as a rarity.

The experiments just described were carried out on a big scale and involved the artificial release of a large number of animals. Extensive preparation was needed which involved, among other things, a huge breeding programme. Many species of woodland moths, however, occur naturally in large numbers and are often abundant in favoured localities. Among these are a number of polymorphic species which have never been investigated, including many with well-known industrial melanics.[1] Others, such as the spring usher (*Erannis leucophaearia*) possess dark forms which are not associated with pollution at all and whose significance has yet to be determined.

Anyone interested in protective devices among insects and the general problem of industrial melanism in moths should consult E. B. Ford's admirable account where numerous suggestions are made for further study.[2]

(ii) *Warning adaptations*. Animals which employ cryptic protective devices are generally palatable to predators and, if their concealment is not of a high order, are likely to suffer a big mortality. The reverse is true of species which possess noxious properties such as an evil taste or smell, irritant hairs on their bodies or a means of retaliation such as the powerful bite of the badger. The effectiveness of such methods is to a large degree dependent upon self-advertisement so that potential predators may be warned to keep away. Devices of this kind are known as

[1] A number of other moths with industrial melanic forms are shown in Plate 6.

[2] Ford, E. B. (1955). *Moths*. Collins.

aposematic and include bright colours, particularly red and yellow, and threatening postures such as that adopted by the larva of the puss moth (*Cerura vinula*) which, when alarmed, extends two whip-like processes at the posterior end of the body.

As in cryptic resemblances, the study of aposematic adaptations can be both subjective and objective, and there is a great deal still to be discovered about them. The difference between the two forms can be conveniently demonstrated on any patch of cabbages where caterpillars of the large and small white butterflies often abound. The larva of the large white (*Pieris brassicae*) possesses warning colours being predominantly green with a row of large black spots on the back. Numerous short, white hairs arise from small warts on the back and sides, the latter being yellow with a sprinkling of black dots. By contrast the caterpillar of the small white (*P. rapae*) is cryptically coloured being uniformly green except for a sprinkling of minute black and yellow dots. An examination of the two forms using 'visibility' tests such as those already described in *Biston betularia*, will reveal important differences in behaviour. While the larvae of the large white tend to expose themselves on the upper surfaces of leaves where they are plainly visible, those of the small white are mostly confined to crevices between the leaves or to their lower surfaces. Such comparisons provide excellent opportunities for the use of objective and quantitative methods. Direct proof of distastefulness is difficult to obtain and requires a great deal of patient observation – and trial! It is an interesting fact that most species whose protection appears to be aposematic prove, when tasted, to be unpalatable to man!

The study of aposematic adaptations may well lead to the discovery of mimicry – a situation in which two or more different species have evolved a common appearance and mode of behaviour. Sometimes, only the species copied (model) is, in fact, distasteful, the other (mimic) being readily preyed upon. Examples are the various clearwing moths, many of which have black and yellow bands on their bodies thus resembling different species of wasps. The bee hawk moths resemble humble bees in a remarkable way, both in appearance when on the wing, and in general behaviour. Mimetic resemblances of this kind which involve an element of deceit (sometimes known as Batesian mimicry after their discoverer) are, of necessity, a rare occurrence. A much commoner type is that found among many species of wasps, all of which are aposematic, in which a common warning mechanism is used, such as black and yellow banding. Communal resemblances of this kind are sometimes known as Müllerian mimicry and are of frequent occurrence among insects possessing a noxious taste or a sting. Quantitative studies are, again, badly needed but they need careful planning and inevitably involve a considerable expenditure of time.

Distracting mechanisms

Brief mention must be made of another type of device commonly employed by birds and insects, in which brightly coloured parts are exposed suddenly as the animal starts to move and therefore gives away its position. Conversely, a structure which is conspicuous in flight may suddenly vanish when its possessor comes to rest. Such species are generally palatable and use these devices (sometimes known as flash colours) to distract or confuse any potential predators which may be in their vicinity. The precise significance of flash colours and the advantages gained by their use are difficult to determine. White tail feathers only exposed in flight are often used by birds such as the wheatear and the various pipits, while the brilliantly coloured hindwings of red and yellow underwing moths are always concealed by the cryptically coloured forewings when the insects are at rest.

MOVEMENT AND DISPERSAL

One of the characteristic features of animal communities is that the distribution of the different species is in a constant state of change. The various methods of marking described in Chapter III provide good opportunities for studying dispersal in the larger terrestrial forms.

The types of movement occurring among animals can be classified roughly as follows.

(a) *Long-range movement* (migration). A great deal has been written on this subject, particularly in birds. Suffice it to say here that such journeys are seasonal, two-way, and always associated with breeding. From the practical viewpoint, one of the most interesting results of migration is its influence on the composition of animal populations. This is an aspect which is well worth investigating in any locality, particularly one which is fairly restricted and clearly defined, such as a patch of heathland or a small wood. Typical of this kind of study is one made in the Winchester College Nature Reserve – a 2½-acre area of *Glyceria* fen which has been artificially planted with trees such as elm, alder, poplar, willow and hawthorn (Plates 5b and 7). The monthly average population of some common birds during part of 1954 is shown in Table 10.

	Jan.	Feb.	Mar.	May	June	Oct.	Nov.	Dec.
Blackbird	4	3	4	3	6	5	6	8
Mistle Thrush	—	2	1	—	1	1	—	1
Wren	1	2	2	2	2	7	6	4
Blue Tit	4	3	3	1	15	6	5	3
Great Tit	1	2	1	2	1	—	1	—
Chaffinch	1	1	1	1	2	1	1	—
Hedge Sparrow	1	2	1	2	—	—	1	—
Snipe	5	10	1	—	—	—	—	—
Sedge Warbler	—	—	—	4	6	—	—	—

TABLE 10. Monthly average density of some common species of birds in Winchester College Nature Reserve (2½ acres) during 1954.

It will be noted that the density of most resident species remained fairly constant, an exception being the blue tits which tended to pass through in flocks during late June. Snipe were only present during the cold weather of the first three months. The chief migrants were sedge warblers which arrived in late April and left again after breeding, in early July.

Seasonal fluctuations of this kind present all sorts of interesting secondary problems such as competition between different species occupying similar ecological niches and the availability of suitable nesting sites (*see* p. 202).

(b) *Short range movement.* This is often of an erratic kind and is chiefly concerned with the search for food.

It is a subject on which a considerable literature is available but much of it is only of a descriptive kind. Systematic marking and sampling by the methods already described can provide much fascinating and original information on animal activity or the lack of it. Moreover, a situation which is well known as typical of one area may not be in the least characteristic of another. Again, there are marked differences in activity even among species whose ecology is superficially similar. Thus, L. E. Brown, studying local movement in three small mammals, the short-tailed vole (*Microtus agrestis hirtus*), the field mouse (*Apodemus sylvaticus*) and the bank vole (*Clethrionomys glareolus britannicus*) has shown that while the daily range of 92 per cent of *Apodemus* and *Clethrionomys* amounted to less than 60 yards that of 92 per cent of *Microtus* was less than half this distance. It would be interesting to know if the situation existing in Silwood Park, where these studies were made, is typical of other localities.

Little attention has been paid so far to the investigation of local movement even among our common animals. Thus, bird-ringing can provide useful data on the distribution of species such as the house sparrow which often strays into quite unexpected places, particularly during winter. Furthermore, it provides an opportunity of discovering what proportion of a population is resident in a certain area also the rate of turnover and expectation of life in different species. Slowly moving forms such as the garden snail also afford excellent material for study. Little is known about the extent of their movement and, as we have already seen (p. 84), colour marking can provide much useful information both on mobility and on predator-prey relationships.

Investigations of this kind are bound to lead to a better appreciation of the dynamic nature of animal communities. If carried on for several years, they may also reveal the extent to which different species are expanding or decreasing their range.

BREEDING ACTIVITIES

The life history of any animal is always well worth study both under natural conditions and in the laboratory. Indeed, it is surprising how few of the breeding cycles of our common species are really well known. Just as the movement of an animal community is subject to changing circumstances, so, too, are the characteristics of its breeding. Thus, a species which is single-brooded in one place may be multi-brooded in another; while at the extremity of its range, it may only be able to breed in alternate years. Incidently, it is worth noting here that the habits, requirements and restrictions of animals may also differ from normal at the limit of their distribution.

The study of breeding cycles in small animals such as insects presents many difficulties particularly under natural conditions, where observation tends to be restricted to distribution, structure and habits. Details of a life history must generally be worked out, either indoors under controlled conditions or by covering an appropriate portion of vegetation with a 'sleeve' of some light material such as muslin. If possible the two methods should be employed together, one as a check upon the other.

Some of the most rewarding studies of breeding activity are those carried out with birds and mammals. Mention has already been made of the possibilities of investigating badger sets (p. 188), but the disadvantage of badgers and of all the smaller mammals is that their activities are almost entirely nocturnal.

The selection of nesting sites by birds involves a great variety of habits and adaptations. An instructive study can be made by selecting a restricted area and endeavouring to find as many nests as possible within it. This is no easy matter, but some indication of their whereabouts can generally be gained by watching the parent birds, particularly the perching place adopted by the male for singing before building actually starts. Records are kept for each nest[1] of the number of eggs laid, the proportion that hatch and the number of fledglings which eventually leave. An estimate can then be made of the breeding success achieved by different species and the possible causes of failure. A summary of a small survey made by Blundell's School in 1949 is shown in Table 11.

[1] A national scheme for recording nesting success is organized by the British Trust for Ornithology who supply specially printed Nest Record Cards with spaces provided for all relevant information.

Species	No. of nests	Average clutch size	% hatched	% that flew of those hatched	% that flew of eggs laid	% mortality
Hedge Sparrow	5	4·2	66·7	75	57·1	42·9
Song Thrush	5	4·2	76·1	100	38·1	61·9
Greenfinch	4	4·3	72·2	31	22·2	77·8
Spotted Flycatcher	3	4·5	66·7	100	66·7	33·3
Blackbird	7	4·3	60·2	58·7	38·1	61·9
Chaffinch	3	4·3	80	80	66·7	33·3
Reed Bunting	3	4·3	85	100	60	40
Willow Warbler	5	5·2	100	43	40	60

TABLE 11. Nest records for eight species from a locality near Tiverton, Devon in 1949.

The number of nests found was small and the conclusions to be drawn from these records are of no more than local interest. However, they demonstrate clearly what an enormous wastage occurs during the early stages of a bird's life.[1] In the 43 nests found (all species included), only 53 per cent of the eggs laid were successfully reared to a stage at which the young flew. Of 194 eggs laid, 75 per cent hatched, and of the resulting young, 70 per cent left the nest.

Attempts to establish the causes of failure among eggs and young produced the following results:

(i) *Eggs.* Of 194 eggs laid, 49 (25 per cent) failed to hatch for the following probable reasons:

Cause	No. of eggs destroyed
Egg collectors	9
Predators (unidentified)	14
Parents deserting (reasons unknown)	10
Infertile	7
Ejected by cuckoo (Hedge Sparrow)	1
Broken by parent bird	1
Causes unknown	7
	49

[1] For an excellent summary of information available on bird survival see: Hickey, J. J. (1952). 'Survival Studies of Banded Birds', U.S.A. Dept. of Interior Fish and Wild Life Service. Sp: Sci: Rep: *Wild Life*, **15**, 177.

(ii) *Young*. Of 145 birds hatched, 43 (30 per cent) died during the nesting period due to the following probable causes:

Cause	No. of young killed
Trampling by cattle (Willow Warblers)	12
Dead in nest (cause of death unknown)	12
Predators (unidentified)	8
Destroyed accidentally (grass-cutting with scythe)	6
Fell out of nest	3
Ejected by Cuckoo (Hedge Sparrow)	2
	43

Another aspect of bird breeding activity which is well worth study, is the way in which a locality is divided up among the individuals of the same and different species into a series of breeding strongholds (territories). Territorial behaviour has now been described for many species but, since it varies considerably from one locality to another, there is a great deal still to be found out. Detailed consideration of the subject is outside the scope of this book but appropriate references are included in the Bibliography.

Territories vary somewhat in different species, but the following generalizations hold good for land birds and may serve as a basis for practical study.

(i) The limits of a territory are first established by the male who generally arrives in the locality a few weeks in advance of the females. He selects a prominent song post from which he sings and displays.

(ii) After pairing, the nest is built within the territory, often in the vicinity of the male's song post.

(iii) Both sexes fight readily to maintain the boundaries of their area against intruders of the same species. The extent to which other species are tolerated varies considerably. For instance, in his studies of blackbird territories near Winchester, H. E. Norton found that starlings, robins, chaffinches and house sparrows enjoyed unrestricted access. Song and mistle thrushes, however, were sometimes tolerated but frequently driven away.

(iv) The outlines of territories often follow natural boundaries such as buildings, walls and hedges. For a particular species, they remain surprisingly constant from year to year both in their distribution and size. Norton observed the layout of blackbird territories in a garden for a period of seven years; their distribution in 1951 and 1952 is shown in Fig. 53. He concluded that the average size was about one seventh of an acre and that the boundaries fluctuated within certain limits depending mainly upon the pugnacity of neighbouring pairs. Thus, in 1952 the cock in the Pine Tree territory started by occupying a rather restricted zone, but eventually succeeded by a process of continual attrition in driving his next door neighbour westwards until he had appropriated a considerable portion of the Home territory as well (Fig. 53b). The size of territories is no doubt governed to some extent by the food available. The more open the country, the greater is their area likely to become. Lack found that in a locality consisting of woodland, orchards and quarries, the size of robin territories averaged about $1\frac{1}{2}$ acres. In the water meadows of the River Itchen, those of the yellow wagtail are approximately twice as large.

(v) Territorial behaviour is not entirely confined to the breeding season: some species, such as the robin, maintain a territory in the winter as well. The significance of this, also the incidence of similar behaviour in other species, are still little known. Further observations are needed before any definite conclusions can be drawn.

(vi) The primary function of a territory seems to be to ensure that a male acquires a mate. Once pairing has taken place, the area no doubt serves as a rendezvous in keeping the pair together. Although food collecting takes place partly within its confines it is never entirely restricted to them. Foraging excursions frequently range far away from the nesting site.

The essence of any study of bird territory is careful routine observation and recording. Once an area is well known the individual birds can often be identified at sight by slight colour differences or characteristic variations in behaviour. Trapping and colour-ringing during the winter, also the ringing of nestlings, are

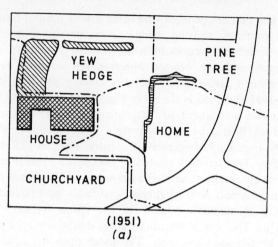

(1951)
(a)

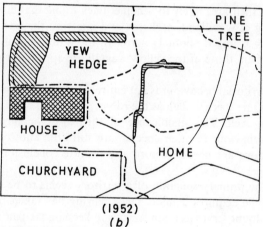

(1952)
(b)

Fixed boundaries —.——.——.——.——.——.

Maximum and minimum boundaries
of pine tree territory ————————————

├─────── 50 yards ───────┤

FIG. 53
Blackbird territories in a garden near Winchester.
(*After Norton.*)

valuable means of building up a large marked population among the resident species as a prelude to a study of their breeding activities the following spring. The use of nest boxes to provide artificial breeding sites is a way of overcoming the difficulties in built-up areas where facilities are restricted for the observation of territorial behaviour.

CHAPTER IX

The Study of Freshwater Habitats

Compared with terrestrial conditions described in the previous chapter, the various types of aquatic habitat present a relatively stable environment for animal life. While it is true to say that the predominant physical factors fluctuate considerably, the magnitude of their changes, also the speed with which they occur, never approach those on land.

The nature of all permanent freshwater habitats depends upon four main features:

(i) The kind of the geological formation in which they occur

(ii) The chemical composition of the water. This is closely related to (i). For instance, the water flowing over calcareous deposits is generally 'hard' with a high value of pH

(iii) Their depth. This is of particular importance in determining the amount of plant growth on the bottom

(iv) The existence of a current which influences the density of the plankton population.

There are also a large number of other temporary or artificial localities such as cattle troughs, water butts, puddles and ditches, all of which provide suitable conditions for a limited range of animal life.

One of the advantages of using a freshwater habitat to illustrate the basic principles of ecology is that the number of resident animals and plants is relatively small compared with those on land. This greatly eases the problem of identification. Furthermore, marked climatic variations such as changes in illumination frequently take place within very short distances, thus facilitating the comparison of one locality with another. Seasonal changes, too, may quickly transform the appearance of a locality (Plate 7) and, incidentally, exert a profound effect on the distribution of its animal population.

208

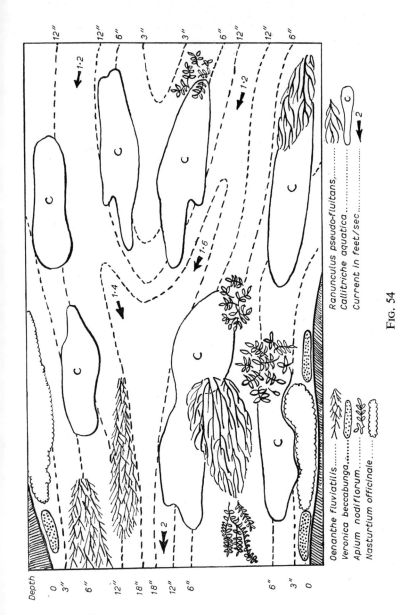

Fig. 54

Plan of part of a Hampshire chalk stream

Ranunculus pseudo-fluitans........
Callitriche aquatica...............
Current in feet/sec...............

Oenanthe fluviatilis........
Veronica beccabunga........
Apium nodiflorum...........
Nasturtium officinale.......

The basic principles guiding the selection of an area for elementary classwork are similar to those obtaining on land (*see* p. 175). In general, it is better to study a small locality intensively than to attempt to cover a wider area superficially. In our annual studies of a small chalk stream near Winchester we find a sector of 25 to 50 square yards quite sufficient for a pair of students working together.

Mapping is an essential preliminary to any ecological study of a natural habitat and the same general principles apply to the cartography of water as obtain on land. The most useful kind of map is generally a surface plan such as that shown in Fig. 54. This should record variations in the nature of the bed, changes in depth (shown by contours) and the distribution of vegetation. In addition, other relevant data can be added such as variations in illumination and changes in the speed of the current. When studying conditions near the bank of a pond or stream it will

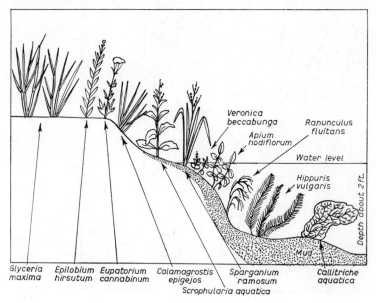

FIG. 55
Transect through a fenland ditch (*see also* Plate 7)

210

generally be necessary to take into account the shading effect of land plants. The construction of a line transect (as in Fig. 55) will often be helpful in providing a more accurate idea of the relative heights of the various zones of vegetation.

STUDY OF CLIMATIC FACTORS

The various physical factors which exert a predominant effect in fresh water are comparatively easy to detect and measure. The apparatus required is not elaborate and full details of its construction are given in Chapter II.

Light

The influence of illumination on freshwater animal communities is of three main kinds.

(i) It exerts an indirect effect by controlling the growth of plants. Most shallow and well illuminated waters support an abundance of plant life which constitutes the basis of the animal food chains. Static waters often contain a rich plant plankton such as the coenobiate Alga *Volvox* (Plate 8a), and teeming myriads of unicellular forms such as diatoms (Plate 8b). The level of illumination falls rapidly with increasing depth, and in most ponds and lakes whose waters tend to be fairly turbid, there is little growth of green plants below about 3 feet.

(ii) It enables the animals to see and be seen. The majority of the larger species occurring in fresh water are insects most of which have the compound type of eye. This is well adapted for working at low levels of illumination among weeds and on the bottom of streams. The background of most freshwater habitats is of a uniform and somewhat sombre kind, the variety of colour and tone seldom approaching that on land or in the shallow reaches of the sea. This, no doubt, largely accounts for the lack of variation in colour and pattern among freshwater animals. Moreover, the majority of the larger carnivores such as fishes have relatively poor eyesight and all of them are colour-blind.

211

(iii) It evokes certain characteristic responses which are vital to the organisms concerned. For instance, the nymph of the may-fly, *Ephemerella ignita*, is a common inhabitant of chalk streams where it is invariably found sheltering under stones and vegetation

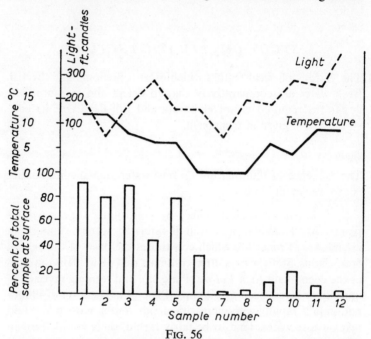

FIG. 56

Relationship between plankton density, temperature and light in a small pond. (*After Borneman.*)

on the bottom. If a stone is lifted and turned over, the nymphs soon move round again to the lower side. At first sight this appears to be a simple example of negative phototaxis. In fact the situation is more complex, for nymphs kept in still water very soon lose their power of response, which is regained once more when they are returned to their natural conditions.

The combination of two or more factors to control a single reaction is widespread among freshwater animals. A situation well worth study is the characteristic vertical movement of plankton by day and night. The various water fleas (Cladocera) such as *Simocephalus* (Plate 9) often abound in ponds and lakes. Samples obtained by sweeping with a plankton net through a fixed distance at various depths will reveal a marked variation in distribution at different times of the day. Estimates of density can easily be made by filtering known volumes of water through a Büchner funnel and counting the animals left behind. The procedure can be greatly speeded up by dividing the filter paper by pencil lines into, say, eight equal segments each of which is examined in turn. The errors involved in this method of sampling are considerable (*see* p. 78), but since the results are required only for comparative purposes, this is not a serious objection. During the warm weather it will be found that the vertical movements of the plankton are fairly regular, the majority of the population coming to the surface at night and moving downwards during daytime as the light intensity increases. The situation becomes more complicated during the winter, when the temperature of the water drops to about 5°C. or below. Fig. 56 shows the results obtained by R. G. Borneman in a small pond near Winchester. Collections of *Daphnia pulex* were made at weekly intervals from mid-October onwards and comprised a single sweep with a net along the surface and another of equal distance along the bottom. The average number of animals per 7 c.c. sample of water was counted in every instance using three different estimates for each level. The 'total sample' (*see* Fig. 56) represents the results for the two levels added together. When the percentage of *Daphnia* at the surface was plotted against temperature (measured with a resistance thermometer) and light (estimated with a photoelectric meter) an interesting and unexpected relationship emerged. Provided the temperature remained above about 5°C., illumination seemed to exert a predominant influence on the vertical movement of the crustaceans. But once colder conditions set in, light was no longer the primary factor concerned.

Such studies are quite easy to carry out using simple apparatus and are well worth while. In a general investigation of fresh water, numerous similar situations will be encountered many of which have never been fully analysed.

213

Temperature

The peculiar thermal properties of water combine to provide a medium for life very different in its characteristics from anything to be found on land. These properties include:

(i) A high specific heat (1 calorie is required to raise 1 gm. 1°C.)

(ii) A high latent heat of fusion (80 calories per gram) and the highest known latent heat of evaporation (536 calories per gram)

(iii) A maximum density at 4°C.; both above and below this temperature, water expands, becoming lighter. This peculiarity accounts for the fact that static waters such as lakes and the deeper ponds never freeze solid in cold weather.

The combination of these properties results in temperature variations which are considerably less than any occurring on land. Moreover, such changes as do occur take place far more slowly. Most aquatic organisms are well able to tolerate the normal range of seasonal fluctuation (eurythermous). A few species, however, such as the ice-age relic *Planaria alpina*, are restricted in their distribution to regions with an almost constant temperature (stenothermous) such as the sources of mountain streams.

As we have seen in the previous section, when studying the behaviour of animals in their natural environment it is often difficult to discern the influence of a single factor. More often than not several factors together exert a combined effect, for instance, in governing the characteristic vertical movements of the plankton and nekton (larger swimming organisms) in deeper waters, which generally exhibit a considerable temperature gradient from top to bottom. The behaviour of *Daphnia pulex*, already described (p. 213), provides an admirable example of the control of vertical distribution by light and temperature acting together. By contrast, flowing waters show little or no evidence of a thermocline.

The development in recent years of the resistance thermometer using a thermistor has revolutionized the measurement of temperature in water. This can now be carried out rapidly even in the deepest lakes without disturbing the natural temperature gradient.

Current

The effects of a current on an animal population are always difficult to study on account of the rapid variation in conditions which may occur from day to day. Thus a gentle stream can become a raging torrent after only a few hours of heavy rainfall.

Flowing water in general exerts an influence on animal and plant communities in the following ways:

(i) The physical impact of a current tends to wash away all organisms, other than those that are either rooted or capable of taking shelter, or are powerful swimmers. Plankton is virtually absent from streams and rivers, which accounts for the relative poverty of their fauna by comparison with static waters. The distribution of species of aquatic animals can often be related to current variations in a convincing way. Thus, the common amphipod *Gammarus pulex* occurs in huge numbers in a chalk stream near Winchester where a proportion of the population can always be found among the gravel on the stream bed. When the water is flowing slowly (less than about $\frac{1}{2}$ foot per sec.), young and old individuals are always found together. But when the sluice gates higher up the stream are periodically opened or during periods of heavy rainfall, the stream becomes a torrent and the speed of the current rises to 2 feet per sec. or more. In these conditions the adult *Gammarus* all move into the calmer eddy pools at the edge of the stream, those remaining among the gravel being seldom more than 4 mm. long.

Measurements of current with a meter such as that described on p. 41 will show a characteristic decrease in speed with increasing depth of water. This accounts for the fact that all the smaller animals tend to remain on the bottom among the stones and roots of plants where the flow of the water is least. For the same reason, fishes are often to be seen motionless near the stream bed apparently maintaining their position without any muscular exertion. The fact that they invariably face up-stream (positive rheotaxis) is no doubt due:

(a) To the necessity for expelling water efficiently through the gills

215

(b) To the advantage of looking in the direction from which food is most likely to come.

(ii) The continual passage of water is bound to cause erosion of the stream bed with periodic accumulations of silt in the vicinity of obstructions such as the larger stones. The plant colonists of stones and gravel are mainly Algae, particularly the filamentous forms such as *Vaucheria* and *Cladophora*. Mud banks support a variety of rooted flowering plants such as the water buttercup *Ranunculus aquatilis* and starwort *Callitriche aquatica*, and the gradual accumulation of silt around their roots may lead eventually to the formation of small islands where true land plants can grow.

(iii) The churning action of the water maintains it in a state of almost permanent saturation with air. Moreover, it brings about a state of uniformity in pH, temperature and the distribution of dissolved minerals, such as never occurs in ponds and lakes.

When studying the effects of a current on an animal population, it is important to bear in mind the possibility of its interaction with other factors such as light. A typical example of this has already been considered, namely, the behaviour of nymphs of the may-fly *Ephemerella ignita* (p. 212).

Hydrogen-ion concentration

In most inland waters the variation in pH is comparatively small and well within the range of tolerance of all the animals living there. Conditions in flowing waters tend to remain fairly constant while ponds and lakes generally exhibit a certain amount of vertical stratification which is subject to seasonal change. The activities of bacteria in breaking down detritus tend to promote acid conditions, both in the mud itself and in the water immediately above it. Some typical measurements of pH made during March in a fenland ditch (Plate 5b) are shown in Table 12.

Seasonal fluctuation in pH is generally due to variations in the amount of carbon dioxide present. The outburst of photosynthesis among green plants in spring and early summer normally causes conditions to become more alkaline, while the cessation of activity during autumn and winter has the opposite effect.

Zone	pH
Water at surface	8·5
Water at 2 ft (above mud)	7·5
6 in. below mud surface	7·0
1 ft below mud surface	6·5
1 ft 6 in. below mud surface	6·4

TABLE 12. Measurements of pH in a fenland ditch (Winchester College Nature Reserve). March 1956.

The normal limits of pH in fresh water lie between 4·7 and 8·5, a range which the majority of species are able to tolerate. Extreme acidity is characteristic of peat bogs and the streams associated with them, the pH of the water being sometimes as low as 4·4. The colonization of such habitats by animals is always comparatively meagre, but whether this is due to the acid conditions or to an excess of substances such as iron compounds dissolved or suspended in the water, is difficult to say.

Dissolved gases

The estimation of oxygen and carbon dioxide in water is a comparatively simple matter and suitable methods are described in Chapter II. In general, all flowing waters tend to be saturated or even super-saturated with air, the amount present being dependent upon the temperature. In static water, however, there is generally a distinct gradient of oxygen from top to bottom which continues into the mud below. Where there is an abundant growth of plants the concentration of oxygen will tend to reach a maximum in the summer months when photosynthesis is at its height and to fall again during the autumn and winter. In the deeper ponds and lakes stagnant conditions normally prevail at a depth below the level of illumination. This is a zone where large quantities of plant debris (detritus) tend to accumulate requiring much oxygen for its decomposition by bacteria.

The characteristic stratification of dissolved oxygen is evident

217

even in comparatively shallow waters. For instance, in the fenland ditch considered in the previous section (Plate 5b), estimates made during March (using the phenosafanine method) gave the following results.

Zone	Per cent saturation with oxygen
Water 6 in. below surface	63·5
Water 2 ft below surface (above mud)	41·2
6 in. below mud surface	33·3
1 ft below mud surface	25·8
1 ft 6 in. below mud surface	29·6

TABLE 13. Measurements of oxygen in a fenland ditch (Winchester College Nature Reserve). March 1956.

The above data show that there was a slight and unexpected rise in the concentration of oxygen in the deepest layers of mud. The reasons for this are not clear, but it proved to be a constant feature of all samples taken during the winter months.

The distribution of carbon dioxide can be studied by similar means to that of oxygen using the methods of estimation already described. In acid waters the gas will be present in solution, while under neutral and alkaline conditions it is combined mainly in the form of bicarbonate. In the brightly illuminated zone containing an abundance of green plants, the carbon dioxide concentration will bear an inverse relationship to that of oxygen. Thus, the active photosynthesis of spring and summer, while causing a rise in the oxygen, brings about a corresponding reduction in the available carbon dioxide. The reverse is true during the winter, carbon dioxide reaching its maximum concentration during January and February. In stagnant waters and in anaerobic, organic mud the situation is somewhat different, for continuous bacterial activity tends to maintain the carbon dioxide at a high level all the year round. The periodic appearance of bubbles at the surface of such waters is a sure indication of the accumulation of gases below.

In addition to carbon dioxide, these bubbles usually contain methane, nitrogen, hydrogen, hydrogen sulphide and often a little hydrogen phosphide as well.

Dissolved minerals

The distribution of a few species of freshwater animals is directly dependent upon the presence of certain minerals in sufficient

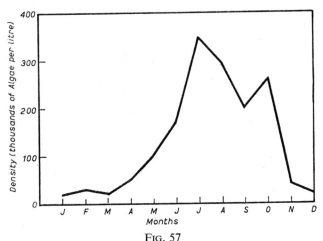

FIG. 57

Typical pattern of variation in the density of plant plankton in a pond (based partly on actual samples)

amounts. For instance, the crayfish, *Astacus fluviatilis*, requires adequate amounts of calcium compounds and is never found in lime-free conditions. But the concentration of dissolved substances in typical habitats such as ponds, streams and lakes seldom amounts to more than a few parts per million, and the influence of these minute quantities on the animal population is largely indirect in controlling the extent of plant growth. This fact can be strikingly demonstrated by a study of the phytoplankton in a pond (Fig. 57). During April and early May the temperature of the water is rising and the concentration of salts has reached a maximum as a result of the active breakdown of detritus by bacteria during the winter. Conditions are thus favourable for the great outburst of algal growth which characterizes static waters in spring. As the summer proceeds, predation by small herbivores and a drop in mineral supplies both contribute towards a marked reduction in the plankton populations. During the warm spells in late September and early October the Algae sometimes stage a partial recovery as the supply of manurial salts starts to increase once more.

Chemical changes in natural waters thus take place with a cyclical periodicity which parallels in many ways those occurring in the soil. The study of such changes involves extensive sampling both of the water and its plankton populations; also the determination of the varying mineral content. Details of these procedures are given in Chapters III and VI. Suffice it to say here that such studies are somewhat time-consuming and hardly suitable for ordinary classwork. They can be invaluable, however, as individual projects, for there is no better way of acquiring a truly dynamic picture of a changing animal and plant environment than by following the fortunes of a plankton community.

THE VARIETY OF FRESHWATER HABITATS

One of the chief aims of any ecological survey is to break down a complex community into a number of simpler parts and to relate these, as far as possible, one to another. Fresh waters provide good subjects for elementary study because the various kinds of microhabitat are generally fairly clear cut and therefore easy to examine independently. Once a locality has been selected and the range of the various climatic factors assessed, the collection of animals can be begun from each microhabitat in turn. The chief types of locality can be summarized briefly as follows.

(i) *Sand, silt and mud.* These are generally characteristic of slowly flowing or static waters. They may also be found in streams and rivers, on the bottom of backwaters and eddy pools, or in regions where obstructions such as large stones and roots have caused an accumulation of silt. Such habitats generally provide an admirable rooting medium for plants provided the water is not too deep for light to reach the bottom. The animal colonists are, for the most part, burrowers feeding on detritus, such as oligochaete worms, the bivalve mollusc *Pisidium*, the larvae of various Diptera like *Tipula* and the nymphs of several may-flies of the

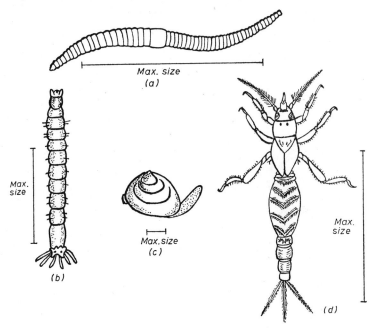

FIG. 58
Animal colonists of sand, mud and silt.
(*a*) Annelid worm, *Eiseniella* (*b*) Dipterous larva, *Tipula* (*c*) Mollusc, *Pisidium* (*d*) Nymph of may-fly, *Ephemera*

genus *Ephemera* (*see* Fig. 58). Some species can colonize the surface of the mud and browse upon the detritus and small Algae that grow there, an example being the gastropod *Hydrobia jenkinsi*.

(ii) *Stones and gravel*. Both of these are associated with the presence of a current whose eroding action tends to remove any accumulations of silt or mud. The medium is a poor one for rooted plants, the chief colonists being various filamentous Algae

221

such as *Draparnaldia* on which numerous herbivores feed. Stones provide good protection from the current and from predators, and often support a large fauna including weak swimmers such as

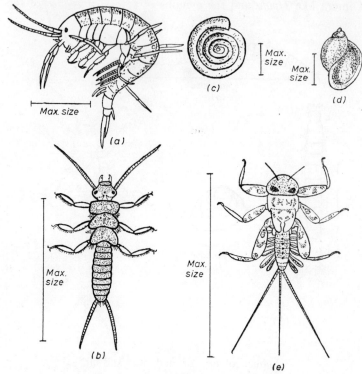

FIG. 59

Animals living among stones and in gravel.

(*a*) Crustacean, *Gammarus pulex* (*b*) Nymph of stone-fly, *Perla* (*c*) Mollusc, *Planorbis* (*d*) Mollusc, *Limnaea pereger* (*e*) Nymph of may-fly, *Ecdyonurus*

Gammarus pulex, nymphs of may-flies (Ephemeroptera) and stone-flies (Plecoptera), and a variety of molluscs of the genera *Planorbis* and *Limnaea* (*see* Fig. 59).

(iii) *Rooted plants.* The many species of plants rooted in water also provide important means of protection for aquatic animals.

222

Indeed, this may well be their most important contribution to the animal community. In streams, the roots of the various pond weeds generally conceal a vast community of weakly swimming forms such as *Gammarus pulex* and many insect nymphs. Similarly, under still conditions, stones and leaves often support

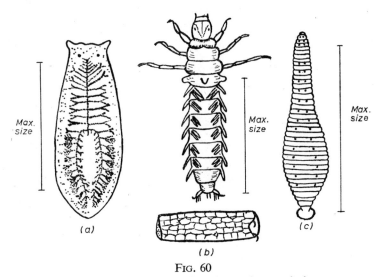

FIG. 60

Some animals commonly found on submerged plants.
(*a*) Planarian, *Dendrocoelum lacteum* (*b*) Larva of caddis-fly, *Phryganea* and its case (*c*) Leech, *Glossosiphonia*

large colonies of planarians, leeches and caddis-fly larvae of the genera *Phryganea* and *Trianodes* (*see* Fig. 60). Very few herbivores eat the leaves of the larger plants; the majority browse on the layer of small Algae which almost always encrusts their surface.

(iv) *Open water*. With the exception of fishes, the colonists of the open water are mainly confined to still conditions. They include the multitudinous plankton already considered, also a great number of powerful swimmers such as the larger Hemiptera, e.g. the water boatmen *Notonecta* and *Corixa* (Fig. 69). Many of these species are capable of surfacing in order to breathe atmospheric air but none is able to survive for long in a current. We have seen (p. 220) how the margins of streams and rivers are often sidetracked into small eddy pools and backwaters which support a flourishing static water fauna. Periods of flooding must bring

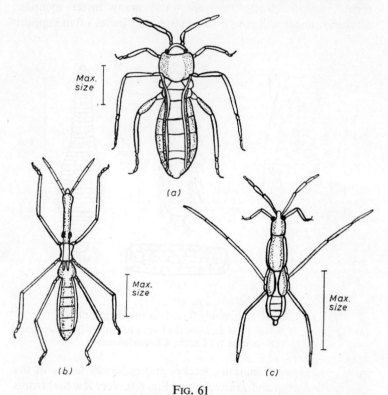

FIG. 61
Colonists of the water surface (all Hemiptera).
(*a*) Water cricket, *Velia currens* (*b*) Water gnat, *Hydrometra stagnorum* (*c*) Pond-skater, *Gerris*

about a frequent turnover in such communities so that the current no doubt provides a powerful, if accidental, means of dispersal. The study of these small, temporary colonies is in itself an interesting one and involves a number of peculiar ecological problems.

(v) *The water surface.* The surface of the water is colonized by

224

a small, specialized community of animals all of which are insects and only capable of existence in the absence of a current. They are frequently to be found in eddy pools at the side of streams. Their weight is supported by the force of surface tension on their legs as can easily be proved by adding a detergent to some water in an aquarium. When introduced into this medium the animals immediately sink while those acting as a control swim effectively on the surface of untreated water. All the larger species are carnivorous Hemiptera, such as the pond-skaters (e.g. *Gerris*), the water gnats (e.g. *Hydrometra*) and water crickets (e.g. *Velia*) (Fig. 61). Some of the smallest forms like the spring-tails (Collembola) are capable of jumping on the surface film just as if they were on land!

ADAPTATIONS OF ANIMALS TO THEIR PHYSICAL ENVIRONMENT

Light and vision

The characteristic behaviour of freshwater animals in response to variations in illumination has already been considered in a previous section. Suffice it to say here that many bottom-living forms appear to exhibit a pronounced negative phototaxis which, no doubt, helps them to avoid being washed away by the current and also to escape the attention of predators. Others, such as the planktonic crustaceans, manage to position themselves in the zone of optimum illumination (normally that in which their plant food is most abundant), and to move upwards or downwards as the intensity of the light changes.

The majority of aquatic arthropods are well adapted structurally for this kind of existence. Most of them possess compound eyes which are ideally suited to vision at short range and in widely varying levels of illumination. Lower forms, such as annelids, possess superficial sense cells which enable them to shun light and take refuge in the mud. When studying the apparent influence of light upon animals in their wild state, it is important to remember that their behaviour, more often than not, is conditioned by other factors such as temperature and current which, together with illumination, combine to exert a joint effect (*see* p. 212).

Temperature and the problem of overwintering

We have seen how the majority of the animals living in fresh water are eurythermous and capable of withstanding the normal range of temperature variations in summer and winter. Stenothermous species such as *Planaria alpina* are inevitably restricted to more uniform zones such as the sources of mountain brooks.

Since practically all freshwater animals are cold-blooded (poikilothermous), by far the biggest problem they have to solve as regards temperature is how to keep their metabolism going during cold weather. Larger forms such as fishes, molluscs and crayfish survive by reducing their general activity. This is a dangerous procedure for species like the minnow which are commonly preyed upon by larger vertebrates such as pike. In the River Itchen minnows are seldom to be seen in their usual haunts after the beginning of November and our studies have shown that they invariably move into the backwaters and small streams to shelter during the winter. Seasonal changes in distribution are a characteristic feature of most of the larger aquatic animals and their investigation forms an important part of any ecological survey.

A great number of the smaller forms overwinter by burrowing into the mud, as sampling with a drag net will quickly show. Some are adults such as the common water boatmen *Corixa* and *Notonecta*, but the majority are nymphs or larvae. Their collection and identification, also the mapping of their winter distribution for comparison with that in summer, constitutes an important part of any programme of field-work. More difficult to identify are those insects which pass the winter as a pupa such as many of the caddisflies. However, an indication of the genera to which they belong can often be obtained from the nature of their cases. For instance, the genus *Agapetus* is characterized by the construction of stone shelters (Fig. 62) which are often numerous on the underside of stones in shallow streams. They are easily kept in the laboratory in running water where the adults can be reared for final identification.

Various freshwater animals pass the winter as eggs but, as might be expected, these are mainly confined to static waters. They include such diverse forms as the different species of *Hydra*,

Max.size

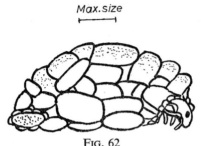

FIG. 62
Larval case of the caddis-fly, *Agapetus*

numerous small crustaceans like *Daphnia*, many planarians and most rotifers. Their eggs can be classified for convenience into two kinds depending on when they are laid:

(i) 'Winter eggs' with a thick, waterproof case containing an abundant supply of yolk

(ii) 'Summer eggs' with a thin shell and relatively little yolk. These are produced only when the temperature is suitable and food abundant. *Hydra* provides an exception to this generalization in forming the 'winter' type of egg only.

Current

Animals inhabiting streams and rivers display a variety of adaptations for maintaining themselves against the force of the current. These can be classified roughly as follows:

(i) *Permanent or semi-permanent attachment to a firm base.* The familiar species which are anchored throughout their life are all primitive forms such as the river sponge *Ephydatia fluviatilis*, and stalked ciliate protozoans of the genus *Vorticella*. Other sedentary ciliates have become epizoic on the larger animals; thus *Carchesium* and *Epistylis* are generally to be found attached to the legs of the freshwater shrimp *Gammarus pulex* (Fig. 63).

227

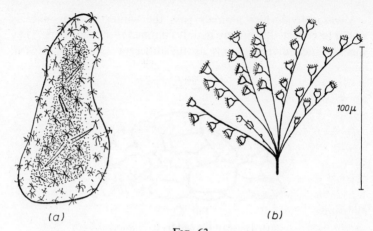

FIG. 63

Sessile animals living in a current and attached to solid objects
(*a*) River sponge, *Ephydatia* (*b*) Ciliate protozoan, *Carchesium*

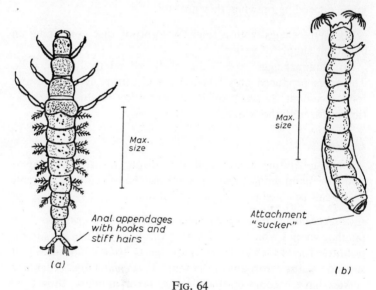

FIG. 64

Animals using hooks and suckers for anchorage in a current
(*a*) Larva of caddis-fly, *Hydropsyche* (*b*) Larva of black-fly, *Simulium*

Other animals pass only part of their life in a static phase, examples being the numerous caddis-flies whose pupae are enclosed in a case of sand, stones or vegetation and adhere to some solid object below the surface.

(ii) *The possession of hooks and suckers.* The development of hooks on the legs and at the posterior of the abdomen is characteristic of many larvae and nymphs. An example is the larva of *Hydropsyche*, a common genus of caddis-flies associated with swiftly flowing streams (Fig. 64). Suckers are also widely used as a means of temporary anchorage and are particularly well developed among leeches such as *Glossosiphonia* (Fig. 60). They are of importance, too, among smaller forms like the larvae of Diptera. A common sight in small brooks are groups of black-fly larvae (*Simulium*) attached to the surface of stones by their anal suckers and swaying to and fro in the current (Fig. 64).

(iii) *Adhesive surfaces.* The body wall of many invertebrates is equipped with mucous glands but few make use of the slime produced for adhesive purposes. Exceptions are planarians such as *Dendrocoelum lacteum* (Fig. 60) and *Polycelis nigra* which glide about on the surface of stones by means of their ciliated underside and superficial musculature. The principle of adhesion over a wide area has been elaborated in Gastropod molluscs typified in streams by the genera *Limnaea* and *Planorbis* (*see* Fig. 59). All of these move and adhere to their surroundings by means of a muscular foot well supplied with mucous glands.

(iv) *Streamlining and flattening of the body.* The bodies of all the more mobile aquatic animals are streamlined to some extent, not only to enable them to withstand a current but also to allow of more rapid movement. In general the outline of these forms, both vertebrate and invertebrate, is much the same – bluntly rounded in front and tapering to a narrow point behind. From a mechanical point of view this is the most efficient shape for a moving object in water since the 'drag' exerted on the body by the passing current is reduced to a minimum.

Many species living in midstream have managed to achieve some degree of flattening as well. A typical example among fishes is the bullhead, *Cottus gobio*, in which the head is much

229

compressed dorso-ventrally (Fig. 65). This odd shape enables it to shelter on the bottom underneath stones or in dense vegetation. Among insects, flattening is sometimes achieved not only by modification of the body-shape, but also by adopting a characteristic posture. Typical of these are nymphs of the large may-fly *Ecdyonurus venosus* (Fig. 59) which habitually crouch on the upper sides of stones in rapidly flowing streams. In general, it will be found that the tendency towards flattening is more pronounced in

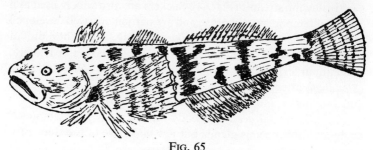

FIG. 65
Bull-Head (*Cottus gobio*)
Note dorso-ventral flattening in head region

nymphs inhabiting this kind of locality than in those living in still water.

(v) *Behaviour responses to the current* (*rheotaxis*) *and to contact* (*thigmotaxis*). The tendency of stream animals to orientate themselves facing into the current (positive rheotaxis) has already been considered (p. 215). Suffice it to say that such responses enable the gills to be used more effectively and also facilitate the capture of food. Furthermore, the natural urge to move upstream has the automatic effect of maintaining stenothermous species within their optimum conditions. A somewhat similar behaviour pattern results from positive thigmotaxis – the tendency to cling to any surface with which the body comes in contact. This is characteristic of most stream species and can be demonstrated in the laboratory with molluscs such as Jenkins's spire snail, *Hydrobia jenkinsi*. If a number of these small snails are placed in the middle of a large, shallow dish of water, they will tend to cling to one another in a solid mass if they can find no other firm surface for attachment.

OXYGEN – ADAPTATIONS FOR EXTERNAL RESPIRATION

Animals which live below the surface of streams and rivers are accustomed to an environment which is permanently saturated with oxygen all the year round. This is very different from the situation in still waters where, as we have already seen, there is always an oxygen gradient from top to bottom which is subject to considerable seasonal fluctuation. As a rule, stream animals fare badly in static conditions and soon show signs of oxygen shortage. This can easily be demonstrated in the laboratory by counting the number of gill movements per minute in a typical stream-dwelling fish such as the loach, *Cobitis barbatula*:

(i) When placed in a shallow dish of water under a running tap
(ii) In the deeper, still water of an aquarium.

Any extraneous interference such as organic pollution which tends to reduce the oxygen supply will thus exert more far-reaching effects on flowing water communities of animals than on those in static localities.

The study of respiratory adaptations forms an important part of any general ecological survey not only from the point of view of structural modifications, but also as a means of contrasting the kinds of community characteristic of different habitats.

The principal methods of respiration employed by aquatic animals can be summarized as follows:

Air obtained in solution

(a) *Through the body surface.* This is the means adopted by all the smaller species, the majority of which do not possess respiratory pigments. The body surface of an organism increases as the square of its linear dimensions, while its volume increases as their cube. Thus, as an animal grows, the efficiency of its gaseous exchange by this means decreases on account of the progressive reduction in the surface/volume ratio. This fact can be demonstrated with nymphs of dragonflies (Zygoptera) which have large projecting caudal gills. Removal of the gills in the early stages

231

makes no apparent difference to the animals' activities. But if the same operation is performed when the nymphs are fully grown they do not survive for long, for cutaneous respiration is no longer sufficient to supply their needs.

(b) *Use of respiratory pigments*. With the exception of the larger species such as fishes and crayfishes whose bodily size and outer covering obviously preclude the uptake of oxygen through the surface alone, those animals which possess respiratory pigments are nearly all either burrowers or free-swimming forms inhabiting static waters. Typical among the former are the various annelids such as the square-tailed worm (*Eiseniella*), a common inhabitant of the bed of streams (Fig. 58). The organic mud of ponds nearly always supports large colonies of midge larvae under somewhat anaerobic conditions. Some of these ('blood worms') belonging to the genus *Chironomus* (Fig. 66), have developed the pigment haemoglobin.

One of the most remarkable instances of the use of a respiratory pigment in free-swimming forms is provided by the common water-flea, *Daphnia* (Plate 9). During the summer, colonies occurring in ponds with an abundance of vegetation are nearly always colourless. But in winter, and also under conditions of stagnation, a great variety of colours is to be found ranging from pale pink to quite deep red. These changes in appearance are now known to be due to the synthesis of haemoglobin in the blood, the concentration of pigment being inversely proportional to the amount of oxygen dissolved in the water. Hence, it is possible to construct a colour chart and from the appearance of *Daphnia*, to predict the percentage oxygen saturation in different habitats.

(c) *Development of gills*. Variation in the structure and distribution of gills among aquatic animals is so great that it is impossible in a small space to contribute more than a few generalizations about them. All animals, no matter where they live, can absorb their oxygen only in aqueous solution. Aquatic species are ideally placed for this purpose, since their specialized respiratory organs have only to be bathed by the natural medium around them (gills). Terrestrial forms, being divorced from direct contact with water, have either to irrigate their breathing devices from their own body fluids (lungs) or to devise some other means of transporting oxygen to their living cells, such as the tracheal system of insects.

Gills in animals are of two kinds:

(i) *Blood gills*. These are projections of the body into which the blood system flows. They are not only characteristic of fishes, but

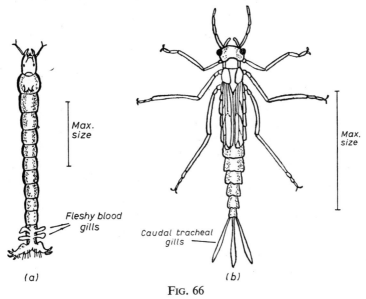

Max.
size

Max.
size

Fleshy blood
gills

Caudal tracheal
gills

(a)

(b)

FIG. 66

Two types of gill used by young stages of insects in fresh water
(a) Larva of midge *Chironomus* (b) Nymph of dragonfly *Coenagrion*

also occur among many smaller forms. For instance, the fleshy posterior projections found in larvae of some Diptera, such as the midge *Chironomus* (Fig. 66), are of this kind.

(ii) *Tracheal gills*. These sometimes have the apearance of blood gills but, instead of a blood supply, they are permeated by branches of the tracheal system. They are entirely confined to arthropods, mainly insects. The shape, number and position of tracheal gills varies a great deal. When occurring at the sides of the abdomen they are often small and numerous as in the nymphs of

233

may-flies, and alder-flies: when at the posterior of the body they are generally larger but few in number, e.g. in the nymphs of dragonflies (Fig. 66).

Atmospheric air

(a) *Breathing tubes and siphons.* Many species of insects inhabiting still water have evolved devices for piercing the surface film

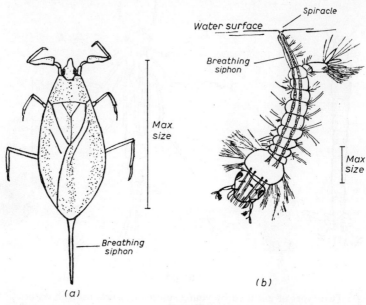

Fig. 67
Two freshwater animals breathing atmospheric air through siphons
(a) Adult water scorpion, *Nepa cinerea* (b) Larva of gnat, *Culex pipiens*

and sucking atmospheric air into the body. Larvae and pupae of the common gnat, *Culex pipiens*, are often to be found in pools, troughs and water butts, while some of the larger Hemiptera such as the water scorpion, *Nepa cinerea*, occur frequently clinging to vegetation just below the surface of ponds and eddy pools (Fig. 67). This method of gaseous exchange depends for its success on three main factors:

234

(i) The absence of a current, which would wash the animals away

(ii) The ability of the individual to steady itself, either by hanging head downwards suspended by surface tension from above, or by gripping some solid object just below the surface such as a stone or plant

(iii) The fringing of the siphon opening with hydrofuge hairs which, by entrapping bubbles, form air-locks and hence prevent the entry of water.

(b) *Spiracles.* These are the external openings of the tracheal system in insects, situated along the sides of the thorax and abdomen. They provide the principal means of entry and exit for gases in all land forms. In aquatic species they are universal among the colonists of the upper surface, such as the water cricket (*Velia currens*). A few submerged larvae and adults have also adopted a similar system of breathing which necessitates their coming to the surface each time a fresh supply of air is needed. The larva of the water beetle *Dytiscus* (Plate 10) is a typical example which possesses a single pair of spiracles at the hind end of the abdomen. These are encircled with a complex fringe of hydrofuge hairs which serve the dual function of preventing waterlogging when the animal is submerged, and of entrapping air bubbles each time it comes to the surface (Fig. 68). The adult beetle is a powerful flier and swimmer spending part of its life on land and part in water. The general structure of its spiracles is therefore very similar to that of the larva.

(c) *Transportation of air bubbles.* The body of many aquatic insects such as beetles and water boatmen appears to emit a silvery sheen. This is due to the adhesion of minute air bubbles which are acquired each time the animal comes to the surface. In the larger beetles, such as *Dytiscus* and *Hydrophilus*, the bubbles are entrapped under the elytra whence oxygen passes via the spiracles into the body. Other insects carry bubbles attached to various parts of their anatomy. For instance, in the whirligig beetle, *Gyrinus natator*, a single bubble is entrapped among the hairs at the posterior of the abdomen, while the water bugs, *Corixa* and *Notonecta* (Fig. 69), are able to accumulate air over

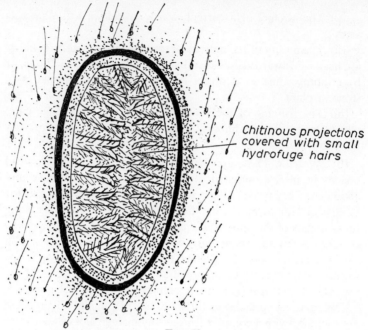

Chitinous projections
covered with small
hydrofuge hairs

FIG. 68
Spiracle of water beetle *Dytiscus marginalis* (×60 approx.)

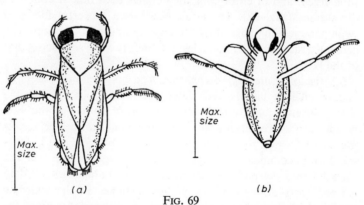

Max.
size

Max.
size

(a)   *(b)*

FIG. 69
Two insects (Hemiptera) which have to rise to the surface periodically
to obtain air. Water boatmen *(a) Corixa* (dorsal view) *(b) Notonecta*
(ventral view)

most of the body surface. The function of this air reserve is not quite the same as in the larger beetles, for it serves as a kind of physical' gill', i.e. as a device which promotes the passage of oxygen out of the water into the animal, also the flow of carbon

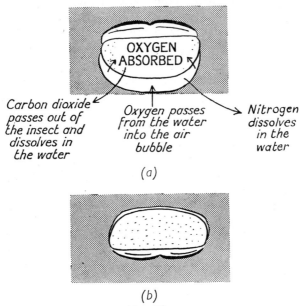

Carbon dioxide passes out of the insect and dissolves in the water

Oxygen passes from the water into the air bubble

Nitrogen dissolves in the water

(a)

(b)

FIG. 70

Diagram illustrating the action of a plastron in water bugs such as *Notonecta*; (a) transverse section of insect just after submerging, (b) the same, some time later. Note that the volume of the bubble has decreased

Popham: *Life in Fresh Water* (Heinemann)

dioxide in the reverse direction. A superficial coating of hairs which entraps air is sometimes known as a 'plastron' and its mode of action is illustrated in Fig. 70. The smallest bugs and beetles are seldom more than about 3 mm. long, and their oxygen requirements are so small, even during periods of maximum activity, that they can breathe permanently through the plastron without ever having to surface at all.

237

(d) *Swallowing air*. This is a valuable means of supplementing a limited air supply and is used by fishes inhabiting static or slowly flowing water. Members of the carp family (Cyprinidae), in particular, are capable of absorbing considerable amounts of oxygen through the well vascularized wall of the intestine. Small species such as the minnow (*Phoxinus laevis*) can be observed in an aquarium periodically to rise to the surface and gulp in a mouthful of air. Similarly, by employing this auxiliary method of aeration, the goldfish is often able to withstand conditions of domestication which would be quite intolerable to any other aquatic animal.

(e) *Development of lungs*. A lung is essentially a respiratory structure kept moist by the organism itself and adapted for the absorption of atmospheric air. It is rare among truly aquatic animals being confined solely to the Gastropod molluscs. These are divided for the purpose of classification into two groups according to their mode of breathing:

(i) Those possessing a horny plate (operculum) on the foot which serves to close the aperture of the shell when the animal has contracted. There are ten freshwater species in Britain all of which breathe by gills

(ii) Those without an operculum in which the inner surface of the mantle is highly vascularized and acts as a lung.

The behaviour of the two groups of snails is characteristic, for while operculate species such as Jenkins's spire snail, *Hydrobia jenkinsi*, can remain submerged indefinitely, pulmonate forms such as the various species of *Limnaea* and *Planorbis* (Fig. 59) have to surface periodically to breathe. The differences in habit of the two groups are easily observed in an aquarium.

BIOTIC FACTORS

Food and feeding habits

The study of the foods and feeding devices of freshwater animals involves much the same general approach as that already described for terrestrial forms (pp. 182–188). The various species can be roughly divided on the basis of their requirements into herbivores, carnivores and detritus feeders (Plates 9–10), but this classification is never absolute for the following reasons:

(i) Many vertebrates such as fishes eat a wide variety of food, both plant and animal

(ii) The composition of a diet frequently varies with the age of the individual. Thus, young may-fly nymphs are mostly herbivores or detritus feeders, but as they get older, many species, such as *Ecdyonurus venosus*, are predominantly carnivorous

(iii) It is often impossible in practice to draw a precise distinction between fresh plant material and detritus. In all probability the majority of the so-called herbivores devour a proportion of both.

The accumulation of evidence on food preferences is somewhat laborious and generally impossible under natural conditions alone. In order to form a reliable opinion on the diet of a particular species, the following classes of information will be required:

(i) The association of the species with a particular kind of microhabitat. For instance, is it an active swimmer, a burrower in mud or a browser on vegetation like a pond snail

(ii) The nature of the mouth parts of captured animals. This can be a valuable source of evidence when used to supplement other observations. For example, the radula of a pond-snail is clearly a device adapted for rasping vegetation, while the 'mask' of a dragonfly nymph (Fig. 71) is an unmistakable organ of predation. But many caddis-fly larvae also have quite well developed jaws and these are used largely for grasping plant material.

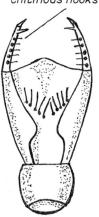

Chitinous hooks

FIG. 71

Mask of dragonfly nymph (*Coenagrion puella*)

(iii) Analysis of gut contents. This procedure is of limited

239

application among aquatic species and is mainly useful in studying the diet of fishes.

(iv) Evidence derived from the study of behaviour in the laboratory. The careful observation of animals in an aquarium is

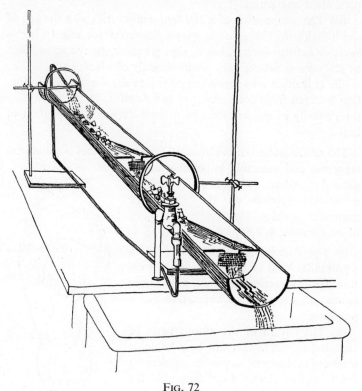

FIG. 72

Artificial stream constructed from a piece of guttering

undoubtedly the most reliable method of learning about their feeding habits. The first step is to simulate as nearly as possible the conditions obtaining in nature. This task is greatly simplified if the area chosen for study is a small one containing relatively few animal and plant species. The setting up of a static-water aquarium

PLATE 13

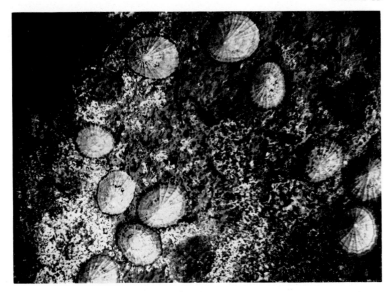

(*a*) Limpets (*Patella vulgata*), on a rock surface (× ½)

(*b*) Limpet holes in soft Lias rock (near Lyme Regis)

PLATE 14

(*a*) Tubes of the small polychaete worm *Spirorbis* on *Fucus* (× ¾)

(*b*) The burrowing sea-cucumber, *Labidoplax digitata*, and two other common inhabitants of its burrow (commensals), the polychaete worm *Harmothoë lunulata* and the small lamellibranch mollusc *Mysella bidentata* (× 1) generally presents little difficulty; small battery jars are quite easily obtainable and serve as suitable containers in the absence of more elaborate equipment. Artificial aeration is generally unnecessary provided there is a good supply of green plants and plenty of light (either natural or artificial).

The study of stream animals presents greater difficulties, but given the necessary space, it is quite easy to construct an 'artificial stream' indoors. One kind that works well consists of a length of guttering inclined at an angle with water from the main running in at the top end and draining into a sink at the bottom. Asbestos gutter is preferable to metal as this avoids the difficulty of corrosion and also provides a rough surface which most clinging species prefer. The depth of the water can be controlled by inserting a series of wooden partitions held in position by Plasticine (Fig. 72). Each has a small notch at the top through which the water pours like a miniature waterfall from one compartment into the next. The 'bed' of the stream can be lined with stones and gravel as required, and provided the light is good and the temperature not too low, green plants such as *Ranunculus aquatilis* can be established without difficulty.

The conditions obtaining in eddy pools and the more slowly flowing stretches of streams can be simulated by a series of shallow dishes arranged one above the other (Fig. 73). Each is fitted with an overflow pipe held in position by Plasticine or sealing compound, with a wire gauze filter in front of it to prevent the smaller animals being washed away. Plastic (PVC) tubing is easier to handle than other kinds and does not deteriorate, while holes are most easily drilled in dishes of the papier mâché type. One advantage of this apparatus is that if the incoming water is allowed to fall from a height of about 9 inches, the oxygen concentration in the top dish will be approaching saturation, while that in the others can be controlled to some extent by adjusting the vertical distance between them.

Observations on feeding made in this way should, as far as possible, be both subjective and quantitative. For instance, the larger specimens of the water boatman *Notonecta* habitually kill young minnows by first attacking their eyes, while a fully grown

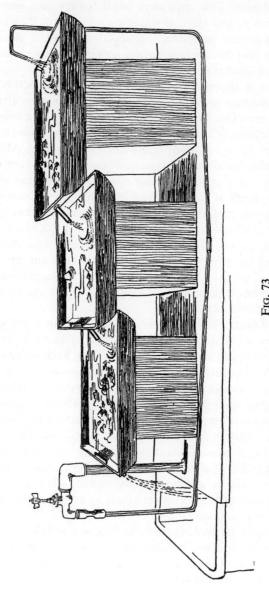

Fig. 73

Shallow pools simulated by a series of dishes with slowly flowing water

larva of the diving beetle *Dytiscus* (Plate 10) can devour as many as four large frog tadpoles in a day.

Food relationships

Once the food preferences of various animals are known, it should be possible to construct part of a simple food chain for a particular habitat. Viewed as a whole, this is almost certain to prove a highly complex affair, since the majority of animals not only vary their diet as they get older but also change it at different times of the year. The guiding principle in elementary work should be that a few links discovered with certainty by personal observation are of far more value than a large number derived from the study of books. Even so, the results obtained by a whole class when pooled together can often provide quite an impressive picture. The method of constructing food chains and the information they provide have already been described (pp. 182–188) in connection with land habitats and need not be considered further here.

Study of density

Communities of freshwater animals, being generally accessible and comparatively easy to sample, provide excellent opportunities for the study of population density and its fluctuations. Mention has already been made (p. 212) of a means of studying populations of the water flea, *Daphnia pulex*, using simple sampling and counting methods. The larger swimming species such as beetles and water boatmen lend themselves readily to marking with the various kinds of paint such as 'Necol' (manufactured by I.C.I.), which adhere readily to wet surfaces. The capture-recapture method (*see* Chapter IV) can, thus, be used for estimating their numbers in small localities. Molluscs such as *Hydrobia jenkinsi* can be sampled by the quadrat method (p. 91) and their distribution in streams related to various physical factors such as the nature of the bed, the speed of the current and the depth of water. Similar studies can be carried out with more mobile forms such as the Amphipod *Gammarus pulex*, using the kind of quantitative sampling net described in Chapter III. We have already seen how the density of young and old populations in this species can

243

fluctuate with environmental conditions such as changes in the speed of the current.

While it is important not to become a slave to the quantitative side of ecology, it is desirable that the kind of studies enumerated above should be carried out whenever conditions permit – as they generally do. Such simple investigations, no matter how imperfect they may be, cannot help but contribute to a better understanding of the fluctuating nature of animal and plant communities. Moreover, they provide opportunities for application of elementary statistical procedure – the side of mathematics most closely allied to the study of biology in general.

Breeding activities

The problems involved in elucidating animal breeding cycles have been considered at some length in the previous chapter. Suffice it to add that in spite of the energy devoted to the study of fresh water in all its aspects, surprisingly little reliable information is available concerning the breeding activity of even the commoner animal species. Moreover, the position is complicated by the fact that a situation regarded as characteristic in one part of Britain may not be in the least typical of another.

The evidence needed to solve such problems as these is obtainable from two sources:

(i) By rearing animals in the laboratory and comparing the various stages with those attained at a corresponding time under natural conditions

(ii) From an analysis of size-distribution in selected species throughout the year. This procedure is particularly applicable to the larger aquatic animals such as the crustacean *Gammarus*, the larvae of caddis-flies and the nymphs of may-flies. It involves the collection of periodic random samples and the measurement of each individual. The results are best expressed graphically and provide a ready means of detecting variations in the age-distribution of a population at different times. The recent work of Hynes (1955) on *Gammarus pulex* in a small stream near Shotwick (Cheshire) provides an excellent example of the way in which this method can be employed. The results of a year's work using

244

samples of about 400 are shown in Fig. 74. Periods of breeding
activity are those where large numbers of the smallest individuals
are present. Following the histograms from the top left (11th

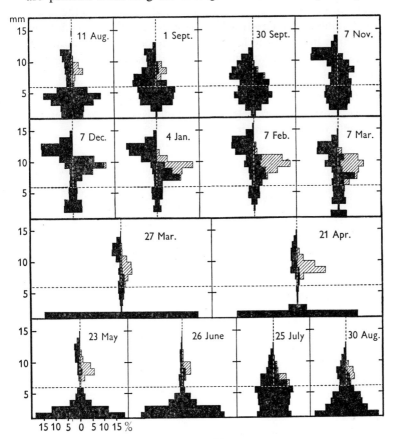

FIG. 74
Size and sex-distribution in samples of *Gammarus* from Shotwick
(1949–50). The length of the shrimps is given by the vertical scale; the
extent of each horizontal block represents the percentage of the total
in that size-group. The horizontal dotted line (at 6 mm. length) shows
the lower limit of sex-distinction. Below it the blocks are centred;
above it, males are shown on the left and females on the right. Females
indicated by cross-hatched areas were fully mature.

Hynes: *Journal of Animal Ecology*

August) shows that the appearance of young slowed down rapidly from September onwards and did not recommence to an appreciable extent until early March. It attained a peak in late March and April thereafter slowing down to a steady rate for the rest of the summer. An interesting feature of these results is the different size-range in males and females from the same sample, indicating either an unequal distribution, or differential survival in the two sexes.

Studies of this kind are hardly suitable for classwork but they provide excellent projects for individuals or small groups of students working together.

CHAPTER X

The Study of Sea Shores and Estuaries

Of all the haunts of animal life the sea is by far the most prolific and complex, and in the narrow compass of a single chapter it would be unprofitable even to attempt a comprehensive survey of the variety of animal habitats which exist around our coasts. The first encounter with the animals and plants of the sea shore is apt to be a rather bewildering experience. For here are to be found representatives of almost every group in the animal kingdom exhibiting an endless diversity of adaptations to a variety of environments which far exceed that on land and in fresh water. In previous chapters I have stressed the advantage to be gained from selecting strictly limited and clear-cut localities as a means of illustrating the general principles of ecology. These considerations apply with even greater force to the study of sea shores and estuaries.

The sea shore is that zone of the coast which exists between high- and low-tide marks and which is exposed, at least for a short period, each day. The various animal habitats which it provides are therefore subject to inherent instability and so differ fundamentally from any that occur elsewhere. This feature is also true of estuaries but for a different reason. Thus, while the greatest problem facing shore animals is the avoidance of desiccation at low-tide, those inhabiting estuaries are largely concerned in adjusting themselves to changes in salinity as the tide ebbs and flows.

One of the great merits of the sea shore as a training ground for biologists is its comparative accessibility. Interesting animal communities can be found almost anywhere no matter how exposed or sheltered the coast may be. In general, the kinds of habitat which predominate on shores are rock faces, rock pools, and sand. In estuaries circumstances are less diverse and include mud, brackish pools and the roots and stems of plants such as rushes (*Juncus*) and cord grass (*Spartina*).

The principles governing the selection of a locality for elementary study are much the same as those which apply elsewhere. If possible the area chosen should be reasonably clearly defined, not too large, and easy to collect. A rock pool or portion of a rocky shore (Plate 11a) are ideal starting-points for each poses a number of ecological problems peculiar to itself.

Mapping is an essential preliminary to any ecological study and this can generally be done without much difficulty. Rock pools are usually small enough for a grid to be constructed over the top consisting of light strings with lead weights attached at each end to keep them in position. This procedure greatly increases the speed and accuracy of mapping the vegetation on the bottom in a manner similar to that already described for fresh water (pp. 210–211). The depth of the water frequently plays an important part in determining the distribution of animals and plants in a pool. It may therefore be necessary to construct at least one line transect (*see* p. 210). Variations in depth can also be represented in plan view by means of contours. A line transect is generally a useful kind of map for a rocky shore, since it will show the vertical distance between one point and another. This information will be needed when making a comparison of two or more localities at different levels. Such measurements can normally be made with sufficient accuracy by using pieces of string, a spirit level and a measuring staff. The optical level is fixed at the highest point and the vertical distance of points lower down is then measured in relation to it. The most important factor influencing animals and plants on a shore is the period of exposure between tides. When making estimates of this it must be borne in mind that tidal flow is not at a constant rate but accelerates up to half-tide and retards from then onwards. Hence the relative height of different localities is not in simple proportion to the speed of tidal movement. Periods of exposure and immersion are, therefore, best determined by direct observation.

Sandy and muddy shores are somewhat variable in composition

and their constituents are subject to a distinct vertical zonation: so, too, are the animal species which live there. The most suitable kind of map for such localities is the profile chart as is used in the study of soils (Fig. 36). This can easily be constructed by examining the vertical face of a trench.

STUDY OF CLIMATIC FACTORS

The problems of studying climatic factors in sea and brackish waters are, in general, similar to those in freshwater habitats. By far the greatest difficulty is to determine the extent to which particular environmental conditions exert specific effects. For instance the reaction of many shore animals to light is unmistakable, but a precisely similar response can often be induced by lack of water. Evidently, the effects of these two factors, and probably a number of others as well, are closely interrelated. In spite of the great amount of study that has been devoted to the animals of our shores, surprisingly little is yet known about their characteristic reactions and the nature of the stimuli which cause them. Measurement of the predominant climatic factors on sea shores and in estuaries presents little difficulty, and the various items of apparatus described in Chapter II will be found suitable for this purpose.

Light

Rocky shores are generally regions of brilliant illumination as is evidenced by the wealth of Algae which grow there. Two main factors contribute to this situation:

(i) The water is clear owing to a lack of sediment

(ii) Even at high tide, the covering of water is never sufficiently deep completely to exclude light from the bottom during day-time.

In the vicinity of estuaries the conditions are somewhat different for the abundance of mud and silt inevitably imparts a considerable turbidity to the water. The penetration of light is then much reduced as is also the growth of green plants.

On close examination, the various microhabitats are found to display a wide variation of environmental conditions even within a matter of a few inches. This fact is well illustrated in a small rock pool such as that shown in Plate 11a. Some typical measurements of illumination taken during a morning in mid-August are summarized in Table 14. They range from almost uninterrupted sunlight in the surface water to total darkness underneath the deepest seaweeds.

Locality	Illumination (ft-candles)
Daylight	2400
Exposed by tide	
Shadow of rock (partial shade)	1950
Shadow of rock (deep shade)	450
Under *Fucus vesiculosus*	0
In rock pool	
6 in. depth	1600
1 ft depth	1400
Shadow of rock (1 ft)	1100
Under fringing *Corallina officinalis* (6 in.)	62
Under *Fucus vesiculosus* on bottom (1 ft)	0

TABLE 14. Illumination of various microhabitats on a Dorset shore. August, 1957. (*A. S. and W. H. Dowdeswell.*)

The principal influence of light on animal communities is an indirect one in promoting the vast growth of littorine Algae on which many species depend for their food and shelter. The effect of illumination on the animals themselves is more difficult to assess. Among freely swimming forms such as small fishes and crustaceans found in pools and gulleys the general reaction to light is to shun it whenever possible. This is obvious enough from the study of any locality by day when practically the whole of the animal population will be found in crevices and among the fringing seaweeds. The onset of darkness brings about a marked change in the activity of many forms such as the crustaceans *Hippolyte* and *Palaemon* which swim about actively feeding on small Algae.

The reverse is true of most of the shore molluscs such as the periwinkles (*Littorina*), which swarm on to the wet surfaces of seaweed as the tide goes out. At first sight this would appear to be a simple instance of positive phototaxis. However, as is so often the case, the situation is more complex. It can be shown quite easily in an aquarium that one of the most powerful influences causing animals to take shelter is the impact of moving water on their bodies. Under laboratory conditions this sensitivity to shaking is retained for some time after the individuals have left their normal environment. Thus, while light undoubtedly plays some part in inducing the various species of *Littorina* to emerge from shelter, the absence of wave-action may well be the predominant factor involved.

In both the examples of phototaxis quoted above there is evidence of a marked diurnal change in the lives of the species concerned, due partly to the alternation of night and day, and partly to the ebb and flow of the tide. Sometimes these two forces act in a complementary manner; sometimes their effects are antagonistic. The result is a cyclical rhythm of activity which is a characteristic feature of all marine animals. From a practical point of view it is clear that collecting during day-time will, at best, provide evidence of only half the life of a community. Sampling must also be carried out at night if a true picture of animal activity is to be obtained.

One other striking feature of the animals of the sea shore compared with those in fresh water is their brilliant coloration. At first sight this would appear to add to their general conspicuousness. But it must be remembered that nearly all predators, both vertebrate and invertebrate, are colour-blind, and that tone, not colour, is therefore the important factor in enabling any potential prey to achieve some measure of concealment. The variation in colours of some gastropods such as the flat periwinkle, *Littorina littoralis*, is probably an advantage in the brilliantly illuminated surface waters with rapidly fluctuating contrasts in light and shade.

The significance of many of these colours is still far from clear and further information, particularly of a quantitative kind, is badly needed. For instance, it would be interesting to know if the variable shell-colour of *Littorina littoralis*, just mentioned, is of any adaptive value. We have seen (pp. 183–184) how colour and marking in the land snail, *Cepaea nemoralis*, are related to the animal's mode of life and the selective action of predatory birds. Is it not possible that a somewhat similar situation exists in marine molluscs as well? Such questions can only be resolved by extensive collecting from a number of localities exhibiting a variety of backgrounds and different levels of illumination. A word of warning is necessary at the outset against drawing too close an analogy between the situation of *Cepaea* on land and that of marine gastropods. It is now known that in some of the most variable species there is a close connection between the colour and pattern on the shell, and the nature of the diet. Thus, in the carnivorous dog-whelk, *Nucella lapillus*, the dark brown and mauve coloured individuals are those which feed primarily on mussels while white shells indicate a barnacle diet. Quite an abrupt change in the colour of the shell can be brought about by switching animals from one kind of food to the other. But the situation is even more complex than this for yellow shells have been shown to be associated not with diet, but with the degree of exposure to wave-action.

Here is a field which would amply repay further study. The majority of sea-snails with multi-coloured shells are herbivores (e.g. the various species of *Littorina*) and the influence of diet is unlikely to be so significant in these as it is in carnivorous forms.

Humidity and oxygen

Practically all marine animals respire externally by gills or through the surface of the body, both methods necessitating the permanent provision of a moist surface through which gases in solution may pass. For the occupants of the sea shore, the problems of breathing and avoidance of desiccation are, thus, closely related.

At high tide the shallow water covering sand and rocks is maintained in a state of permanent saturation, or even supersaturation with air as a result of the churning action of the waves. Respiration thus presents little difficulty to the animals living below. But tidal ebb inevitably causes serious problems both of water shortage and lack of oxygen. Just how serious these problems can be is easily gauged by keeping some typical marine animals in the laboratory in a dry state or in an aquarium which is insufficiently aerated. In neither instance will they survive for long.

Under natural conditions such difficulties are overcome in one of four ways:

(i) The animals may remain in the water either by retreating with the tide or by becoming isolated in gulleys and pools. The tendency of some species to lurk among the fringing weeds of rock pools is advantageous in that it concentrates them in the zone of active photosynthesis and hence of high oxygen content. Little experimental work has been done on the conditions of aeration in such habitats and this is an investigation that would be worthwhile. Suitable apparatus and methods are described in Chapter II.

(ii) Various species may take refuge underneath the carpet of seaweeds covering exposed rocks where humidity is high and oxygen abundant. Such action is typical of poorly protected forms such as the sea anemone, *Actinia equina*.

(iii) Others remain exposed on the surface of rocks, stones and weed making use of their natural ability to withstand drying up. Such behaviour is typical of many molluscs such as the periwinkle, *Littorina littorea*, which is capable of closing the branchial chamber by an operculum, also of highly specialized crustaceans like the acorn barnacle (*Balanus balanoides*) with its four valve-like calcareous plates which can be closed to form a tightly fitting cover (*see* Fig. 83).

(iv) The occupants of sand and mud are faced with a special problem since few of them are able to withstand exposure on the surface. Such forms as polychaete worms (e.g. the lugworm, *Arenicola marina*, Fig. 77) and bivalve molluscs (e.g. the cockle, *Cardium edule*, Fig. 79) burrow downwards to varying depths where conditions remain more or less unaltered after the retreat of the tide.

ZONATION IN SHORE ANIMALS

One of the most characteristic features of shore communities is the varying ability of the different plant and animal species to withstand exposure by the tide. This results in a fairly clear-cut zonation which is shown particularly clearly among the common seaweeds covering any stretch of rocks. Thus, at the seaward edge the predominant form is generally *Fucus serratus*, often in company with various oar-weeds such as *Laminaria digitata*. Higher up the shore is the zone of *Ascophyllum nodosum*, which overlaps to varying extents those of *F. serratus* below and *F. spiralis* above. Still further up the shore and extending to the level of the highest tides is the region of the channelled wrack, *Pelvetia canaliculata*. Beyond this again we come to the splash zone which remains clear of the water but is subject to a good deal of spray. This is the home of a true land flora such as lichens and various halophytic flowering plants like samphire (*Crithmum maritimum*) and golden samphire (*Inula crithmoides*).

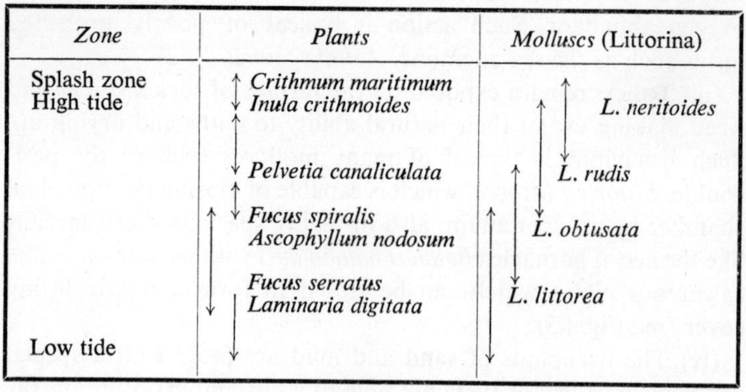

Zone	Plants	Molluscs (Littorina)
Splash zone High tide	Crithmum maritimum Inula crithmoides	L. neritoides
	Pelvetia canaliculata	L. rudis
	Fucus spiralis Ascophyllum nodosum	L. obtusata
	Fucus serratus Laminaria digitata	L. littorea
Low tide		

FIG. 75

Diagrammatic representation of the zonation of some common plants and molluscs (*Littorina*) on a rocky shore

The animals of the rocky shore are similarly zoned according to their ability to withstand exposure, a beautiful illustration being the distribution of the various species of periwinkles (*see* Fig. 75 and Plates 15–16). Thus, the lower part of the shore is dominated by the common periwinkle, *Littorina littorea,* which extends over the zones of *Fucus serratus, Ascophyllum* and *F. spiralis.* Slightly higher up, but overlapping the distribution of *L. littorea* to some extent is the flat periwinkle, *L. obtusata.* The *Pelvetia* zone is characterized by two further species, the rough periwinkle, *L. rudis,* which often extends downwards into the region of *Fucus spiralis* and the small periwinkle, *L. neritoides.* The latter could be classed with some justification as a partial land animal for it can exist for days in the splash zone well above high-tide mark. Similar distributions are found in many shore animals including various other gastropod molluscs. Like the various species of *Littorina,* these are particularly suitable for study on account of the ease with which they can be collected and identified. The various top shells of the genera *Osilinus, Gibbula,* and *Calliostoma,* are zoned in a manner somewhat similar to those of *Littorina* but their distribution is seldom so clearly defined.

The zonation of animals and plants on a rocky shore thus provides ideal opportunities at a comparatively elementary level for the descriptive study of distribution. An aspect less often considered is the quantitative relationship existing between the different species as one replaces another. Much valuable work can be done in this field using comparatively simple sampling techniques and statistical procedures such as those described in Chapters III and V.

A typical survey involving a single belt transect on a rocky shore (Plate 11a) is summarized in Table 15.

The quantitative estimation of Algae is difficult to achieve with any accuracy, but the rather crude procedure adopted provides a reasonably reliable means of detecting variations in density. A more accurate method would have been to count the number of stones colonized in each square and express this figure as a percentage of the whole. Reference to Table 15 shows clearly that among the plant and animal species studied there were two distinct patterns of distribution:

(i) A clear-cut zonation within the inter-tidal regions, as illustrated by the alga *Enteromorpha intestinalis* and the gastropod *Littorina neritoides.*

255

(ii) A gradually increasing density extending from part-way down the shore to low-tide mark and beyond. *Ulva lactuca* and *Fucus serratus* provide typical instances among the plants while the molluscs *Patella vulgata* and *Osilinus lineatus* are similarly distributed.

No. of 1 yard quadrat	Plants					Animals					
	Enteromorpha intestinalis	*Pelvetia canaliculata*	*Ulva lactuca*	*Fucus vesiculosus*	*Fucus serratus*	*Littorina neritoides*	*Patella vulgata*	*Osilinus lineatus*	*Gibbula umbilicalis*	*Gibbula cineraria*	*Littorina rudis*
1 (High-tide mark)	R	—	—	—	—	—	—	—	—	—	—
2 (mark)	R	—	—	—	—	—	—	—	—	—	—
3	R	—	—	—	—	5	—	—	—	—	—
4	C	—	—	—	—	5	2	—	—	—	—
5	C	R	R	—	—	13	—	5	—	—	—
6	C	R	R	—	—	14	4	2	—	—	—
7	C	R	C	—	—	6	5	7	1	—	—
8	R	R	C	R	R	31	10	18	2	1	—
9	—	R	C	—	R	65	24	24	5	3	—
10	—	—	R	—	C	47	28	22	25	7	12
11	—	—	A	A	C	8	16	18	8	1	14
12	—	C	A	C	C	—	36	14	7	4	9
13	—	C	A	A	A	—	21	11	14	7	7
14 (Low-tide mark)	—	—	A	C	A	—	50	29	12	11	2

Plant distribution:

R (rare)=Less than 25 per cent of stones colonized.
C (common)=25–75 per cent of stones colonized.
A (abundant)=More than 75 per cent of stones colonized.

Animal distribution:
Numbers=density per 1 yard square

TABLE 15. Belt transect of a gently sloping Dorset shore between tide marks to show densities of certain species of plants and molluscs. (*A. S. and W. H. Dowdeswell.*)

The vertical distribution of animals in sand and mud is more obscure than that on rocks and its study involves the somewhat laborious process of careful digging and sifting. Moreover, the zonation of species is variable depending on their position in relation to the tide and the structure of the shore. In most localities at least three different animal strata are generally well defined:

PLATE 15

(*a*) Small periwinkle, *Littorina neritoides* (×2)

(*b*) Rough periwinkle, *Littorina rudis* (×1)

Common molluscs inhabiting the intertidal zone

PLATE 16

(*a*) Flat periwinkle *Littorina obtusata* ($\times \frac{3}{4}$)

(*b*) Common periwinkles, *Littorina littorea*, with acorn barnacles, *Balanus balanoides* ($\times \frac{1}{2}$)

Common molluscs inhabiting the intertidal zone

(i) Surface-dwelling forms including small amphipod crustaceans such as *Corophium* and numerous actively swimming polychaete worms like *Nereis diversicolor* and *Harmothoë lunulata.*

(ii) The zone of the bivalve molluscs which generally extends downwards from two to eight inches. The most characteristic inhabitants are cockles (*Cardium edule*), often accompanied by various species of *Tellina*, the razor shell (*Ensis*) and many other lamellibranchs (*see* Fig. 79).

(iii) The region of the burrowing polychaetes, by far the commonest species being the lugworm, *Arenicola marina.* Its presence is easily recognizable by the multitudinous worm casts which are a characteristic feature of most sandy shores containing a certain amount of organic material. The galleries which it constructs below ground by eating its way forward like an earthworm, are U-shaped and may extend downwards to a depth of about eight inches (Fig. 78).

The reasons underlying animal zonation in sand and mud are by no means clear: a varying tolerance of exposure by different species is not a contributory factor as it is on a rocky shore. Food requirements probably play an important part; so may the different methods of external respiration. Both these factors are considered further in later sections of this chapter.

Temperature

Most of the animal inhabitants of our shores are eurythermous species and well able to tolerate all normal fluctuations in temperature, both diurnal and seasonal. In general, sea water presents a much more stable environment than fresh; the deeper it is, the more uniform do conditions become. Ultimately, a point is reached at the bottom of the great oceans where the temperature remains almost unchanged the whole year round. This is the home of a strange host of stenothermous vertebrates and invertebrates which modern deep sea diving expeditions are only just beginning to reveal.[1]

[1] For good recent accounts see:
Günther, K., and Deckert, K. (1956). *Creatures of the Deep* (Allen and Unwin).
Spärck, R., *et al.* (1956). *The Galathea Deep Sea Expedition* (Allen and Unwin).

In our offshore waters diurnal fluctuations in temperature are never more than a degree or so, while the maximum seasonal variation seldom exceeds 10° C. On the shore itself, conditions are much more unstable but the changes are of short duration between one high tide and the next. Nevertheless, while they are exposed, the occupants of the various microhabitats may be subjected to the greatest temperature extremes of any marine animals. A study of these variations therefore forms an important part of an ecological survey. Some typical readings taken with a resistance thermometer are summarized in Table 16.

Locality	Temperature (°C.)
Open sea	16
Air	22·5
Exposed by tide	
Shadow of rock	21·5
Under *Fucus serratus*	18
Rock Pool	
Surface water	21·5
4 in. depth	21
8 in. depth (bottom)	20

TABLE 16. Temperature of various microhabitats on a Dorset shore. August 1957.
(*A. S. and W. H. Dowdeswell.*)

The day in question was rather cool with intermittent sunshine and a strong wind. In such conditions it is unlikely that an appreciable thermocline could have existed even in the deepest rock pools. During the warmest weather in Britain, temperature variations in deep water seldom exceed 4° C., while the maximum reached in small isolated pools near high-tide mark must sometimes approach that of the surrounding air.

Conditions in sand and mud are much more stable and, apart from small abrupt changes in the top few inches, they remain remarkably uniform for several feet below the surface. Burrowers such as the lugworm, *Arenicola marina*, and the brackish ragworm *Nereis diversicolor*, thus enjoy almost complete immunity to the temperature variations resulting from tidal change.

As we have seen, the greatest fluctuations in temperature occur in rock pools, particularly if these are shallow, and it is not uncommon during a hot summer's day to find small crabs and fish such as the sand-goby (*Gobius minutus*) which have succumbed, probably on account of the rapid heating of the water.

In general, reactions which enable animals to resist desiccation also assist them in avoiding over-heating. Species which tend to remain exposed on rocks and weeds are those with a formidable waterproof covering such as molluscs and barnacles. Poorly protected forms like sea anemones, which inhabit rock faces tend to shelter under overhanging seaweeds and in shaded gulleys, while nearly all the inhabitants of pools are to be found during daytime in the cool of the seaweed curtain fringing the edge, or on the bottom.

Salinity

Sea water is a complex mixture of suspended matter and minerals in solution. From the point of view of animals, the most important ingredients are the chlorides of sodium and magnesium which amount to about 3·1 per cent by weight of the water around our coasts. The salinity of the sea varies little both from one locality to another and at the different seasons, so that in this respect the animals of the shore and open waters enjoy an almost constant environment. The majority are incapable of tolerating any but the smallest change in chloride content (stenohaline).

In the rather restricted circumstances which we are considering, there are only three types of locality where significant variations in salt concentration may occur:

(i) *Pools.* These are of two kinds, those habitually covered at high tide and those above the normal tide-level where the sea water is liable to dilution by rain. The concentration of salts in shallow pools often rises rapidly on a hot day as a result of evaporation and it is not uncommon in water only a few inches deep to find a tenfold increase of chloride. On the other hand, dilution with fresh water may occur to a comparable or even greater extent in localities at the landward edge of the shore. Only a few plant and animal species are able to tolerate such

259

variations but these provide most interesting subjects for study (*see* p. 267).

(ii) *Seepage streams.* It is not at all uncommon to find small streams of fresh water from the land traversing the sea shore at low tide. The salinity of such waters rises progressively as they near the sea. These conditions are inimicable to most marine animals and only a few species such as the planarian *Procerodes ulvae* are able to tolerate them for long.

(iii) *Estuaries.* The zone in which river waters join the sea is always well-defined and fluctuates with the state of the tide. Salinity variations in this region are the most extreme possible ranging from the pure sea to fresh water through every grade of dilution. The colonization of this unstable brackish environment demands great adaptability on the part of the animals concerned, particularly in their power of osmotic control. The majority of marine and freshwater species are excluded on this account and there remains a fascinating community of polychaete worms, arthropods and molluscs whose members have achieved varying degrees of compromise with their surroundings.

It will be seen from this brief survey that variations in salinity provide a promising topic for study since suitable localities will almost certainly be available on any shore. The procedure for estimating chloride is not difficult to carry out and details of it are given in Chapter II.

ADAPTATIONS OF ANIMALS TO THEIR PHYSICAL ENVIRONMENT

Light and vision

The brilliantly illuminated waters of the shore and shallow sea provide unlimited opportunities for animals to see and be seen. Their characteristic and varied reactions to light have already been described in a previous section; it remains to consider briefly the kind of sense organs used in achieving these responses. The only vertebrates found in our seas are fishes and mammals nearly all of which are equipped with well developed eyes, similar in general structure to our own. Evidence derived from a study of the structure of the retina and of the animals' behaviour suggests that while they are probably capable of forming quite a clear image at short range, none is able to perceive colours. Colour-blindness is almost certainly a feature of all invertebrate vision as well. This is an important point to bear in mind when attempting to interpret the vivid coloration in gastropod shells such as periwinkles and in many other marine animals (*see* p. 251).

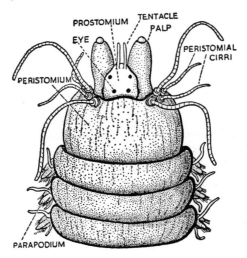

FIG. 76

Head of *Nereis* (dorsal view) showing eyes and
other sense organs

Grove & Newell: *Animal Biology* (Univ. Tutorial Press Ltd.)

In general, the animals of the shore tend to shun bright sunshine and to become active in the fading light of dusk. Invertebrates exhibit a variety of eyes which are well adapted for this kind of behaviour. These are of two types:

(i) The compound eye characteristic of most arthropods, and found in shrimps, prawns and nearly all the smaller Crustacea. To what extent these animals can form an image it is difficult to say, but there is no doubt that this kind of sense organ is ideally suited for vision at low light intensities and also for detecting movement, the shadows of potential predators and other nearby objects.

(ii) Simple eyes consisting of hollow vesicles lined with a sensory epithelium supplied by an abundance of nerves. A few species such as some of the periwinkles possess a rudimentary lens but the majority, if they are capable of forming an image at all, do so on the pin-hole camera principle. Eyes are also widespread among lower forms such as the actively swimming polychaete worms (Fig. 76) but these amount to little more than cup-shaped areas of light-sensitive tissue. It is doubtful if they enable their possessors to achieve much more than a discrimination between light of different intensities.

Colour-change

The unending variety in illumination and background which is so characteristic of marine habitats provides excellent opportunities for the employment of colour variation as a means of conceal-ment. Such changes can be observed without difficulty in a labora-tory aquarium. For instance, the skin of flat fishes contains many chromatopores whose expansion and contraction causes the animal to become darker and lighter. This reaction is apparently under nervous control for a portion of skin in which the super-ficial nerve supply has been severed is incapable of carrying out the response. Small specimens of the dab (*Pleuronectes limanda*) are often to be found stranded in sandy pools at low tide and these provide good material for study.

Many of the small decapod crustaceans show a remarkable rhythmic cycle of colour-change being dark by day and light by night. Such variations extend uniformly over the whole body and the animals are incapable of matching a dappled background. Coloration of this sort, as might be expected, is under the control of hormones secreted by the sinus gland at the base of the eye-stalk. Good examples for study are the shrimp, *Palaemonetes varians*, a common inhabitant of brackish water pools in salt marshes, also the chameleon prawn, *Hippolyte varians*, which often occurs among seaweeds in rocky gulleys and is best collected just as the tide is retreating.

Oxygen – adaptations for external respiration

Apart from the strange group of insects which habitually colonize the splash zone, such as the beetle *Aëpus marinus* and the spring-tail *Lipura maritima*, no marine animals are capable of breathing atmospheric air alone. All obtain their oxygen in solution in water and get rid of carbon dioxide in the same way. The structural and physiological problems facing them are thus much the same as those in fresh water (*see* pp. 231–238).

Gaseous exchange invariably takes place either through the surface of the skin or by means of gills – organs of respiration which are kept moist by the surrounding water. In the first category are included the young stages of practically all animals, also the smaller adults like planarians and most polychaete worms. In these the ratio of surface area to volume is high so that the whole body acts as a gill which is sufficiently effective to satisfy the animals' modest needs for oxygen. Some of the larger species also employ this method of respiration but these are mostly sluggish creatures with a low metabolic rate such as the sea anemones. The use of respiratory pigments is generally associated with special breathing organs although some of the larger polychaetes such as *Nereis* carry haemoglobin in their blood although they do not possess any structures which could be regarded as gills.

Respiratory organs among the higher animals assume a number of forms and are often beautifully adapted to the environment in which they are employed. Their efficiency is often increased by the presence of a variety of respiratory pigments. By far the commonest of these are haemoglobin used by most annelids, and the bluish haemocyanin characteristic of the decapod crustaceans, some molluscs and a few echinoderms. At their simplest, gills may be merely blind outgrowths of the body wall within which the blood circulates. These are often arranged in tufts giving a somewhat feathery appearance (Fig. 77) as in the lugworm *Arenicola marina* – a common inhabitant of sand and mud. The animals burrow into the mud and form tunnels as shown diagrammatically in Fig. 78. The nature of the burrow varies somewhat with the conditions, but three distinct regions can generally be recognized:

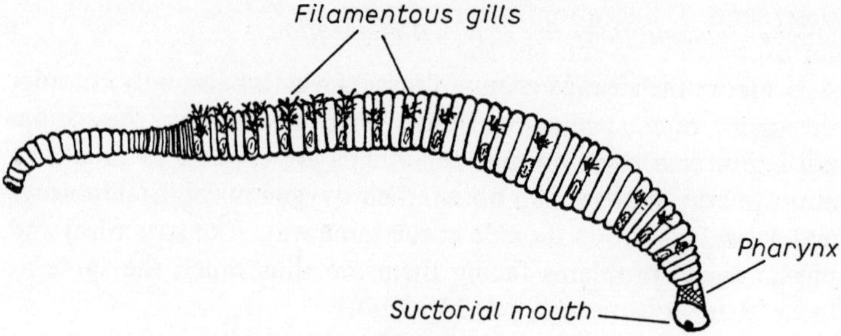

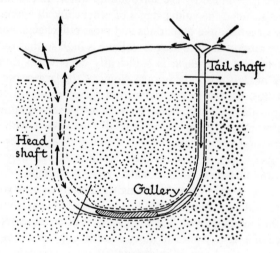

Filamentous gills

Pharynx

Suctorial mouth

FIG. 77
Lugworm, *Arenicola marina* (× ⅔ approx.)

Tail shaft

Head shaft

Gallery

FIG. 78
Structure of burrow of lugworm, *Arenicola marina*

Yonge: *The Sea Shore* (Collins)

an anterior head shaft, a middle gallery and a posterior and narrower tail shaft. The walls of the gallery are lined with mucus and the worm is able to move backwards and forwards in this region by muscular expansion and contraction. In feeding, mud is sucked down the head shaft and this is therefore lined with soft,

264

loose sand. Defaecation is achieved by the worm extending the tail backwards up the tail shaft whence the characteristic worm casts are extruded on to the surface. The backward and forward movement of the animal inside its burrow somewhat resembles the action of a piston and it has been shown by Wells that this serves to keep the sand loose and freely irrigated with water. When at rest, continuous waves of contraction pass backwards along the worm's body from tail to head and these set up a current of water which flows down the tail shaft, through the gallery and out by the head shaft. Exposure of the sand at low tide brings the process of irrigation to a halt and it is at this stage that the haemoglobin of the blood must be of particular value in providing a reserve of oxygen. There is also evidence that *Arenicola* is capable of trapping air by coiling the posterior of the body and pushing it through the mouth of the tail shaft. When contraction occurs air bubbles are carried into the close proximity of the gills which then function temporarily as a kind of lung. Many other worms possess gills of varying complexity but a great deal remains to be discovered about their effectiveness and mode of use.

Some of the most elaborate respiratory devices are to be found among the various bivalve molluscs many of which, as we have already seen, are burrowers in sand and mud. In all of these the cavity containing the gills (mantle cavity) extends the whole length of the body so that the maximum respiratory surface is presented to the water. The efficiency of the gills is further increased by complex folds and intercommunicating channels whose surfaces are lined with cilia. By their rhythmic beating the cilia promote a continual turnover of the water which enters and leaves the mouth cavity through the siphons (inhalent and exhalent) at the posterior end. The structure of the siphons is of particular interest being closely related to the mode of life of the species concerned. Thus, in the mussel (*Mytilus edulis*), a surface dweller (*see* Fig. 82), they are little more than mere slits in the mantle cavity, while in typical burrowers like *Cardium* and *Tellina* they take the form of tubes of varying length (Fig. 79). The breathing mechanism used by gastropods is similar in principle to that of Lamellibranchs the entry of water into the mantle cavity being

265

through a slit-like extension of the mantle. In some species such as the whelk (*Buccinum undatum*), this may be drawn out into a long tube. The respiratory surface is mainly provided by the inside of the mantle and the gills tend to be reduced. When exposed at low tide, forms such as *Littorina* are capable of retaining moisture inside the mantle cavity in spite of the fact that it is now full of air.

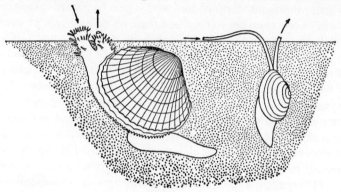

FIG. 79

Two common sand-burrowing bivalve molluscs, *Cardium edule* (left) and *Tellina tenuis*, (right) The length of the siphon is beautifully adapted to the depth at which the animals live

Yonge: *The Sea Shore* (Collins)

The gill is then functioning more like a lung and in drought-resistant species such as *L. neritoides* the replenishment of water is necessary only during the fortnightly spring tides or even less often. This accounts for its position on the shore (p. 254).

A comparable situation exists among the larger crustaceans in which the gills are invariably housed in a spacious branchial chamber protected by the outer carapace. The movements of the limbs cause a continual replenishment of the water in contact with the respiratory surfaces. Many of the larger Decapoda such as the shore crab *Carcinus* are perfectly capable of living on land and breathing atmospheric air. Indeed, immobilization of the gills will cause rapid death in water but no apparent inconvenience on land, showing that when oxygen is plentiful, sufficient can be absorbed through the thin parts of the body. The requirements of sessile forms such as the acorn barnacle, *Balanus balanoides*, are so modest that the animal can close the plates surrounding its body completely during periods of exposure, thus bringing the action of the gills to a standstill (Fig. 83).

Among fishes, several tropical forms such as the well-known climbing perch (*Anabas scandens*) are able to live on land and breathe atmospheric air, but this is not so in any British species, all of which die if exposed for more than a few minutes.

Salinity and life in estuaries

Of the various habitats already considered which are liable to changes in salinity (see pp. 259–260) the regions of estuaries provide by far the sternest test of adaptability among plants and animals. The gradient of chloride concentrations is often exceedingly complex and varies from one estuary to another, but within the transition zone there can always be found every gradation from sea water to fresh.

Fishes such as the salmon which live mainly in the sea but spawn in the rivers and the eel which matures up-river but breeds in the sea, have achieved considerable powers of water regulation. But these must be regarded as only temporary inhabitants of estuaries. Most of the marine animals we have considered are incapable of penetrating far into the brackish zone, for they would not be capable of dealing with the inrush of water into their bodies which would occur as a result of osmosis. Similar difficulties face freshwater species attempting to colonize estuaries, but for them the problem is to avoid desiccation rather than waterlogging.

The true colonists of estuaries thus represent a unique ecological adjustment since all of them have achieved some degree of osmotic independence (euryhaline). This has been attained in two ways; by adjusting the mechanism of osmotic control and by burrowing. Comparatively little is known about the first category which includes fishes such as the flounder (*Pleuronectes flesus*) and the shore crab, *Carcinus*. Experimental work has been concentrated particularly on the various species of the small amphipod crustacean *Gammarus* (e.g. *G. pulex*, see Fig. 59) which are found throughout the whole range of estuarine conditions. Hynes has divided the various species into five categories according to their adaptability:

(i) Marine forms which are incapable of osmoregulation in brackish or fresh water, e.g. *G. locusta.*

(ii) Those whose cuticle is relatively impermeable to chlorides and which can enter brackish waters from the sea, at least for a short time, e.g. *G. salinus.*

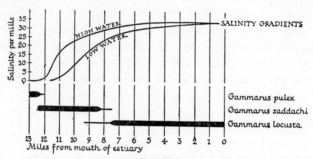

FIG. 80

Distribution of three species of *Gammarus* in relation to the salinity of an estuary

Yonge: *The Sea Shore* (Collins)

(iii) Species with impermeable integuments which are nonetheless able to absorb chlorides selectively against the osmotic gradient, e.g. *G. zaddachi* and *G. chevreuxi.* These live in the sea and brackish conditions but not in fresh water.

(iv) Those capable not only of retaining and absorbing salts, but also of producing dilute urine, e.g. *G. duebeni.* This species can tolerate the whole range of estuarine conditions.

(v) Freshwater forms possessing blood with a low osmotic pressure which are incapable of withstanding even dilute sea water, e.g. *G. pulex.*

Mapping the range of different species can provide a fascinating study of animal distribution in relation to a single physical factor. A typical result obtained from such a study involving three species of *Gammarus* is shown in Fig. 80. Other crustaceans with a capacity for some degree of osmotic control include the prawn, *Palaemonetes varians*, and the opossum-shrimp, *Praunus flexuosus*. Gastropod molluscs are poorly represented in estuaries, but the small snail *Hydrobia ulvae*, like its fresh water counterpart, *H. jenkinsi*, frequently swarms on the surface of the mud.

Species which burrow no doubt enjoy some degree of immunity to variations in salt concentration. They include several poly-chaetes such as *Nereis diversicolor*, which are also able to control the salt concentration in their blood to some extent. Several bivalve molluscs penetrate some distance up-river, one of the commonest being the cockle, *Cardium edule*. Comparatively little is known about environmental conditions at different depths of estuarine mud, and there is a fruitful field here for ecological studies of all kinds, particularly the influence of tidal change on the vertical distribution of the various animal species.

Wave action and the problem of anchorage

One of the greatest problems facing shore animals is how to avoid being washed away by the pounding action of the waves. Many beautiful adaptations for anchorage exist and their study should form part of any general ecological course. The various structures involved and the characteristic behaviour patterns associated with them combine to play a significant part in determining the distri-bution of different species.

Protective adaptations are, in general, of three main kinds:

(i) *Burrowing*. This kind of behaviour, as we have already seen, is typical of residents in sand and mud. Annelids such as *Nereis* penetrate the soft surface by a muscular wriggling action, while species like *Arenicola marina* eat their way downwards like an earthworm. Bivalve molluscs all possess an efficient structure for burrowing in the form of a muscular foot which is used like a ploughshare. Some gastropods can colonize the surface of sand (e.g. the dog whelk, *Nucella lapillus*), or the mud of estuaries (e.g. the spire-snail, *Hydrobia ulvae*). Both species take refuge during rough conditions by burrowing downwards a few inches.

(ii) *Sheltering in crevices and under seaweed*. This is a charac-teristic reaction of many species which habitually colonize rock faces. With the retreat of the tide the less well protected forms like the beadlet anemone, *Actina equina*, are reluctant to show themselves on account of the danger of desiccation. They are generally to be found sheltering underneath the overhanging seaweeds. Other species such as the multitudinous periwinkles (*Littorina*) and top-shells (*Gibbula, see* Plate 12a), swarm on to the surfaces of rocks and weeds, the herbivores among them profiting by the period of calm for active feeding.

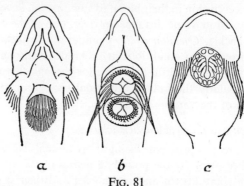

a b c

FIG. 81

Fishes with ventral suckers formed from modified pelvic fins

(*a*) Goby, *Gobius paganellus* (*b*) Sucker, *Lepadogaster* (*c*) Sea-snail, *Liparis* (various magnifications)

Yonge: *The Sea Shore* (Collins)

(iii) *Structural modifications*. Shore animals display a remarkable variety of structures for anchorage. In most fishes the general shape of the body is either streamlined like the pipe-fish or flattened as in the sole. They are thus able to take refuge in crevices or on the surface of the sand. A few shore-dwelling species such as the rock goby, *Gobius paganellus*, have undergone extreme specialization and possess a ventral sucker (Fig. 81), derived from the modified pelvic fins. This enables them to cling tightly to rock surfaces while the flattened body offers little resistance to the water. Similar modifications are found among the various species of sucker-fish (*Lepadogaster*) and the so-called sea-snails (*Liparis*). Molluscs also show a variety of adaptations for fixation, the most

270

obvious being the muscular foot of gastropods typified by the limpet, *Patella vulgata* (Plate 13a). Rock surfaces are never perfectly flat and it is essential for the shell to make complete contact, not only for adhesion, but also to avoid the danger of desiccation at low tide. The alternatives facing *Patella* are, therefore, either to grind the rock to fit the shell or to modify the edge of the shell to conform to the irregularities of the surface. Both methods can be used and which is adopted depends upon the

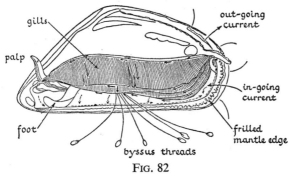

FIG. 82

Common mussel, *Mytilus edulis*, with left shell and
mantle removed to show internal structure

Yonge: *The Sea Shore* (Collins)

hardness of the rock. In soft deposits such as the Lias of Lyme Regis, it is not uncommon to find rocks pitted with limpet holes as much as an inch in depth (Plate 13b). Numerous bivalves are colonists of rock faces, notably the mussel, *Mytilus edulis*, which is often to be found in huge numbers when exposed at low tide (Plate 12b). Their efficient means of adhesion is the byssus – sticky thread-like strands of material secreted by glands associated with the foot (Fig. 82).

Most of the shore-dwelling Crustacea either possess flattened bodies like crabs, or are well streamlined like prawns, and so able to shelter in rock crevices without much difficulty. But structural adaptation *par excellence* has been achieved by the acorn barnacle, *Balanus balanoides* (Fig. 83), one of the commonest colonists of the rocks around our coasts. The creature has undergone such

271

specialization that it is hard to identify it as a crustacean at all. The whole body is encased by two concentric layers of calcareous plates, six on the outside and four within. These open when the animals are submerged but close tightly during periods of exposure. Adhesion to rocks is achieved by a rigid cement secreted by glands on the lower surface which represent the highly

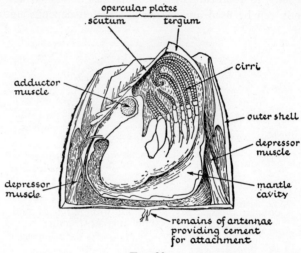

FIG. 83

Vertical section through an acorn barnacle (*Balanus balanoides*)

Yonge: *The Sea Shore* (Collins)

modified remains of the antennae. Adhesive substances are similarly employed by numerous species of tube-building poly-chaete worms which often abound on seaweeds and rocks. The minute coiled tube-worm, *Spirorbis borealis*, frequently lives upon serrated wrack, *Fucus serratus* (Plate 14a), while the much larger *Pomatoceros triqueter* is a characteristic colonist of rock faces in the intertidal zone. A great variety of attachment devices is employed by other sessile forms but the secretion of mucus plays a part in nearly all of them. Sea anemones are notable examples among the larger coelenterates, while small colonial species such as *Tubularia larynx* utilize the same means for communal anchorage.

A similar process is employed by tunicates, polyzoans and sponges.

Mucous surfaces must also play a large part in preventing many small, soft-bodied species from being washed away. Nemertine and platyhelminth worms possess numerous glands in their epidermis, and in some species of the planarian *Convoluta*, the hind end of the body is raised into adhesive papillae to enable the animals to maintain themselves on fronds of seaweed.

BIOTIC FACTORS

Food and feeding habits

Methods of observing the foods and feeding habits of freshwater animals have been considered in some detail in Chapter IX (pp. 238–243). Marine communities are subject to much the same general principles but are more difficult to study since practically all the microhabitats observable at close quarters suffer an almost complete turnover in their populations at each high tide. This fact greatly enhances the value of an aquarium as a medium for studying food relationships, where the conditions prevailing in localities such as rock pools can be simulated with some degree of realism.

Structural modifications can also be a valuable guide to food preferences and it is with these that we shall be mainly concerned in the following pages. Animals can be divided for the sake of convenience into carnivores, herbivores and detritus feeders although, as we have already seen, such a clear-cut distinction never obtains under natural conditions.

Carnivores. The presence of well developed jaws and teeth such as are found in fishes, is generally a sign of a carnivorous diet. Some of the commonest pool-dwelling forms are the blennies of which three species are generally to be found in the intertidal zone, the shanny, *Blennius pholis* (Plate 11b), the gunnel, *Centronotus gunnellus*, and the viviparous blenny, *Zoarces viviparus*. All have broad, powerful teeth and are able to crush acorn barnacles and small mussels. Crustaceans form the staple diet of many shore fishes such as the gregarious sand-goby (*Gobius minutus*), and the black goby (*G. niger*), a common inhabitant of estuaries. Among the smaller carnivores are the many species of actively swimming annelid worms such as *Perinereis cultrifera* which often occurs in the surface layers of sandy pools and *Nereis diversicolor*, an estuarine species. These have an eversible pharynx armed with powerful jaws (Fig. 84) with which they can prey upon other small annelids and crustaceans such as the amphipod *Gammarus*. Most of these species appear to supplement their animal diet with a good deal of plant material and detritus as well.

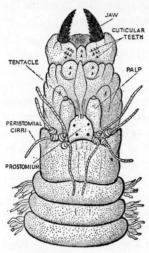

FIG. 84

Head of *Nereis* with jaws everted (dorsal view)

Grove & Newell: *Animal Biology*
(Univ. Tutorial Press Ltd.)

A different method of predation well worth close study in an aquarium is that practised by the common starfish, *Asterias rubens*, which frequently occurs under rocks in the intertidal zone. Its diet is almost exclusively bivalves, mainly mussels, which it opens with its powerful arms equipped with rows of sucker-like tube-feet on their lower surfaces. Starfishes have no teeth the mouth being adapted for sucking only. The problem of ingestion is overcome by everting the stomach and pouring digestive juices on to the prey outside. The semi-digested remains are then sucked in through the mouth. A suctorial method of feeding is also used by the various ribbon-worms (Nemertines) the commonest being the reddish-brown *Lineus ruber* which reaches a length of about six inches. This feeds on small polychaetes which it engulfs whole by means of an extensible proboscis. The animal has no teeth and is incapable of mastication so that an unusually large morsel often appears as a distinct bulge as it passes down the alimentary canal.

Gastropod molluscs are all equipped with the same type of feeding mechanism – a horny, strip-like radula covered with numerous teeth and used as a file for rasping. Most species are herbivorous, but a notable exception among shore-dwelling species is the dog-whelk, *Nucella lapillus,* which inhabits much the same zone as the common periwinkle, *Littorina littorea,* itself a typical herbivore. The radula of *Nucella* resembles that of other marine snails but is peculiar in that it is carried on the end of a long protrusible proboscis. The animal preys upon other molluscs such as *Littorina* by slowly boring a hole through the shell. This is achieved entirely by mechanical means, but in some forms such as *Natica* the process is aided by the secretion of acid substances as well. Once the shell has been pierced the proboscis is inserted through the hole and the contents rasped out by the radula.

Finally, brief mention must be made of that remarkable group of sessile carnivores, the sea anemones. The commonest of these is the beautiful beadlet-anemone, *Actinia equina,* notable for its colour variations and often found in pools far up on the rocky shore. Like all its coelenterate relatives, the body consists of a hollow sac with single opening serving both as mouth and anus surrounded by a fringe of delicate tentacles. Aided by the batteries of stinging cells (nematoblasts) on their surface, these creatures are capable of siezing a variety of animal prey and pushing it into the mouth. Their diet includes worms, crustaceans and even small fishes, and their graceful feeding activities are fascinating to watch in an aquarium.

Herbivores. The plant-eating animals of the shore are all relatively small and few of them utilize the larger Algae as food to any appreciable extent. Gastropod molluscs such as periwinkles and limpets can sometimes be found rasping at the surface of growing seaweeds with their powerful radulas but they mostly prefer to browse upon torn-off pieces of finer weed which are frequently in a state of partial decomposition. As the tide retreats a fine layer of the multitudinous floating plants is deposited on the surface of rocks and exposed vegetation, and this also provides an important source of food for the smaller species.

The shore-inhabiting fishes are predominantly carnivores but many of them such as the shanny (*Blennius pholis,* Plate 11b) also include a certain amount of weed in their diet. Similarly, bristle-worms, like the various species of *Nereis,* invariably devour

275

appreciable quantities of plant material and detritus. All the larger Crustacea such as the crabs, lobsters and prawns are scavengers feeding on the remains of plants and animals, both fresh and decomposing. They have powerful mandibles with which they are able to sieze and masticate their food. Small forms like *Gammarus* feed on minute Algae, particles of larger plants and detritus which are wafted towards the mouth by the active movement of the limbs.

Finally, there is the host of filter feeders to be considered in the next section which, in addition to detritus, also absorb large quantities of living plant plankton.

Detritus feeders. Adaptations among marine animals for feeding upon the rotting remains of plants are of two kinds:

(i) Filter mechanisms such as those of bivalve molluscs
(ii) Devices for swallowing mud, as in lugworms.

When considering methods of respiration (pp. 263–267) we saw how lamellibranch molluscs such as mussels and cockles possess elaborate devices for maintaining the passage of a current of water over the gills. Such structures, in fact, serve the dual purpose of respiration and of wafting minute floating Algae and particles of detritus towards the mouth. These are absorbed, apparently unselectively, and pass down the alimentary canal where the nutritive portions are digested.

Similar methods of feeding have been adopted by many sedentary forms. For instance, the acorn-barnacle, *Balanus balanoides*, opens its covering plates when submerged and thrusts the modified thoracic legs (cirri) to and fro in a kind of rasping motion (Fig. 83). This seems to set up a current of water which carries particles into the mouth. Most of the tube-building poly-chaete worms such as *Spirorbis* (Plate 14a) and *Serpula* feed on detritus in much the same kind of way, a water-current being set up by cilia which cover the surface of the tentacles and gill fila-ments.

The annelid occupants of mud, typified by *Arenicola* and its allies, literally eat their way downwards through the surface layers. They are well adapted structurally for this mode of life, possessing a suctorial mouth and pharynx which can be expanded and contracted with the aid of powerful muscles. A similar method of feeding is employed by some echinoderms notably the burrowing sea-cucumber, *Labidoplax digitata*. This is one of the longest of the holothurians (Plate 14b) and may grow to about a foot. It is found in sheltered areas along the south coast in localities of mixed sand and mud.

The various detritus feeding species occupy an important place in the economy of our shores. Not only do they help to remove any excess of organic debris, but by the processes of digestion and defaecation, they aid its ultimate breakdown by bacteria into the simple manurial salts required by plants. The physiology of this mode of nutrition is undoubtedly complex and little is known about it; nor is it clear how its efficiency compares with that of the carnivores and herbivores.

Density and distribution

Mention has already been made elsewhere in this chapter of the distribution of animals and plants characteristic of sand, mud and rocky shores, also of ways in which it can be studied, mainly from a descriptive point of view. Such investigations inevitably provide only a partial picture of distribution. For instance, they give no precise indication of the circumstances in which one species replaces another – whether there is a gradual changeover involving a region of overlap, or if transition takes place quite abruptly. Information of this kind, which forms an essential part of ecology, can only be obtained from a study of the actual numbers of animals present. This is no easy matter, for fluctuations in physical conditions on a sea shore are enormous; so too are the variations in animal density. However, there are certain compensating advantages when compared with similar situations in fresh water and on land. At low tide, a high proportion of shore animals are relatively sessile so that sampling with simple apparatus such as small quadrats is a fairly simple operation. A typical study of shore plants and animals has already been described (pp. 254–257). Gastropod molluscs, barnacles and tube-building worms such as *Spirorbis*, lend themselves particularly well to investigations of this kind. Two kinds of study will be found well suited to ordinary classwork. One involves a detailed investigation of single species in some well defined microhabitat such as a rock face or particular species of seaweed. Distribution and density can often be related quite clearly to the influence of one or more predominant physical factors already discussed such as light, temperature and humidity. The other sort of survey necessitates the laying out of a transect down the shore as already described (p. 248), and sampling particular species at regular intervals. Exercises of this kind are well worth while, even if they are rather incomplete – as they are bound to be when time is limited. For it is only by the use of elementary sampling and statistical techniques in the field that students will gain a true idea of their value and appreciate the objective information on distribution which they can provide.

All animal populations fluctuate in numbers, many with a fairly regular periodicity, but these changes are often too slow to be detected except as a result of many years' continuous study. However, violent fluctuations in physical conditions such as periods of extreme heat or cold, also the sudden incidence of disease, may have disastrous effects on shore animals. For instance, the small sea-urchin, *Psammechinus miliaris*, which was formerly common at Whitstable in Kent, was completely exterminated during the exceptionally cold winter of 1928–9. Circumstances of this kind are fortunately rare, but when they do happen to occur, the labour involved in keeping continuous records for a particular area may prove unexpectedly to have been well directed.

Fluctuations of quite another kind occur daily every time the tide ebbs and flows over the many microhabitats, such as rock pools that comprise the sea shore. Such localities are ideal for elementary study as they are generally small, their boundaries are clear-cut and the number of animal and plant species is not excessive. Their populations can be divided roughly into two groups – residents such as sea-anemones, and temporary visitors like fishes and shrimps. In between these two categories there is a third comprising such animals as crabs which can be regarded as partial residents. Honey carried out a survey of a Guernsey rock pool with an area of about 250 square feet and maximum depth of $3\frac{1}{2}$ feet. He observed the crab population (*Carcinus*) for a period of 18 days during April, all new arrivals being marked with dots of 'Necol' paint (*see* p. 87) each time a visit was made to the pool. His results are summarized in Table 17.

Date (*April 1946*)	7	9	11	13	15	17	19	21	23	25
Carcinus (unmarked)	2	2	3	2	0	4	0	0	1	2
Carcinus (marked)	0	1	0	0	1	1	5	4	1	0
Total population	2	3	3	2	1	5	5	4	2	2

TABLE 17. Turnover in the crab population of a Guernsey rock pool. (*After Honey.*)

These rather limited data give some idea of the transient nature of the *Carcinus* population. Thus, of the 7 crabs marked during the previous 6 days, none was still in the pool on 13th April, while at least 4 of the total of 13 individuals marked up to the 17th returned to the locality two days later. In all some 14 *Carcinus* were marked during the period of observation but all had disappeared by April 25th. Simple studies like this are also instructive in showing the comparatively narrow limits within which the density of a small population normally varies in a temporary habitat of restricted size subject to constant change. During the same series of observations, Honey found the number of fishes (all species) in this Guernsey rock pool averaged 3, the maximum being 6 and the minimum 2. In marked contrast are some of the more permanent communities of animals such as lugworms and barnacles whose density fluctuates within wide limits. The numbers involved are often huge but we still have little idea of the factors which ultimately control them.

CHAPTER XI

Field-work Procedure

Of the various branches of biology, there is little doubt that ecology is one of the most difficult both to teach and to learn. Moreover, at an elementary level, the study of an animal community presents far greater problems than does one of plants. No doubt this accounts for the emphasis on plant ecology which seems to be almost universal among our schools. An additional complication arises from the fact that the ecological approach does not come naturally to many students and its acquisition is often rather a slow process. This is partly due to the inherent difficulty of the subject, but the undue emphasis still placed on comparative anatomy in our examination syllabuses is also a contributory factor.

In the preceding chapters I have attempted to show that animal ecology is a subject worth teaching and that valuable work of an elementary kind can be carried out by classes and small groups of students. The excuse sometimes put forward that no suitable habitats exist in or near a particular area is seldom valid except, perhaps, within large cities.

The successful running of a school or university ecology course, as in any other branch of teaching, depends primarily on the personality and enthusiasm of the teacher. It is unlikely that he will stimulate a class to great activity if he has had no previous practical experience of ecology himself. If possible he should have made some original observations of his own even of an elementary kind. One of the points stressed repeatedly in the later chapters of this book is the scope for original work in the vast field of animal ecology which still remains to be explored. Teachers in secondary schools are particularly fortunate in having their own journal – the *School Science Review* — in which their findings can be published and quickly brought to the notice of a wide scientific circle.

Equally important with the personal side of teaching is the care with which a course of study is planned in advance. This is axiomatic but applies with particular force to ecology since plant and animal communities are in a constant state of change. Mention has already been made elsewhere of the wide variety of small habitats which are suitable for elementary study, and it may be helpful in the remaining pages to consider the problem of planning a course of field-work once the site has been determined.

THE PLANNING OF FIELD-WORK

Selection of projects

Much the most valuable experience a student can acquire is that derived from an investigation carried out, under supervision, on his own or in a small syndicate. A number of suitable elementary projects have been suggested in the course of Chapters VII–X. Practical introduction to ecological procedure is a necessary preliminary to independent studies and this will normally be achieved through classwork. Regarding the selection of a locality, little need be added to what has already been said in the chapters dealing with particular habitats. It is, perhaps, worth stressing once again that the ideal site for beginners should be small, clearly defined and should not support more species than it will be possible to identify. A difficulty which generally arises in practical work is that not all students work at the same speed. Some will have completed a project when others are only half-way through it. When planning a piece of field-work, therefore, it is advisable to bear this possibility in mind and to devise a number of additional problems to occupy the abler pupils. For instance, if the locality chosen for study is in full sun, it may be possible to find one nearby in partial shade with which it can be compared. Alternatively, numerical aspects can be introduced involving elementary sampling which will appeal to the more mathematically minded. All animal habitats are subject to a good deal of variation even over quite short distances, so that a teacher should seldom have much difficulty in chosing a project with the right amount of flexibility.

281

Reconnaissance

The old army dictum that 'time spent on reconnaissance is never wasted' applies with particular emphasis to the planning of a practical ecology course. This is obvious enough, but the point needs stressing because a preliminary survey inevitably means an extra demand on a teacher's time and therefore may tend to be overlooked. Moreover, it is by no means certain that a survey of a locality made one year is necessarily adequate for the next. Some habitats are capable of altering completely in a matter of a few hours, possibly with disastrous consequences. For instance, a heavy downpour can turn a clear, shallow chalk stream into a raging, muddy torrent, thereby ruling out any possibility of practical work.

Equipment

Mention has already been made in earlier chapters of apparatus suitable for studying particular kinds of ecological problems. None of this need be expensive and most of it can be made in a laboratory workshop. In addition there is a certain amount of standard equipment which is bound to be needed sooner or later and which it is advisable to buy at the outset.

Microscopes will only be required for the identification of the smallest animals, and even then, the power required is not high. The ideal instrument is of the low-power binocular type, preferably with several objectives and eyepieces so as to give a fairly wide range of magnification. The maximum power normally necessary with a monocular microscope is that of a $\frac{2}{3}$-inch objective ($\times 10$) used with a $\times 5$ eyepiece ($= \times 50$). Lower magnifications are often an advantage and a 3-inch objective ($\times 1 \cdot 7$) will be found invaluable on account of its wide field. A hand lens is an indispensable item of ecological equipment and students should be encouraged to buy one for themselves. The folding 'doublet' type with a metal case will be found most satisfactory and a pattern with adequate correction is now obtainable for about six shillings. The working distance (gap between lens and object) decreases with increasing magnification and a $\times 8$ lens provides a satisfactory compromise.

The marking out of an area and subsequent collection of plants and animals inevitably requires a good deal of measuring and storage equipment. The construction of Ecology Field Boxes is sometimes advocated, each being designed to hold a specified set of apparatus. Such items can be purchased from biological dealers if required, but there is little need for anything so elaborate, at any rate in schools. Most of the apparatus likely to be needed is not fragile and can be packed in any container of convenient size. Linear measurements, if required accurately, are best made with a measuring tape although string knotted at appropriate intervals is a perfectly satisfactory substitute for most purposes. Vertical distances in water and on land can be measured with a home-made version of the surveyor's staff painted red, white and black in six-inch lengths; this can also be used as a post for marking part of an area or the direction of a transect.

Once collecting begins a large number of labelled containers will be needed. Small amounts of plant material can be kept in tobacco tins (flat type) several of which can be carried in a pocket. An alternative method is to use polythene bags which are cheap and easily obtainable from dealers. Large plants are best stored in a botanist's vasculum, but this is a cumbersome object to carry about. The ideal container for small animals, both terrestrial and aquatic, is a transparent plastic tube with a tightly fitting bung. These are easily obtainable from dealers but are rather expensive if used in large numbers. An alternative is the glass specimen tube with a cork but this is apt to get broken. For most aquatic animals and plants the salad dressing jar will be found an excellent substitute. It is reasonably large and watertight, the stoppers are generally interchangeable in the event of breakage or loss, and storage presents little difficulty. Moreover, hotels are generally only too delighted to get rid of their accumulated stocks.

One final point must be made concerning containers in general: before use each should be provided with a blank label so that the necessary information about the contents can be clearly recorded. Remember that bungs are easily misplaced so that labels should always be fixed to the container itself and *never* to the stopper or lid.

Suitable utensils must also be available in the laboratory so that a catch can be decanted and examined quickly on return. Watch and clock glasses are ideal for small species and have the advantage that they will fit on an ordinary microscope stage. When using a hand lens, animals are best observed on a black and white tile – those with transparent bodies are most easily seen against the black surface while pigmented individuals show up well on a white background. Aquatic animals should be transferred with some of their natural water to a shallow dish and provided with a little weed in moderate light (not full sun). Many types of plastic

Fig. 85
Widger. A useful tool for
manipulating small animals
and plants
P. K. Dutt & Co. Ltd.

container are now available and old photographic dishes are particularly suitable. The cheapest and most convenient kind of all is probably the small china or enamel pie dish obtainable from any ironmonger.

Special apparatus required for collecting animals in particular habitats has already been described in Chapter III and need not be considered further here. An indispensable item of personal equipment for any ecological work is a fairly stout penknife. This is needed for prising insects out of bark crevices, removing barnacles from rocks, lifting insect nymphs from the surface of stones and similar sorts of collecting. A partial substitute for many purposes is a section lifter which can easily be made by flattening one end of a six-inch length of stout copper wire with a hammer. An invaluable device of fairly recent origin is the 'widger';[1] a piece of stainless steel about seven inches long with two concave blades of different widths (Fig. 85). It costs only a few shillings, is easy to carry about and ideal both for removing small animals and for collecting plants such as toadstools and mosses.

[1] Obtainable from P. K. Dutt & Co. Ltd, 1 Alfred Place, London, W.C.1.

Other essential items of field equipment are a small notebook, preferably of a size that will fit easily into the pocket, and a supply of graph paper for map-making. Reference books for identification will also be needed, mainly in the laboratory. A classified list of suggested works is included in the Bibliography.

Organization of classwork

The complexity of even quite small animal and plant communities necessitates that before embarking upon a piece of fieldwork, a class must be quite clear as to its aims and the means by which they are to be achieved. At the same time it is important that as much as possible should be left to the originality and ingenuity of the students themselves. These two requirements are bound to conflict, and the position is made more difficult by the fact that the circumstances in which different groups of students are working may themselves vary appreciably. There is no easy answer to these problems, but a partial solution which works quite well in practice is to provide the class in advance with a set of notes on the project to be undertaken. These should not be regarded as instructions and are best framed as a series of questions to which answers must be found. The success achieved by different students, also their speed of progress, will vary greatly, and for this reason it is an advantage to classify questions under a series of numbered headings. This enables the teacher to 'take stock' at frequent intervals and to keep the work of the class together by comparing the results of different syndicates or individuals. Mention has already been made (p. 281) of the problem of keeping the clever pupil interested and the desirability of having a number of small related problems available in case of need. Some notes on the ecology of a small Hampshire chalk stream are included at Appendix C as an example of the kind of directive envisaged. In this instance, the whole class was expected to complete section A, while the cleverer members mostly finished B as well.

The organization of a practical class is largely dependent on local circumstances, in particular the number of students and their seniority. Experience with school classes at all levels suggests that they should never exceed 24, while the optimum is about 16 or less.

The formation of a number of small syndicates (2 or 3 in each) eases the demand on apparatus and is a great help in reducing the time spent on such items as mapping, collecting and identification. As to the best means of organizing these small groups, there are two distinct schools of thought. Some teachers believe in splitting up a problem into its component parts and delegating one or more aspects to each syndicate. The final result is a synthesis of a number of independent investigations. The advantage claimed for this method is that it enables a relatively wide field to be covered. On the other hand it means that each student gains first-hand knowledge of only a small fraction of the complete study; the remainder has to be accepted on trust from his companions. The alternative course of allowing each syndicate to achieve as much as it can would seem to be infinitely preferable, even if the results are less complete in the end. The selection of strictly limited habitats advocated elsewhere in this book, greatly aids ecological work conducted on this basis.

A word of warning may be helpful to the beginner concerning the ease with which breakage and loss of equipment can occur in the field. Although little of the apparatus is likely to be expensive, continual replacement is tedious and a waste of time. The relatively small amount of trouble involved in keeping a written check on equipment issued to syndicates and ensuring its safe return will be amply repaid later on in reduced expenses and labour saved.

Consolidation of results

The final stage in any practical work consists in the analysis of results and the writing of a complete account. It is important that sufficient time be allowed for this to be done thoroughly and that the class should have ample opportunity for discussing the various aspects of the problem both before and after the project is completed. The value of a preliminary questionnaire (*see* p. 285) is particularly evident here in providing a guide to the order in which different items should be considered. Moreover, it enables the various sections of the work to be discussed and written-up as they are completed instead of leaving the task of compiling the whole account until the end.

The study of even a small area necessitates systematic collection from a number of different microhabitats – possibly as few as half a dozen, but often more. The various species occurring in each place must be accurately recorded and it is often a help to construct a simple table of the kind shown in Table 18. This will serve both as a guide in writing a detailed account and also as a convenient key to the distribution of different species.

SPECIES	Water crowfoot (stems and leaves)	Water crowfoot (roots in mud)	Gravel	Stones (upper surface and sides)	Stones (underneath)	Open water
Fishes						
Salmo trutta	—	—	—	—	—	✓
Cobitis barbatula	✓	—	—	—	✓	—
Cottus gobio	✓	—	—	—	✓	—
Annelids						
Eiseniella sp.	—	✓	—	—	—	—
Crustaceans						
Gammarus pulex	—	✓	✓	—	✓	—
Astacus fluviatilis	✓	—	✓ (young)	—	✓	—
Molluscs						
Ancylus fluviatilis	—	—	—	✓	—	—
Hydrobia jenkinsi	✓	—	—	✓	—	—

TABLE 18. Part of a summary of animal species occupying certain microhabitats in a chalk stream.

Mention has already been made elsewhere of the effects of seasonal change on animal communities. In order to appreciate these and the various methods of overwintering adopted by different species, visits to a locality studied during the summer should also be made in the autumn, winter and spring. Provided the preliminary work has been thorough and well-recorded, such expeditions need each occupy little more than an hour or two.

Value of photography

To conclude, mention must be made of the use of photography as a means of retaining a permanent record, not only of whole localities, but also of microhabitats, apparatus and even of animals and plants themselves. The development of the 35 mm. camera together with efficient small projectors has brought about a revolution in photographic methods, so that the making and showing of first rate lantern slides is now a practical possibility in all schools. Ideally, all pictures should be taken as colour transparencies since these achieve a degree of realism which is unobtainable in black and white. Unfortunately, colour film is expensive and it has the additional disadvantage of being rather 'slow'. In practice, this means that snapshots can only be taken in good light. Fortunately, the production of black and white lantern slides is now an easy matter and no longer necessitates the tedious procedure of converting an ordinary negative into a transparent positive. The introduction by Gevaert of 35 mm. 'Dia-dircct pan reversal' film[1] has enabled positive transparencies to be taken which need only be mounted between two glasses to make them into permanent lantern slides. The quality of this film compares favourably with that of the best British makes of the normal kind. Moreover, compared with colour film, it possesses the advantage of being more than twice as fast and reasonably cheap (each exposure costs only a few pence). Development, like that of colour film, is carried out by the manufacturers and the cost is included in the initial price.

The many possibilities of photography as an aid to the learning and teaching of ecology have so far been only partially explored. Fully utilized, they should prove invaluable, particularly in those schools which have to rely on a single annual visit to a distant locality such as a Field Centre. Moreover, good black and white prints or enlargements can help to enliven any account of ecological field-work, as well as providing a lasting record of what may well be the most enjoyable part of a school biology course.

[1] Obtainable from photographic dealers or from Gevaert Ltd, Acton Lane, Harlesden, London, N.W.10.

The Theory of Line Transects

The following is a brief summary of an account by W. B. Yapp.[1] The original paper should be consulted for fuller information, including details of the mathematics involved.

The problem of encounters between moving objects is essentially the same whatever the nature of the objects concerned. The frequency of 'impact' depends upon three factors:

(i) The size of the objects
(ii) Their speed
(iii) Their density.

Applying this idea to the counting of animals in the field, we can assume that an 'impact' has occurred each time an observation is made. If an observer moves in a predetermined direction counting all the animals of a particular kind (e.g. a species of bird), then, making a few approximations, the number of individuals per unit area (D) can be calculated from the formula

$$D = \frac{z}{2R(\bar{u}^2 + \bar{w}^2)^{\frac{1}{2}}},$$

where z = the number of encounters between observer and organism in a unit time,

R = the 'effective radius' of the organism,

$\bar{u}$ = the average speed of the organism,

$\bar{w}$ = the average speed of the observer.

The application of this formula to findings in the field clearly depends upon the extent to which valid values can be given to the different variables.

(a) In order to obtain a fairly accurate estimate of D, it is essential that the numbers should remain reasonably constant

[1] Yapp, W. B. (1956). 'The Theory of Line Transects', *Bird Study*, **3**, 93–104.

during the period of observation. Tit populations in winter are in a constant state of movement and provide rather unsuitable material for this kind of study. Resident populations of birds tend to be more stable during the summer and this is the best time to apply the line transect method of estimating their numbers.

(b) The number of observers is one and his size is arbitrarily fixed at zero. His speed can be determined quite easily; apparently about 2 m.p.h. is regarded as the best compromise between covering too little ground and uncertain identification at greater speeds. Pauses to make records must be taken into account in calculating the average speed; these must obviously be reduced to a minimum.

(c) The speed of the organism ($\bar{u}$) is a highly variable quantity and no satisfactory means has yet been devised for assessing it. That of tits seems to vary from $\frac{1}{8}$ to 2 miles per hour, but birds may remain stationary for periods of up to 25 minutes. This suggests that a number of small samples is likely to provide more reliable estimates of density than a few larger ones.

(d) The effective radius of the organism (R) is really the range at which it can be recognized, thus implying that its 'sensory tentacles' stretch out towards the observer through the 'recognition distance'. This distance can be either auditory or visual. The former is, in many ways, the easier to measure, and is particularly applicable to birds. There is, however, a large personal variation, and noisy days with a high wind are useless. More important is the fact that birds do not call continuously, although woodland species generally sing in stanzas, each lasting from 2 to 10 seconds, according to species. The average audible range for many species of birds is about 200 yards. Moving at 2 miles per hour (i.e. covering approximately 200 yards in 3 minutes) observers should have a reasonable chance of encountering the majority of woodland species in a single transect.

Long periods of silence serve to reduce the 'effective diameter' of the bird; these vary in extent from day to day. As far as possible, therefore, counts should be made at fairly frequent intervals and at about the same time.

In open country, visual contacts will be more important. For instance, observations from railway trains provide an excellent opportunity for estimating the density of large species, such as magpies. The speed of the train is easy to determine, and it is a good plan to confine counting to birds within an arbitrary radius of, say, 50 yards.

(e) The number of contacts per unit time (z) is a function of the four other variables already considered. While D (the density of organisms) and $\bar{w}$ (the average speed of the observer) are likely to remain reasonably constant throughout a series of observations, there are bound to be wide variations in R (the effective range of the organism) and $\bar{u}$ (its average speed). Some means is needed for assessing a mean value of these two quantities for particular species under different circumstances.

For birds, at least, we can formulate certain general conditions which must obtain if valid estimates and comparisons are to be achieved.

(i) The observations must be made in the same phase of the life cycle, e.g. nest-building, incubation, winter flocking, etc.

(ii) Weather conditions, the time of day and the season of the year must be reasonably comparable

(iii) Those features of the environment which affect recognition must be uniform. It seems unlikely that variations in woodland (e.g. presence or absence of leaves) will influence the range of auditory identification to an appreciable extent, but this needs further investigation. Visual identification in such circumstances is likely to vary a good deal and will generally be impracticable. In open country, the nature of the vegetation may have an effect on the distance at which different species of birds can be flushed. Here again, a great deal more careful observation is required.

The line transect method for estimating densities clearly opens up considerable possibilities for experiment, particularly in the determination of the larger variables involved. Where conditions are carefully chosen and tend to remain uniform for an appreciable period, there seems to be no reason why it should not provide a satisfactory means of making quantitative comparisons both between different species, and between the occupants of various habitats.

The Analysis of Data Obtained by the Method of Capture-Recapture

We have seen in Chapter IV how direct calculations made from this kind of data are open to certain limitations. The more detailed mathematical treatment outlined here has been developed by R. A. Fisher, and the following is a summary of a paper by E. B. Ford[1] explaining the procedure step by step.

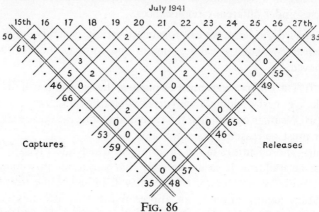

July 1941

FIG. 86

Capture-recapture data from a small colony of the scarlet tiger moth (*Panaxia dominula*) in 1941

Capture-recapture data are best recorded in the form of a triangular trellis (*see also* pp. 94–98, and Fig. 29). The example given in Fig. 86 is a short one and represents captures, releases and recaptures in a small colony of the scarlet tiger moth, *Panaxia dominula*, during 1941. The method of constructing such a table is explained in Chapter IV and need not be repeated here.

Having assembled the data, the next step is to construct a table (as shown in Table 19) consisting of fourteen columns. Column 1

[1] Ford, E. B. (1951). 'The Experimental Study of Evolution', *Australian and New Zealand Association for the Advancement of Science*, **33**, 143–54.

1	2	3	4	5	6	7
July	r	Releases	% survival as decimal raised to power of r	C4×C3	Entries in C5 summed from bottom	Entries in C6 summed from bottom
26	1	—	0·84	—	101·8755	584·0646
25	2	—	—	—	101·8755	482·1891
24	3	55	0·5296	32·5978	101·8755	380·3135
23	4	49	0·4978	24·3957	69·2768	278·4380
22	5	—	—	—	44·8811	209·1612
21	6	—	—	—	44·8811	164·2801
20	7	65	0·2951	19·1809	44·8811	119·3989
19	8	46	0·2479	11·4023	25·7003	74·5178
18	9	—	—	—	14·2980	48·8176
17	10	—	—	—	14·2980	34·5196
16	11	57	0·1469	8·3746	14·2980	20·2217
15	12	48	0·1234	5·9237	5·9237	5·9237

8	9	10	11	12	13	14
Recaptures	Observed survival in days	Expected survival in days $= \dfrac{\text{C8}\times\text{C7}}{\text{C6}}$	Excess of observed survival over expected	Captures	Estimated $= \dfrac{\text{C6}\times\text{C12}}{\text{C8}\times\text{C4}}$ no.	July
0	—	—	0	35	∞	27
—	—	—	—	—	—	26
5	18	20·10	−2·09	59	1,379	25
4	21	18·64	2·36	53	1,194	24
—	—	—	—	—	—	23
—	—	—	—	—	—	22
4	10	11·60	−1·60	66	1,437	21
8	29	27·31	1·69	46	332	20
—	—	—	—	—	—	19
—	—	—	—	—	—	18
4	4	4	0	61	615	17
			0.36			16

TABLE 19. Daily survival = 84 per cent. C = column. The dating (relative to C1 or C14) changes between C7 and C8.

bears the dates according to the trellis, while column 14 is redated, one day later.

This procedure is necessary because the individuals caught on any particular date refer only to releases on previous dates, while those released at the same time refer only to subsequent dates. Entries prior to column 8 are dated similarly to column 1, while those from column 8 onwards are dated relative to column 14.

Column 2 shows the interval between each day of release and the last day on which captures were made (July 27th); this period is denoted as r days. Column 3 gives the number of releases per day. Column 4 shows the rate of survival adopted (p. 295), which is here 84 per cent, expressed as a decimal and raised to the corresponding power of r. The entries in column 3 are now multiplied by those in column 4, the products forming column 5. It should be noted that at any date (s days) prior to July 27th, the totals available for capture will be the sum of the products in column 5 divided by $(0.84)^s$.

For this reason, the entries in column 5 are now progressively summed from the bottom and constitute column 6. We are also concerned with the time intervals between marking and recapture, and column 7 shows a second summation, being the values in column 6 summed from the bottom. Thus, after an interval of t days, every marked specimen is counted t times. In this way an estimate is obtained of the total number of days between marking and recapture to be expected among all recaptures on a particular date. Column 8 thus contains the number of recaptures per day, dated relative to column 14, and column 9 the total number of days which these have survived (obtained from Fig. 86). For example, reference to the trellis diagram will show that on the 19th, 5 specimens have survived 4 days (=20 days of survival), and 3 have survived 3 days (=9 days of survival). Therefore, the figure 29 is entered in column 9 corresponding to the 19th in column 14.

It is now possible to determine the number of days it is *expected* that marked specimens have survived at the particular survival rate assumed (here 84 per cent – p. 295). This is obtained by multiplying the figures in column 8 by those in column 7, and dividing by those in column 6. Such multiplications are, of course, made along the same line, so involving entries for C8 dated relative to C14, and for C6 and 7 relative to C1. The results are tabulated in column 10. The excess of *observed* values (C9) over *expected* (C10) appears in column 11, and is summed at the foot. In column 12 the daily captures are entered, dated in accordance with C14.

We are now in a position to estimate the number of individuals per day which is shown in C13 and dated relative to C14. The calculation is made (as shown at the head of C13) by multiplying the appropriate number in column 12 (dated to the *same* day) with that in column 6 (dated to the *previous* day), both entries, therefore, being on the same line. The product is now divided by that of columns 8 and 4 (both now dated relative to C14, i.e. to the *previous* day). Thus in determining the value for column 13 on any particular date, it will be noted that the figures in C6, 8 and 12 will appear on the same line while that in C4 will be on the line above.

On dates when there are no recaptures, there can be no estimate of population size. However, an approximation can often be obtained by combining such an entry on the table with a preceding or following one for which recaptures are available.

The daily rate of elimination of 16 per cent (i.e. 84 per cent survival) is arrived at by reducing approximately to nothing the discrepancy between the total days of survival *observed* and *expected*. This comparison appears in column 11. It will be seen that the individual divergences are small, those of opposite sign generally cancelling one another. The appropriate survival rate must, of course, be obtained by a process of trial and error.

The procedure outlined above thus provides a means of determining the number of individuals inhabiting a particular area per day, and provides a reliable estimate of total population size in communities which are long-lived and non-migratory, like a breeding colony of birds. Difficulties arise, however, in short-lived, rapidly fluctuating populations such as those of insects, where quick hatching or emergence may soon raise the density from almost zero to a maximum. Subsequent deaths may exert an equally rapid effect in the opposite direction.

For the estimation of numbers in short-lived populations, we require to know how many marks they carry during a given period of their life. Thus the number of marked individuals surviving on the second day of study should be equal to the number of releases on the first day multiplied by the percentage survival (calculated as a decimal, as already explained). The number of *marks* (as opposed to individuals) present on the third day equals that on the second plus the number of releases on that day, if any, the total again being multiplied by the survival rate. This procedure is repeated for each subsequent day.

In our example, the number of marks present on July 20th was 87·0929. The necessary calculation is shown in Table 20 (data obtained from Fig. 86).

Date	Releases on previous day	Previous marks × survival-rate	Marks present per day
16.vii	48	48 × 0·84	40·32
17	57	(40·32 + 57) × 0·84	81·7488
18	—	81·7488 × 0·84	68·6692
19	—	68·6692 × 0·84	57·6820
20	46	(57·6820 + 46) × 0·84	87·0929

TABLE 20. Marks present up to July 20th, in the population described in Fig. 86, at the daily survival-rate of 84 per cent.

In arriving at the average daily population, the number of marks present on each day is multiplied by the number of captures on that day. The products are summed for the days to be averaged and the result is divided by the number of marks recaptured over the period in question. The result for the five days July 16th–20th is shown in Table 21.

The daily population-size, averaged for the three days for which information exists is then estimated as 10861/16=678·8. This presumably represents approximately the size of the population on the two dates (July 17th and 18th) when no sample was obtained.

Date	Marks in population	Captures	Marks × Captures	Recaptures
16.vii	40·32	61	2,459·5	4
17	81·7488	—	—	—
18	68·6692	—	—	—
19	57·6820	46	2,653·4	8
20	87·0929	66	5,748·1	4
			10,861·0	16

TABLE 21

Towards the end of the season, data may become unobtainable and the calculation of population size must then be made using the known death rate. The average total estimated for about the last three occasions of adequate sampling, is multiplied by the survival rate for a succession of days until the value finally becomes negligible.

Notes on the Ecology of a Chalk Stream

The following notes are not intended to be a directive but merely to serve as a guide to the sort of questions which must be answered in an ecological study of this kind. As such, they provide a background to field-work and a basis for writing-up results.

A.

1. *General*

To what extent was the sector chosen representative of the locality as a whole?

2. *Physical factors*

What are the chief factors likely to influence colonization by: (i) plants; (ii) animals?

How can they be measured? Record any special apparatus required and say how it was used.

What is the best way of recording these measurements in the small sector studied?

To what extent are the physical factors likely to fluctuate: (i) over short periods; (ii) at different times of the year?

3. *Colonization*

(a) *Plants.* Make sure that the area chosen for investigation is thoroughly mapped in both plan and vertical section. Examine the soil (edaphic) factors (the nature of the stream bed).

Is there any sequence in the colonization of a bare patch? If the river were left alone what would be the likely succession and final climax vegetation?

What sort of changes might be expected to occur throughout the year: how do the plants overwinter?

How far do the water conditions appear to affect the growth of plants, e.g. mud and silt coming downstream?

Does the colonization of the stream bed by plants alter its nature by causing the accumulation of silt and mud?

How far do the aquatic plants spread up the banks? To what extent are they able to survive out of water?

What special adaptations do the plants possess for living in this type of habitat?

Examine the larger plants, also rocks and stones for the presence of smaller plants such as Algae and Cryophytes. How far are each of these found on a specific type of substrate?

(b) *Animals.* What are the main types of microhabitat occurring in the locality, e.g. roots of plants, undersides of stones, gravel, etc.?

What species colonize these places and approximately in what numbers? Note whether the animals are young (larvae or nymphs) or adults. N.B. When removing stones or vegetation, place a net *downstream* to catch the animals which are dislodged.

Work out a chart system for recording distribution of species in relation to habitats.

In what ways are the animals adapted to their environment in respect of (i) respiration; (ii) movement; (iii) ability to withstand the force of the current?

Is there any evidence to show how the various species pass the winter?

4. *Biotic factors*

(a) *Plants.* Do the plants produce flowers? If so, how do they: (i) become pollinated; (ii) disperse their seed?

Do the plants reproduce themselves asexually? If so, by what means?

Is there any visible evidence of plants being eaten by animals? Try to find those plants which might be useful as food for the animals. Examine the smaller forms carefully.

How far is human interference responsible for keeping the stream in its present condition?

(b) *Animals.* To what extent does the presence of particular species of plants influence colonization by animals in providing: (i) shelter; (ii) food?

299

Is it possible to determine the food of different species: (i) from observation under natural conditions; (ii) from study in an aquarium; (iii) from examination of gut contents; (iv) from evidence provided by mouthparts and other feeding structures?

Is a classification into carnivores, herbivores and detritus feeders justified?

From your findings construct any portions of a food chain that you can.

N.B. The information used *must* be gained from your own observations and not derived from a book.

To what extent is it possible to discover whether the density of species in a particular locality is uniform or not (*Gammarus pulex* and *Hydrobia jenkinsi* are good material for this study)? What are the most suitable sampling and statistical methods to employ? What deductions can be made from your results?

Note. If possible, sampling should be carried out at least twice on different occasions, in order to determine whether the conditions are constant or not.

B.

When you have completed A above, select a second small stretch of the stream as unlike the other as possible. If the first locality was in the sun, choose one in the shade. If the current was strong, try an eddy pool at the stream edge. Repeat the procedure in A as far as you can and compare the two sets of results. What general conclusions can you draw?

Bibliography

References marked (A) are advanced accounts or standard works. Those marked (G) are suitable for general reading and are more elementary.

General Ecology
(G) Brimble, L. J. F. (1951), *Nature Studies for Schools.* Macmillan
(G) Dale, A. (1960), *Observations and Experiments in Natural History.* Heinemann (Good suggestions for elementary work.)
(G) Edlin, M. L. (1952), *The Changing Wild Life of Britain.* Batsford
(A) Elton, C. (1958), *The Ecology of Invasions by Animals and Plants.* Methuen
(G) Fitter, R. S. R. (1963), *Wildlife in Britain.* Pelican
(G) Friedlander, C. P. (1960), *Heathland Ecology.* Heinemann
(G) McLean, R. C., and Cook, W. R. I. (1943), *Practical Field Ecology.* Allen and Unwin
(G) Neal, E. G. (1960 2nd edition), *Woodland Ecology.* Heinemann
(A) Odum, E. P. (1954), *Fundamentals of Ecology.* Saunders
(G) Pearsall, W. H. (1950), *Mountains and Moorlands.* Collins
(G) Reid, L. (1955), *Earth's Company.* Murray (Good, readable introduction.)
(G) Sankey, J. (1958), *A Guide to Field Biology.* Longmans (Excellent short introduction.)

Plant Ecology
(G) Ashby, M. (1961), *Introduction to Plant Ecology.* Macmillan (Good introductory account.)
(G) Baron W. M. M. (1963), *Organisation in Plants.* Arnold (Excellent account relating physiology to ecology.)
(G) Bracher, R. (1939), *Field Studies in Ecology.* Arrowsmith
(A) Daubenmire, R. F. (1947), *Plants and Environment.* Chapman and Hall
(G) Gilmour, J. and Walters, M. (1961 3rd edition), *Wild Flowers.* Collins
(A) Godwin, H. (1956), *The History of the British Flora.* Cambridge
(G) Hepburn, I. (1952), *Flowers of the Coast.* Collins
(G) James, W. O. (1957), *Background to Gardening.* Allen and Unwin
(A) Leach, W. (1957, 4th edition), *Plant Ecology.* Methuen
(A) Lousley, J. E. (editor) (1953), *The Changing Flora of Britain.* Botanical Society of the British Isles

(G) Lousley, J. E. (1950), *Wild Flowers of the Chalk and Limestone.* Collins

(G) Matthews, J. R. (1955), *Origin and Distribution of the British Flora.* Hutchinson

(A) Oosting, H. J. (1958, 2nd edition), *The Study of Plant Communities.* Freeman

(G) Raven, J., and Walters, M. (1956), *Mountain Flowers.* Collins

(G) Salisbury, E. J. (1961), *Weeds and Aliens.* Collins

(G) Salisbury, E. J. (1952), *Downs and Dunes.* Bell

(G) Tansley, A. G. (1946), *Introduction to Plant Ecology.* Allen and Unwin

(G) Tansley, A. G. (1949), *Britain's Green Mantle.* Allen and Unwin

(A) Tansley, A. G. (1953), *The British Islands and their Vegetation.* Cambridge (Standard work of reference.)

(G) Tansley, A. G., and Price, Evans (1947), *Plant Ecology for the School.* Allen and Unwin

(G) Turrill, W. B. (1948), *British Plant Life.* Collins

Animal Ecology

(A) Allee, W. C., Emerson, A. E., Park, O., Park, T., and Schmidt, K. P. (1949), *Principles of Animal Ecology.* Saunders

(A) Allee, W. C., Schmidt, K. P., and Hesse, R. (1951), *Ecological Animal Geography.* Chapman and Hall

(A) Andrewartha, H. G. (1961), *Introduction to the Study of Animal Populations.* Methuen

(A) Beirne, B. P. (1952), *The Origin and History of the British Fauna.* Methuen

(G) Besley, M. A., and Meyer, G. R. (1955), *Field Work in Animal Biology.* Methuen

(A) Chapman, R. N. (1931), *Animal Ecology.* McGraw-Hill

(G) Dowdeswell, W. H. (1959, 2nd edition), *Animal Ecology.* Methuen

(G) Elton, C. (1927), *Animal Ecology.* Sidgwick and Jackson

✓ (G) Elton, C. (1953, 3rd edition), *The Ecology of Animals.* Methuen

(A) Lack, D. (1954), *The Natural Regulation of Animal Numbers.* Oxford

(G) Lulham, R. (1949), *Introduction to Zoology through Nature Study.* Macmillan

(A) MacFadyen, A. (1957), *Animal Ecology.* Pitman

(A) Pearse, A. S. (1939), *Animal Ecology.* McGraw-Hill

General Works on Soil Ecology

(A) Bear, F. F. (editor) (1955), *Chemistry of Soil.* Chapman and Hall

(A) Clarke, G. R. (1941), *The Study of Soil in the Field.* Oxford

(G) Darwin, C. (1881), *The Formation of Vegetable Mould Through the Action of Worms, with Observation of their Habits.* Murray

(G) Hall, A. D. (1944, 3rd edition), *The Feeding of Crops and Stock.* (3 volumes) Murray

(G) Jacks, G. V. (1954), *Soil.* Nelson

(G) James, W. O. (1957), *Background to Gardening.* Allen and Unwin.

(G) Kevan, D. K. McE. (editor) (1955), *Soil Zoology.* Butterworth (Includes excellent key to indentification of soil fauna.)

(G) Kevan, D. K. McE. (1962), *Soil Animals.* Witherby

(A) Knowles, F., and Watkin, J. E. (1947, 2nd edition), *A Practical Course in Agricultural Chemistry.* Macmillan

(A) Kühnelt, W. (1961), *Soil Biology.* Faber and Faber

(G) Manley, G. (1952), *Climate and the British Scene.* Collins

(G) Millar, C. E. (1955), *Soil Fertility.* Wiley

(G) Robinson, G. W. (1949), *Soils, their Origin. Constitution and Classification.* Murby

(G) Russell, E. J. (1950, 2nd edition), *Lessons on Soil.* Cambridge (Elementary practical course.)

(A) Russell, E. J. (1954, 8th edition), *Soil Conditions and Plant Growth.* Longmans (Standard work.)

(G) Russell, E. J. (1957), *The World of the Soil.* Collins (Outstanding modern account.)

(G) Smith, A. M. (1952), *Manures and Fertilizers.* Nelson

(A) Waksman, S. A. (1952), *Soil Microbiology.* Chapman and Hall

General Works on Freshwater Ecology

(G) Carpenter, K. (1928), *Life in Inland Waters.* Sidgwick and Jackson

(A) Edmondson, W. T., Ward, H. B., and Whipple, G. C. (1959, 2nd edition), *Freshwater Biology.* Wiley (Standard American work.)

(G) Garnett, W. J. (1953), *Freshwater Microscopy.* Constable

(G) Macan, T. T. (1959), *A Guide to Freshwater Invertebrate Animals.* Longmans

(G) Macan, T. T., and Worthington, E. B. (1951), *Life in Lakes and Rivers.* Collins

(G) Mellanby, H. (1953, 5th edition), *Animal Life in Fresh Water.* Methuen

(G) Popham, E. J. (1955), *Some Aspects of Life in Fresh Water.* Heinemann

(G) Prud'homme Van Reine, W. J. (1957), *Plants and Animals of Pond and Stream.* Murray

General Works on Marine and Estuarine Ecology

(A) Barnes, H. (1959), *Oceanography and Marine Biology. A Book of Techniques.* Allen and Unwin

(G) Barrett, J. H., and Yonge, C. M. (1958), *Pocket Guide to the Seashore.* Collins (Excellent for identification.)

(G) Besley, M. A., and Meyer, G. R. (1955), *Field Work in Animal Biology*. Methuen

(A) Eales, N. B. (1961, 3rd edition), *The Littoral Fauna of the British Isles*. Cambridge (Standard work.)

(G) Ennion, E. A. R. (1946), *Life on the Sea Shore*. Oxford

(G) Fraser, J. (1962), *Nature Adrift. The Story of Marine Plankton*. Foulis

(G) Hardy, A. C. (1956), *The Open Sea I. The World of Plankton*. Collins

(G) Hardy, A. C. (1959), *The Open Sea II. Fish and Fisheries*. Collins

(A) Newton, L. (1931), *A Handbook of British Seaweeds*. British Museum (Natural History)

(A) Nicol, J. A. C. (1960), *The Biology of Marine Animals*. Pitman (Excellent general account.)

(G) Russel, F. S., and Yonge, C. M. (1947), *The Seas*. Warne

✓ (G) Wilson, D. P. (1951, 2nd edition), *Life of the Shore and Shallow Sea*. Nicholson and Watson (Very good introduction.)

(G) Yonge, C. M. (1949), *The Sea Shore*. Collins

Identification of Plants

(G) Barrett, J., and Yonge, C. M. (1958), *Pocket Guide to the Sea Shore*. Collins (Excellent for seaweeds.)

✓ (A) Clapham, A. R., Tutin, T. G., and Warburg, E. F. (1952), *Flora of the British Isles*. Cambridge (Standard work.)

✓ (A) Clapham, A. R., Tutin, T. G., and Warburg, E. F. (1959), *Excursion Flora of the British Isles*. Cambridge (Abridged version of standard work. Pocket size.)

(G) Gilmour, J., and Walters, M. (1961, 3rd edition), *Wild Flowers*. Collins

✓ (G) Hutchinson, J. (1955, 2nd edition), *British Wild Flowers*. (2 volumes) Pelican

(G) Makins, F. K. (1957, 2nd edition), *Concise Flora of Britain*. Oxford

(G) McClintock, D., and Fitter, R. S. R. (1956), *Pocket Guide to Wild Flowers*. Collins (Excellent elementary book, well illustrated mostly in colour.)

(A) Newton, L. (1931), *A Handbook of British Seaweeds*. British Museum (Natural History)

(G) Prime, C. T., and Deacock, R. J. (1952, 2nd edition), *A Shorter British Flora*. Methuen

(G) Skene, M. (1952, 2nd edition), *A Flower Book for the Pocket*. Oxford (Good for beginners; illustrated in colour.)

(A) Smart, J., and Taylor, G. (1953), *Bibliography of Key Works for the Identification of the British Fauna and Flora*. The Systematics Association (c/o The British Museum, Natural History) (An indispensable summary.)

Identification of Animals
(i) *Vertebrates*
Amphibians
(G) Sanders, E. (1937), *A Beast Book for the Pocket*. Oxford
(G) Smith, M. (1949), *British Reptiles and Amphibia*. King Penguin
(G) Smith, M. (1957), *The British Amphibians and Reptiles*. Collins

Birds
(G) Fisher, J. (1951), *Bird Recognition*. (2 volumes) Pelican
(G) Fitter, R. S. R. (1954), *The Pocket Guide to British Birds*. Collins
(Good for beginners.)
(G) Gibson-Hill, C. A. (1947), *British Sea Birds*, Witherby
(G) Peterson, R., Mountfort, G., and Hollom, P. A. D. (1954), *A Field Guide to the Birds of Britain and Europe*. Collins (Outstanding for field identification; beautifully illustrated.)
(A) Witherby, H. F., Jourdain, F. C. R., Ticehurst, N. F., and Tucker, B. W. (1947, 4th edition), *Handbook of British Birds*. (5 volumes) Witherby (Standard work of reference.)

Fishes
(G) Hodgson, N. B. (1948), *Freshwater Fishes of the British Isles*. Crowther
(G) Jenkins, J. T. (1936, 2nd edition), *The Fishes of the British Isles*. Warne

Mammals
(G) Hodgson, N. B. (1945), *Mammals and Reptiles of the British Isles*. Crowther
(G) Matthews, L. H. (1952), *British Mammals*. Collins
(G) Sanders, E. (1937), *A Beast Book for the Pocket*. Oxford (Excellent elementary account.)

Reptiles
(G) Hodgson, N. B. (1945), *Mammals and Reptiles of the British Isles*. Crowther
(G) Sanders, E. (1937), *A Beast Book for the Pocket*. Oxford
(G) Sanders, M. (1949), *British Reptiles and Amphibia*. King Penguin
(G) Sanders, M. (1951), *The British Amphibians and Reptiles*. Collins

(ii) *Invertebrates*
General
(G) Barrett, J., and Yonge, C. M. (1958), *Pocket Guide to the Sea Shore*. Collins

(G) British Museum (Natural History) (1940), *Instructions for Collectors, No. 4A. Insects.*

(G) British Museum (Natural History) (1954), *Instructions for Collectors, No. 9A. Invertebrates other than Insects.*

✓ (G) Cloudsley-Thompson, J. L., and Sankey, J. (1961), *Land Invertebrates.* Methuen (Contains excellent elementary keys and references.)

(A) Eales, N. B. (1961, 3rd edition), *The Littoral Fauna of Great Britain.* Cambridge

(A) Edney, E. B. (1957), *The Water Relations of Terrestrial Arthropods.* Cambridge

(A) Kevan, D. K. McE. (editor) (1955), *Soil Zoology.* Butterworth (Excellent elementary key to soil fauna included.)

(G) Kevan, D. K. McE. (1962), *Soil Animals.* Witherby

(G) Mellanby, H. (1953, 5th edition), *Animal Life in Freshwater.* Methuen

(G) Savory, T. H. (1955), *The World of Small Animals.* University of London Press

For detailed descriptions and keys for the various groups of aquatic invertebrates see the excellent series of pamphlets published by The Freshwater Biological Association, The Ferry House, Ambleside, Westmorland.

Annelids

(A) Cernosvitov, L., and Evans, A. C. (1947), *Lumbricidae, No. 6 of Synopses of the British Fauna.* Linnean Society, London

(G) Roots, B. I. (1956), "Famous Animals—7. The Earthworm". *New Biology 21.* Pelican

(A) Stephenson, J. (1930), *The Oligochaeta.* Oxford

Arthropods

  (a) *Arachnids*

(G) Baker, E. W., and Wharton, G. W. (1952), *An Introduction to Acarology (Mites and Ticks).* Macmillan

(G) Bristowe, W. S. (1947), *Spiders.* King Penguin

(G) Bristowe, W. S. (1958), *The World of Spiders.* Collins

✓ (G) Cloudsley-Thompson, J. L. (1958), *Spiders, Scorpions, Centipedes and Mites.* Pergamon

(A) Evans, G. O., and Browning, E. (1954), *Pseudoscorpions, Synopses of the British Fauna No. 10.* Linnean Society, London

(G) Friedlander, C. P., and Priest, D. A. (1955), *Insects and Spiders.* Pitman

(G) Hughes, T. E. (1959), *Mites, or the Acari.* Athlone Press

(A) Locket, G. H., and Millidge, A. F. (1951–3), *British Spiders.* (2 volumes) Ray Society, London (Standard work.)

(A) Savory, T. H. (1928), *The Biology of Spiders*. Sidgwick and Jackson

(G) Savory, T. H. (1945, 2nd edition), *Spiders and Allied Orders of the British Isles*. Warne

(G) Savory, T. H. (1952), *The Spider's Web*. Warne

(b) *Crustaceans*

(A) Edmondson, W. T., Ward, H. B., and Whipple, G. C. (1959, 2nd edition), *Freshwater Biology*. Wiley (Good for some of the smaller forms. American species only.)

(A) Edney, E. B. (1954), *British Woodlice, No. 9 of Synopses of the British Fauna*. Linnean Society, London

(A) Webb, W. M., and Sillem, C. (1906), *The British Woodlice*. Duckworth

(c) *Insects*

For detailed treatment of the various Orders see the separate parts of the *Handbook for the Identification of British Insects*, Royal Entomological Society, London.

(G) British Museum, (Natural History) (1954), *Instructions for Collectors, No. 4A Insects*. (Includes summary of principal characteristics.)

(G) Burr, M. (1936), *British Grasshoppers and their Allies*. Philip Allan

(A) Chrystal, R. N. (1937), *Insects of the British Woodlands*. Warne

(G) Colyer, C. N., and Hammond, C. O. (1951), *Flies of the British Isles*. Warne

(G) Daglish, E. F. (1952), *Name this Insect*. Dent

(G) Dibb, J. R. (1948), *Field Book of Beetles*. Hull

(A) Donisthorpe, H. St. K. (1927), *British Ants*. Routledge

(G) Ford, E. B. (1946, 2nd edition), *Butterflies*. Collins

(G) Ford, E. B. (1955), *Moths*. Collins

(G) Friedlander, C. P., and Priest, D. A. (1955), *Insects and Spiders*. Pitman

(A) Hickin, N. E. (1952), *Caddis*. Methuen

(A) Imms, A. D. (1938), *A General Textbook of Entomology*. Methuen

(G) Imms, A. D. (1947), *Insect Natural History*. Collins

(A) Imms, A. D. (1959, 5th edition), *Outlines of Entomology*. Methuen

(A) Jeannel, R. (1960), *Introduction to Entomology*. Hutchinson

(G) Joy, N. H. (1932), *A Practical Handbook of British Beetles*. Warne

(G) Joy, N. H. (1944), *British Beetles, Their Homes and Habits*. Warne

(A) Kloet, G. S., and Hincks, W. D. (1945), *A Check List of the British Insects*. Stockport (An invaluable check-list, generally regarded as the standard work.)

(G) Longfield, C. (1937), *Dragonflies of the British Isles*. Warne

(A) Marshall, J. F. (1938), *The British Mosquitoes*. British Museum (Natural History)

(G) Moreton, B. D. (1950), *Guide to British Insects*. Macmillan

(G) Morley, D. W. (1953), *Ants*. Collins

(G) Pickard, B. C. (1954), *Grasshoppers and Crickets of Great Britain*. (Private publication.)

(G) Sanders, E. (1946), *An Insect Book for the Pocket*. Oxford

(G) South, R. (1943, 3rd edition), *The Butterflies of the British Isles*. Warne

(G) South R. (1943, 3rd edition), *The Moths of the British Isles*. Warne

(G) Step, E. (1932), *Bees, Wasps, Ants and Allied Insects of the British Isles*. Warne

(G) Stokoe, W. J. (1944), *The Caterpillars of the British Butterflies*. Warne

(G) Stokoe, W. J. (1948), *The Caterpillars of the British Moths*. (2 volumes) Warne

(d) *Myriapods*

(G) Blower, J. G. (1955), *Yorkshire Centipedes*. Naturalist No. 855

(A) Blower, J. G. (1958), *Synopses of the British Fauna No. 11—British Millipedes (Diplopoda)*. Linnean Society, London

(G) Cloudsley-Thompson, J. L. (1958), *Spiders, Scorpions, Centipedes and Mites*. Pergamon

(e) *Molluscs*

(G) Ellis, A. E. (1928), *British Snails*. Oxford

(A) Quick, H. E. (1949), *Testicellidae, Arionidae, Limacidae (Slugs) No. 8 of the Synopses of the British Fauna*. Linnean Society, London

(G) Quick, H. E. (1960), *British Slugs*. British Museum (Natural History)

(G) Step, E. (1945), *Shell Life*. Warne

Nematodes

(A) Goodey, J. B. (1957), *Laboratory Methods for Work with Soil and Plant Nematodes. Technical Bulletin No. 2*. H.M.S.O. London

(A) Goodey, T. (1951), *Soil and Freshwater Nematodes*. Methuen

(G) Kevan, D. K. McE. (1955), *Soil Zoology*. Butterworth

(G) Kevan, D. K. McE. (1962), *Soil Animals*. Witherby

(A) Southey, J. F. (editor) (1959), *Plant Nematology. Technical Bulletin No. 7*. H.M.S.O. London

Protozoans

(A) Edmondson, W. T., Ward, H. B., and Whipple, G. C. (1959, 2nd edition), *Freshwater Biology*. Wiley

(A) Sandon, H. (1927), *The Composition and Distribution of the Protozoan Fauna of the Soil*. Oliver and Boyd

Coloration and Mimicry

(G) Brown, E. S. (1951), *Mimicry as illustrated in the British Fauna* (New Biology No. 10) Penguin

(A) Carpenter, G. D. H., and Ford, E. B. (1933), *Mimicry*. Methuen

(A) Cott, H. B. (1940), *Adaptive Coloration in Animals*. Methuen

(A) Parker, G. H. (1948), *Animal Colour Changes*. Cambridge

(G) Stephenson, E. M. (1946), *Animal Camouflage*. Pelican

(G) Wilson, D. P. (1951, 2nd edition), *Life of the Shore and Shallow Sea*. Nicholson and Watson

Territorial Behaviour

(G) Buxton, J. (1950), *The Redstart*. Collins

(G) Howard, H. E. (1948), *Territory in Bird Life*. Witherby (The original classic reprinted.)

(G) Lack, D. (1946, 2nd edition), *The Life of the Robin*. Witherby (Also in Pelican edition.)

(G) Smith, J. (1945), *How to Study Birds*. Collins

(G) Smith, S. (1950), *The Yellow Wagtail*. Collins

(A) Thorpe, W. H. (1956), *Learning and Instinct in Animals*. Methuen (Includes territorial behaviour of vertebrates and invertebrates.)

(A) Thorpe, W. H. (1961), *Bird Song*. Cambridge

(G) Tinbergen, N. (1951), *The Study of Instinct*. Oxford

Statistical Analysis and Quantitative Methods

(G) Bailey, N. T. J. (1959), *Statistical Methods in Biology*. English University Press (An excellent guide, clearly written.)

(G) Brookes, B. C., and Dick, W. F. L. (1953, 2nd edition), *An Introduction to Statistical Method*. Heinemann

(A) Fisher, R. A. (1954, 12th edition), *Statistical Methods for Research Workers*. Oliver and Boyd

(A) Fisher, R. A. (1951, 6th edition), *The Design of Experiments*. Oliver and Boyd

(A) Greig-Smith, P. (1957), *Quantitative Plant Ecology*. Butterworth

(G) Loveday, R. (1958), *Statistics*, Pts. 1 and 2. Cambridge (Good elementary course.)

(A) Mather, K. (1951, 4th edition), *Statistical Analysis in Biology*. Methuen

(A) Snedecor, G. W. (1950, 4th edition), *Statistical Methods*. Iowa (An excellent American textbook.)

309

INDEX

Figures in italics refer to text illustrations, those in bold to plates

311

Lumbricus castaneus, *44*, 170
Lumbricus rubellus, 168, 169
Lumbricus terrestris, 80, 157, 168, 171
Lungs, 233, 238
Lycosa, 161
Lydford, W. H., 159
Lyme Regis, **11**, **13**

Macan, T. T., 77
Macfadyen, A., 81, 191
Magnesium sulphate, 82, 93
Mammal traps, 69–71
Maniola jurtina, 94, 110, 123, 190
Manurial salts, 155, 220
Maps, 175–7, 248–9, 286
Marking methods, 84, 86–7, 88, 164, 183, 190
Marsh Marigold, **7**
Mask of dragonfly, *71*, 239
May-flies, 212, 216, 221, 222, 230, 234
May-fly nymphs, *33*, 91, 102–3
Meadow Brown butterfly, 94, 110, 123, 190
Meadow-sweet, **7**
Mean, 105, 106, 123, 190
Melanic moths, **6**, 195–7
Mendelian ratio, 117
Mercury vapour lamp, *13*, *14*, 62
Microhabitats, 179, 181, 186, 191, 239, 249, 258, 278, 287
Microtus agrestis, 25
Microtus arvalis, 25
Microscopes, 282
Migration, 199–200
Millipedes, 157, 159, 161, 162, 164, 165
Mimicry (Batesian), 199
Mimicry (Müllerian), 199
Minnow, 122, 238, 241
Mites, 83, 156, 173
Molluscs, 74

Molybdate-sulphuric acid reagent, 148
Moore, W. H., 78
Mor, 152
Mosquitoes, 21
Mottled Umber moth, 194
Movement, 84, 199–201
Mud, 220–1, 225, 248, 258, 276
Mud – gases in, *40*, 140–1
Mud grab, 73, 76
Mud sampling, *22*, *23*, 71–4
Mullein Shark moth, 178
Murphy, P. W., 152
Mussel, **12**, *82*, 265, 271
Mycorrhiza, 133
Mysella bidentata, **14**
Mytilus edulis, **12**, *82*, 265, 271
Myxomatosis, 25, 193

Naphthylamine, 147
Natica, 275
Natural selection, 88
Neal, E. G., 23, 188, 189
Nekton, 214
Nematoblasts, 275
Nematoda, 167
Nepa cinerea, *67*, 234
Nereis, *76*, *84*, 263, 269, 275
Nereis diversicolor, 257, 258, 269, 274
Nessler's Solution, 143–5
Nessler tube, 144, 146, 147, 148
Nest records, 203
Nets, *3*, 15, *16*, *21*, *24*, *25*, 60–1, 64–5, 71–2, 74–7
Night-flying species, 62
Nitrate; estimation in soil, 145
Nitrite; estimation in soil, 147
Nitrogen cycle, 155, 158
Nocturnal activity, 164
Nocturnal change, 191
Norton, H. E., 204
Norway Rat, 85